PHYSICAL PROPERTIES OF POLYMERS

PHYSICAL PROPERTIES OF POLYMERS

F. BUECHE

DEPARTMENT OF PHYSICS,
UNIVERSITY OF DAYTON, DAYTON, OHIO

1962

INTERSCIENCE PUBLISHERS

A DIVISION OF JOHN WILEY & SONS, NEW YORK • LONDON

Preface

The purpose of this book is to provide an introduction to the underlying molecular principles governing the physical behavior of high polymers. It will serve as a text for the novice in the field of the mechanical properties of polymers, and it is expected that after completing a study of THE PHYSICAL PROPERTIES OF POLYMERS the reader will be well prepared for intelligent research in this area. Although a deliberate effort has been made to emphasize the qualitative factors of analysis so necessary to a thorough comprehension of the phenomena of polymer action, the equally important quantitative aspects of molecular behavior have not been neglected. Furthermore, the discussions have been arranged so as to permit those readers who desire only a qualitative understanding of the significant principles of the subject merely to scan the mathematics.

In view of our current, rather detailed knowledge of polymer behavior it is not surprising that accepted ideas and theories can now be presented in a logical and lucid manner. THE PHYSICAL PROPERTIES OF POLYMERS attempts to do just this by means of a concise and readily comprehensible presentation of fundamental concepts. It is not intended to be a history of the subject and, as a consequence, certain approaches which were once of considerable importance have been only slightly touched upon.

Despite the fact that this volume is primarily directed to those who lack a prior familiarity with polymer physics, many of the topics are developed to a high level of sophistication, thereby providing a worthwhile source of information for the researcher who is better acquainted with this field. Where space limitations have made superficial explanations a necessity, references to pertinent literature are given.

I am deeply indebted to both Miss Clara Pappas, who patiently and skillfully translated my pen scratchings into the final typewritten draft of this book, and Dr. A. Gent for his many useful suggestions concerning the manuscript.

F. Bueche

Dayton, Ohio
November, 1961

Contents

INTRODUCTION

1. Nature of Polymer Molecules

A polymer molecule is a rather large molecule composed of many small primary molecules chemically bound together. Although the number Z of primary molecules composing the polymer molecule is quite definite for any given molecule, the methods of preparation of these macromolecules usually preclude the possibility of a sample in which all the polymer molecules contain the same number of primary molecules. The primary molecules are usually referred to as "monomer units," and Z, the number of monomer units in the polymer, is called the "degree of polymerization." In spite of the fact that even dimers (i.e., $Z = 2$) are polymer molecules, the polymers considered in this book will usually be assumed to have Z larger than about twenty. More often, Z will be of the order of hundreds and thousands. A typical polymer molecule will therefore consist of a long chainlike structure such as that shown in Figure I.1. This chain will in general be of appreciable length, so that it can ordinarily be considered even more flexible than the picture would indicate. Moreover, Brownian motion will cause the chain to writhe and squirm; and it will change its configuration continuously under the action of thermal motion.

One of the two general classifications of polymer molecules is the "condensation" polymer. The basis of such classification is the method by which the monomers react with each other to form a polymer. In this case, two monomer units react with each other to form a larger molecule while simultaneously forming a small, nonreactive molecule. This type of reaction is illus-

1

trated by the reaction of a typical hydroxy acid to form a polyester:

$$HO—R—COOH + HO—R—COOH$$
$$\rightarrow HO—R—COOR—COOH + H_2O$$

$$HO—R—COOR—COOH + HO—R—COOH$$
$$\rightarrow HO[—R—COO—]_2R—COOH + H_2O$$

$$HO[—R—COO—]_2R—COOH + (n-2)HO—R—COOH$$
$$\rightarrow HO[—R—COO—]_nR—COOH + (n-2)H_2O$$

where $—R—$ could be a structure of form $—CH_2(CH_2)_q—CH_2—$.

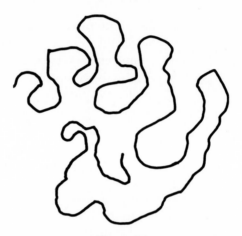

Figure I.1

It is seen in the above reaction that a molecule having a degree of polymerization $n+1$ has been formed by successive splitting out of water. For this type of reaction to occur, the monomer unit must possess reactive end groups at both ends, one end acting as one reactant, which combines chemically with the other end. In certain cases, one uses two different monomer units that are able to condense pairwise. A typical example is polyhexamethylene adipamide (nylon). The first step in this reaction is as follows:

$$H_2N(CH_2)_6NH_2 + HOCO(CH_2)_4COOH$$
$$\rightarrow H_2N(CH_2)_6NH—CO(CH_2)_4COOH + H_2O$$

The ends of this resultant molecule can react further, of course, to extend the molecule to high molecular weights.

A second general type of polymerization reaction occurs through combination of monomers containing double bonds; for example, the making of polyethylene from ethylene occurs by means of this so-called "addition" type of polymerization:

$$H_2C{=}CH_2 + H_2C{=}CH_2 \rightarrow \underset{\displaystyle H \ \ H \ \ H \ \ H}{\overset{\displaystyle H \ \ H \ \ H \ \ H}{-C-C-C-C-}}$$

$$H_2C{=}CH_2 + -CH_2CH_2CH_2CH_2- \rightarrow (-CH_2-CH_2-)_3$$

$$(n-3)H_2C{=}CH_2 + (-CH_2-CH_2-)_3 \rightarrow (-CH_2-CH_2-)_n$$

Notice that no small molecule is split out in this case, for the monomers add directly to each other. Various common condensation and addition polymers are given in Table 1.

The condensation reaction usually takes place as soon as the reactive monomers are added together and ceases only after all the monomer has been used up. This is not true in the case of addition polymers. At the outset a double bond must be broken to form a free radical, i.e., a reactive double bond. The radical then attacks other double bonds, and the reaction indicated above proceeds. To facilitate this reaction, the monomer is usually heated to high temperatures, or catalysts are added. Termination of the reaction usually occurs through the addition of a nonreactive impurity to the chain ends or by means of other mechanisms that will not be discussed here.

Because of the different natures of the initiation, propagation and termination steps in these two classes of polymerization, it is not unexpected that the degree of polymerization differs in the two cases. In general, condensation polymers have much lower molecular weights than addition polymers. A typical condensation polymer may have a molecular weight of 20,000, and very seldom is it as high as 100,000. Addition polymers frequently have molecular weights as high as 1,000,000. Of course, it is clear from the random way in which polymerization proceeds that a given polymer sample will contain chains of

TABLE 1
Common Polymers

Name	Formula
Polystyrene	$-CH_2-CH-$ phenyl group
Polymethyl methacrylate	CH_3 $-CH_2-C-$ $O=C-O-CH_3$
Polymethyl acrylate	$-CH_2-CH-$ $O=C-O-CH_3$
Polybutyl acrylate	$-CH_2-CH-$ $O=C-O-C_4H_9$
Polyvinyl acetate	$-CH_2-CH-$ $O-C-CH_3$ $\parallel$ O
Polyethylene	$-CH_2-CH_2-$
Polyvinyl chloride	$-CH_2-CH-$ Cl
Polyvinyl alcohol	$-CH_2-CH-$ OH
Polyacrylonitrile	$-CH_2-CH-$ CN
Polyvinylidene chloride	$-CH_2-CCl_2-$
Polyethylene oxide	$-CH_2-CH_2-O-$
Polyacrylic acid	$-CH_2-CH-$ $O=C-OH$
Polychlorotrifluoro ethylene	Cl $-CF_2-C-$ F

TABLE 1 (*continued*)

Name	Formula
Polytetrafluoro ethylene	$-CF_2-CF_2-$
Polydimethylsiloxane	$\begin{array}{c} CH_3 \\ \mid \\ -O-Si- \\ \mid \\ CH_3 \end{array}$
Polychloroprene	$\begin{array}{c} Cl \\ \mid \\ -CH_2-C=CH-CH_2- \end{array}$
Polymethyl vinyl ether	$\begin{array}{c} -CH_2-CH- \\ \mid \\ O-CH_3 \end{array}$
Polyisoprene	$\begin{array}{c} CH_3 \\ \mid \\ -CH_2-C=CH-CH_2- \end{array}$ and $\begin{array}{c} CH_3 \\ \mid \\ -CH_2-C- \\ \mid \\ CH=CH_2 \end{array}$
Polybutadiene	$-CH_2-CH=CH-CH_2-$ and $\begin{array}{c} -CH_2-CH- \\ \mid \\ CH=CH_2 \end{array}$
Polyisobutylene	$\begin{array}{c} CH_3 \\ \mid \\ -CH_2-C- \\ \mid \\ CH_3 \end{array}$
Cellulose	$\begin{array}{c} CH_2OH \\ \mid \\ C\underset{H}{\quad}O \\ \end{array}$

TABLE 1 (*continued*)

Name	Formula
Polyesters	$-(CH_2)_n-\overset{\displaystyle O}{\overset{\displaystyle \|}{C}}-O-$
Polyamides	$-\overset{\displaystyle H}{\overset{\displaystyle \|}{N}}-(CH_2)_n-\overset{\displaystyle O}{\overset{\displaystyle \|}{C}}-$
Polyurethanes	$-O-(CH_2)_n-O-\overset{\displaystyle O}{\overset{\displaystyle \|}{C}}-\underset{\displaystyle H}{N}-(CH_2)_n-\underset{\displaystyle H}{N}-\overset{\displaystyle O}{\overset{\displaystyle \|}{C}}-$

widely different molecular weights. In later chapters it will become evident that the distribution of molecular weights in a polymer sample has a marked influence upon the physical behavior of the material; hence it is important to have ways of characterizing the distribution.

2. Average Molecular Weights

A method for expressing an "average" molecular weight of a heterogeneous polymer is a practical necessity. For low molecular weights, one may effectively count the number of molecules present in a polymer solution by measurements of osmotic pressure or change in boiling or freezing point. If the total weight of the polymer is divided by the number of molecules present, the so-called "number-average" molecular weight M_n is obtained.

Let us consider a unit-weight polymer sample containing a distribution of molecular weights. If the number of molecules with molecular weight M_i is given by n_i, then the total weight of the sample is $\Sigma \, n_i M_i$. The summation is to encompass all the molecular species. Similarly, the total number of molecules in the sample is $\Sigma\, n_i$. Therefore, from the above definition of number-average molecular weight,

$$M_n = \Sigma\, n_i M_i / \Sigma\, n_i \qquad (\text{I.1})$$

or

$$M_n = \Sigma\, w_i / \Sigma(w_i / M_i) \qquad (\text{I.2})$$

In the latter expression, the weight fraction of material having a molecular weight M_i, which is $n_i M_i$, has been replaced by the symbol w_i. The common techniques yielding number-average molecular weights are osmotic pressure, boiling-point elevation, freezing-point depression, and end-group titration.

Other types of measurements give a somewhat different average molecular weight. Light scattering, for example, gives the so-called "weight average." It is defined as

$$M_w = \Sigma\, w_i M_i / \Sigma\, w_i \qquad (\text{I.3})$$

This may also be written in terms of the number of molecules in each species n_i by making the substitution $w_i = n_i M_i$. Notice that Eq. (I.3) is the same as (I.1), except that the number of molecules of species i has been replaced by the weight of such molecules; hence the customary terminology—number and weight average.

On occasion, a third basic molecular weight average is also encountered. This is called the Z-average molecular weight, defined as

$$M_z = \Sigma\, w_i M_i^2 / \Sigma\, w_i M_i \qquad (\text{I.4})$$

Finally, dilute-solution viscosity measurements are sometimes used to characterize molecular weights. In general, it is found that the so-called "intrinsic viscosity" of a polymer solution is proportional to M^a for a homogeneous polymer (1). The exponent a will be about 0.50 for solutions in a poor solvent for the polymer and about 0.80 in a very good solvent. If this technique is used to characterize a heterogeneous polymer, the so-called "viscosity-average" molecular weight M_v is obtained. The exact average obtained lies between the weight and number averages, but closer to the weight average. If the exponent a is unity, then $M_v = M_w$. Even for exponents near 0.7 the difference between M_v and M_w will not be too large, provided that no material of extremely high molecular weight is present. These conclusions concerning M_v apply only to linear polymers; when gel is present, the situation becomes very complex.

To see how these averages depend upon the molecular-weight distribution of the polymer, two distributions will be considered. The first of these instances, the "most probable" distribution, is given by the following relation:

$$w_i = (M/M_n^2) \exp(-M/M_n) \, dM \qquad (I.5)$$

which gives the weight fraction of polymer within the range of molecular weight $M \pm dM/2$. This distribution is commonly found for condensation polymers; however, it also occurs in certain addition polymers. If this expression for w_i is substituted in Eqs. (I.2), (I.3), and (I.4) and the summation replaced by an integral, one finds

$$M_n = M_w/2 = M_z/3 \qquad (I.6)$$

It is clear from this that the weight and Z averages emphasize the high-molecular-weight polymer to a greater extent than does the number average.

This fact is even more readily apparent when one considers a low-molecular-weight polymer with a small amount of microgel in it. Consider a polymer for which 99 per cent of the weight is composed of material with $M = 20,000$ and the remaining 1 per cent is microgel with $M = 10^9$. Using the above relations, one finds

$$M_n = 20,200 \qquad M_w = 10^7 \qquad M_z = 10^9$$

Obviously the weight and Z average must be used with care in such an instance. Systems containing a small amount of highly branched polymer will give a large M_w/M_n ratio; for example, this ratio varies from about 2 to 30 for commercial polyethylenes. Although this is somewhat an extreme case, it does indicate that the various average molecular weights of a polymer are relatively complicated measures of polydispersity.

3. Branching and Gel Formation

It is possible for a growing polymer chain to branch and lose its linear form. Although polyethylene is commonly represented as

$$H_3C—CH_2[—CH_2—CH_2—]_nCH_2—CH_3$$

which indicates a linear structure, actual commercial molecules are known to contain branches such as

$$CH_2[—CH_2—CH_2—]_qCH_2—CH_3$$
$$|$$
$$H_3C—CH_2[—CH_2—CH_2—]_pCH—CH_2[—CH_2—CH_2—]_sCH_2—CH_3$$

For the purposes of the above diagram only one branch is shown, but commercial polyethylene will often have many additional branches.

Many polymers undergo small amounts of branching during the polymerization reaction. If some—say, a fraction q—of the monomer units along a chain act as branch points, then a molecule containing Z monomer units will contain, on the average, qZ branches. As long as this product is much less than unity, the fraction of branched molecules will be small, and the effects of branching will be negligible for most purposes. However, if qZ approaches unity, the branching effect becomes serious.

To put this on a more quantitative basis, let us consider the polymerization of a monomer A with a small amount of a second monomer B. Assume monomer A to be a typical vinyl monomer such as styrene, which would polymerize by itself to give a polymer A—A[—A—]$_n$A—A. If monomer B is capable of adding four A monomers to itself, as would be the case for divinyl benzene, then the copolymer would contain branch points of the following form:

$$—A—A—A—A—A—A—A—$$
$$|$$
$$B$$
$$|$$
$$A—A—A—A—A—A—A—A—$$

Since each reactive end of the B monomer has an equal chance of entering a chain, the chains that the B monomer links together will be typical chains. One therefore concludes that, if the reactivity of the B monomer is the same as that of the A, the only effect of the presence of a small amount of this constituent is to link together the A chains which would exist in the absence of monomer B. Thus monomer B will merely act as a crosslinking agent between A chains in the sample.

An analogous situation would exist if one were to crosslink polyisoprene chains (natural rubber) with a vulcanizing agent such as sulfur. This linkage is accomplished as follows:

$$2[-CH_2-\overset{\overset{\displaystyle CH_3}{|}}{C}=\overset{\overset{\displaystyle H}{|}}{C}-CH_2-CH_2-\overset{\overset{\displaystyle CH_3}{|}}{C}=\overset{\overset{\displaystyle H}{|}}{C}-] + X \rightarrow$$

$$-CH=\overset{\overset{\displaystyle CH_3}{|}}{C}-\overset{|}{\underset{|}{C}}-CH_2-CH_2-\overset{\overset{\displaystyle CH_3}{|}}{C}=\overset{\overset{\displaystyle H}{|}}{C}-$$
$$X$$
$$-CH=\overset{}{C}-\overset{|}{\underset{\underset{\displaystyle CH_3}{|}}{C}}-CH_2-CH_2-\overset{}{\underset{\underset{\displaystyle CH_3}{|}}{C}}=\overset{}{\underset{\underset{\displaystyle H}{|}}{C}}-$$

Although the exact way in which the above reaction takes place will influence the structure near the crosslink, the above case is one possibility. The net effect in any analogous reaction is to tie two primary chains together.

It is of interest to examine the end result of such a vulcanization reaction. If the primary molecules have a degree of polymerization Z, there will be qZ crosslink points per average chain, where q is the chance that any given monomer unit in the chain is crosslinked. If $qZ \ll 1$, the chance that a chain Z units long contains a crosslink point is just qZ. The chance that the chain to which it is linked contains two crosslinks, so that it will be attached to yet another chain, is just $(qZ)[q(Z-1)]$, which is equal to $(qZ)^2$ for Z large. In fact, the probability that n chains are all linked together is approximately $(qZ)^n$.

Although the above treatment of the problem is far from rigorous, certain facts appear obvious. First, if $qZ \ll 1$, the number of chains linked together will on the average be very small; however, as qZ approaches unity, the chance that a given chain will be linked to a second, and that chain to a third and so on, will be very good. As a matter of fact, if $qZ = 1$, the probability that a given chain which contains a crosslink will be linked to an infinite number of other chains will be close to unity. When $qZ > 1$, one would therefore expect to find that a molecule of infinite molecular weight constituting an infinite network of chains will be set up in the rubber sample. The critical value of crosslinking, where $qZ = 1$, is called the "gel point," because it is at this degree of crosslinking that an infinite network, or gel, is formed. Of course, the term "infinite" is used somewhat loosely in this discussion, since the number of chains linked together is limited by the size of the polymer sample.

It should not be misconstrued, however, that all the chains in a sample are tied together at the gel point. Many chains are not crosslinked at all when $qZ = 1$. This qualification is readily comprehended from a more familiar problem. If a large number of balls are thrown into a large number of boxes in random fashion, the chance that each box will receive one ball is unity (in the above sense) when the number of boxes equals the number of balls. Obviously, this is the case which applies to a crosslinked system when $qZ = 1$. Enough crosslinked units have been made at random to provide exactly one crosslinked unit in each chain on the average. However, in the case of the balls distributed in an equal number of boxes, it is clear that some boxes will contain more than one ball, while some will contain none at all. Similar results may be predicted for the crosslinked chains; namely, some chains will contain no crosslinks at all. There will, in fact, be a large amount of sol present at the gel point. The sol will consist of single molecules and all combinations of multiple molecules. For a polydisperse system it has been found (1) that the gel point occurs when the number of crosslinked units in unit volume is equal to the number of weight-average chains, i.e., to the density divided by M_w.

It appears from the above discussion that a rubber which is

vulcanized to various degrees will display no exceptional behavior at the gel point. Upon being dissolved in a solvent, a
small amount of the material, the gel, will not dissolve; but
most of the material, the sol, will go into solution. The pure
rubber will appear much the same as the unvulcanized material
and will pull apart readily. However, as vulcanization proceeds
to higher values, the rubber becomes more stable under stress
and no longer undergoes viscous flow. It is evident that the
physical properties of a rubber are seriously dependent upon
the degree of crosslinking, a subject that will be discussed in
greater detail in succeeding chapters.

Chapter 1

CHAIN DIMENSIONS

1. Root Mean Square End-to-end Length R

The size of a linear polymer molecule may be expressed in a number of ways. Since a molecule constantly changes its configuration because of its thermal motion, it is patently impossible to assign a definite unchanging geometrical size to the molecule. For this reason, one must deal with average measures of size, which may be considered time averages that one would obtain by measuring the size from a series of pictures of a particular molecule taken at random times. Fully equivalent to this would be an average size computed from a series of size measurements on many molecules, all being made at the same time.

Quite commonly one expresses the average size of a molecule in terms of its mean square end-to-end length R^2. This end-to-end length is the straight-line distance between the two ends of the molecule. Then, by definition,

$$R^2 = (1/q) \sum_{j=1}^{q} r_j{}^2 \qquad (1.1)$$

where r_j is the end-to-end length of the j'th molecule. This equation merely says that the average value of the square of the end-to-end length is given by selecting at random a large number (q) of molecules and finding the average of the square of their end-to-end lengths.

The calculation indicated in Eq. (1.1) can be carried out as follows. If a chain is composed of N rigid bonds connected end

13

to end and if one assigns to each bond—say, the i'th—a vector $\mathbf{a}_i$, which points from the beginning to the end of the bond, then

$$\mathbf{r}_j = \sum_{i=1}^{N} \mathbf{a}_i \tag{1.2}$$

Substitution of this relationship into Eq. (1.1) results in

$$R^2 = (1/q) \sum_{j=1}^{q} \left(\sum_{i=1}^{N} \mathbf{a}_i \right)_j^2 \tag{1.3}$$

Equation (1.3) is perfectly general for any linear polymer. If one knew exactly how the various chain bonds were oriented in a large number of molecules, it would be possible to evaluate R^2 merely by placing the values in Eq. (1.3). In general, however, one must use more or less realistic *models* for a chain in order to evaluate Eq. (1.3), since the required values of the $\mathbf{a}$'s are not known for real chains. Even though the bond angles along a chain are almost always known, it is a difficult task to ascertain the relative positions of the bonds on their valence cones. Some success has been achieved in this respect for the most simple chains (1), but in a molecule such as polyethyl methacrylate, interferences between chain groups three or four chain bonds away from each other make an accurate evaluation completely intractable.

To proceed further in evaluating Eq. (1.3), the sum in Eq. (1.3) is squared to obtain

$$R^2 = \frac{1}{q} \sum_{j=1}^{q} (a_1{}^2 + a_2{}^2 + \cdots + a_N{}^2 + \mathbf{a}_1 \cdot \mathbf{a}_2$$
$$+ \mathbf{a}_1 \cdot \mathbf{a}_3 + \cdots + \mathbf{a}_{N-1}\mathbf{a}_N)_j \tag{1.4}$$

where $\mathbf{a}_n \cdot \mathbf{a}_m \equiv a_n a_m \cos\theta$, and where θ is the angle between $\mathbf{a}_n$ and $\mathbf{a}_m$.

Now, $a_1{}^2 = a_2{}^2 = \cdots = a_N{}^2 = a^2$; hence

$$R^2 = \frac{1}{q} \sum_{j=1}^{q} (Na^2 + \mathbf{a}_1 \cdot \mathbf{a}_2 + \mathbf{a}_1 \cdot \mathbf{a}_3 + \cdots + \mathbf{a}_{N-1} \cdot \mathbf{a}_N)_j \tag{1.5}$$

Since the quantity Na^2 is the same for any molecule,

$$R^2 = Na^2 + \frac{1}{q} \sum_{j=1}^{q} (\mathbf{a}_1 \cdot \mathbf{a}_2 + \mathbf{a}_1 \cdot \mathbf{a}_3 + \cdots + \mathbf{a}_{N-1} \cdot \mathbf{a}_N)_j \quad (1.6)$$

Equation (1.6) still represents only a general value for any linear chain containing N chain bonds. Until the projection of one chain bond upon every other bond of the same chain is known, or at least the average value thereof, the last term in Eq. (1.6) cannot be evaluated.

It is a simple matter to evaluate Eq. (1.6) in the case of one particular model chain, the so-called "freely orienting" chain. One of the stipulations of this chain is that the junction between two adjacent bonds is perfectly free to rotate. The two bonds may assume any orientation whatsoever with respect to each other. For this reason, the average projection of any one bond upon another will be zero. Hence, the average value of $\mathbf{a}_1 \cdot \mathbf{a}_2$ or any other similar pair will be zero. Equation (1.6) then becomes

$$R^2 = Na^2 \qquad \text{(freely orienting chain)} \qquad (1.7)$$

Other chain models can be used to evaluate Eq. (1.6). If N is assumed large enough for the chain to have considerable flexibility, these other models all yield the following result:

$$R^2 = (\text{constant}) Na^2 \qquad \text{(any long chain)} \qquad (1.8)$$

The constant in Eq. (1.8) varies, depending upon the model; but it is usually between 1 and 10. Eq. (1.6) is evaluated for a few other models in Appendix 1.

It should be noted that for any reasonable chain model leading to Eq. (1.8) the extended or contour length of the chain is of order Na. This observation, together with Eq. (1.8), leads to the fact that the average end-to-end length is of order $1/\sqrt{N}$ times smaller than the fully extended length. It will be seen later that, for moderate size polymer molecules, N will be larger than a few hundred; therefore, R will in general be very much smaller than the contour length of a chain.

2. Radius of Gyration S

Another measure of the size of a molecule is its average radius of gyration S. Qualitatively, this is the average distance of the mass in a molecule from the center of mass. More precisely, it is defined by the relation

$$S^2 = \left\langle \sum_{i=1}^{N} m\mathbf{s}_i^2 \right\rangle_{\text{av}} (1/Nm) \qquad (1.9)$$

where m is the mass associated with each of the N chain bonds and $\mathbf{s}_i$ is the vector distance from the center of mass to the i'th chain bond.

The computation indicated by Eq. (1.9) is carried out in Appendix 2. It is found there that, when Eq. (1.8) applies for the chain-end separation, the following relation also applies:

$$S^2 = R^2/6 \qquad (1.10)$$

As a by-product of this computation, it is also shown in Appendix 2 that the mean square distance of the i'th bond from the center of mass of the molecule is

$$\langle s_i^2 \rangle_{\text{av}} = (R^2/3)[u^3 + (1 - u)^3] \qquad (1.11)$$

where $u \equiv i/N$. It is interesting to note that the center chain segment, the $N/2'$th segment, is at an average distance $R/2\sqrt{3}$ from the center of mass while the chain end is at an average distance of $R/\sqrt{3}$ from the mass center.

3. Distribution Function for Chain-end Separation

Although it is of importance to know the average value of the chain-end separation R, this quantity tells relatively little about the chain-end separation for a given molecule at a given instant. It is for this reason that one is led to compute the distribution of chain-end separations about the average. We therefore define a function $P(x,y,z)\,dx\,dy\,dz$ which gives the probability that, if one chain end is at the origin of coordinates, the second chain end will be within the volume element $dx\,dy\,dz$. This function is obtained in Appendix 3 and, for a freely orienting chain of N bonds each of length a, is given by

$$P(x,y,z) = (3/2\pi Na^2)^{3/2} \exp\left[-(3/2Na^2)(x^2 + y^2 + z^2)\right] \quad (1.12)$$

This quantity is plotted as a function of x/R in Figure 1. The approximations inherent in the computation leading to Eq.

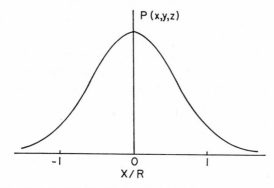

Figure 1.   The chain-end distribution function plotted as a function of the reduced x coordinate, X/R.

(1.12) make the result invalid if the chain is extended to near its maximum length, namely, for $x = Na$. As pointed out earlier in this chapter, the value of N will generally be a few hundred or larger; thus if the chain-end distance x is approximately equal to $(\frac{1}{4})Na$, it follows that (x/R) will be of order 10 or larger. Since $P(x,y,z)$ is already extremely small at such large values of x/R, the fact that the function is in error in this region will usually be of little consequence. Most of the chains will have chain-end separations small enough for Eq. (1.12) to be considered exact.

An interesting feature of the function $P(x,y,z)$ is that it has a single maximum, and this maximum is at the origin. Hence, the most probable chain-end separation in the x direction is zero. This does not mean, however, that most of the chains have an end separation near zero. It should be remembered that the probability of finding the second chain end within a volume element $dx\,dy\,dz$ at x,y,z is proportional to the product $P(x,y,z)\,dx\,dy\,dz$. Since only a very small volume is available near the origin of coordinates, the probability of finding a very small chain-end separation is also very small. That is to say, even though $P(x,y,z)$ is large when x, y, and z are small, there is only a relatively small volume in this region, and accordingly the chance of finding the second chain end there is also small.

This probability is more easily seen if Eq. (1.12) is transferred to polar coordinates. Because of the symmetry of the distribution function [Eq. (1.12)] about the origin, a volume element $4\pi r^2\,dr$ can be assumed, a spherical shell about the origin. Then the probability that the second chain end is in a volume element $4\pi r^2\,dr$ if the first chain end is at the origin is expressed as follows:

$$4\pi r^2 P(r)\ dr\ =\ 4\pi r^2 (3/2\pi Na^2)^{3/2} \exp\,[-(3r^2/2Na^2)]\ dr \quad (1.13)$$

The function $4\pi r^2 P(r)$ is plotted in Figure 2. This plot shows clearly that the most probable value of r is not zero but $(\tfrac{2}{3})^{1/2}R$. Of course, if one multiplies Eq. (1.13) by r^2 and integrates over

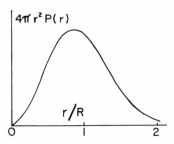

Figure 2.   The radial distribution function for the chain-end separation.

all r, the result will be the average square of the chain-end distance, namely, R^2. It is evident, therefore, that the most probable value of r is not quite equal to the root mean square value R.

4. Distribution about the Center of Mass

Another means for characterizing the size of a molecule is to give the distribution of chain bonds as a function of the distance from the center of mass of the molecule. Consequently, $4\pi s^2 P(s)\, ds$ is defined as the probability of finding any chain bond in a volume element $4\pi s^2\, ds$ at a distance s from the center of mass of the molecule. From the definitions of the center of mass and the radius of gyration S

$$S^2 = \int_0^\infty s^2 P(s) 4\pi s^2\, ds \qquad (1.14)$$

Unfortunately, the correct form for $P(s)$ is a very complicated function, as is shown in Appendix 4. For this reason, $P(s)$ is usually approximated with the following function:

$$P(s) = (9/\pi Na^2)^{3/2} \exp\left(-9s^2/Na^2\right) \qquad (1.15)$$

This function is compared with the correct function in Figure 3. It is clear that Eq. (1.15) is a workable approximation to $P(s)$

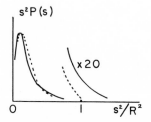

Figure 3. The density function for the distribution of chain segments about the center of mass. The exact gaussian form as found in Appendix 4 is plotted as the continuous curve, while the broken curve is a plot of Eq. (1.15).

except at large values of s. When substituted in Eq. (1.14), this approximation yields the correct value for S^2, namely, $R^2/6$.

It is further shown in Appendix 4 that the probability of finding the i'th chain bond at a distance s_i from the center of mass is

$$P(s_i) = (\phi/\pi)^{3/2} \exp\left(-\phi s_i^2\right) \qquad (1.16)$$

where $\phi \equiv 9N^2/\{2a^2[i^3 + (N - i)^3]\}$. From this relation,

$$\langle s_i^2 \rangle_{av} = \int_0^\infty 4\pi s_i^4 P(s_i) \, ds_i = (a^2 N/3)[u^3 + (1 - u)^3] \quad (1.17)$$

where $u \equiv i/N$. This confirms Eq. (1.11), which was obtained in another way.

5. Other Chain Dimensions

There are many other measures possible for a chain molecule. Actually the molecule may often be better represented by an ellipsoid of revolution with major axis along the line between the chain ends. This is particularly true if the chain is in a stretched configuration (2). It can be demonstrated (3) that the three radii of gyration of the molecule considered as an ellipsoid are given by

$$S_1^2 = S_2^2 = R^2/36 \qquad S_3^2 = (R^2/36)[1 + (3L^2/R^2)] \quad (1.18)$$

where L is the distance between the chain ends, and direction 3 is taken along the line joining the chain ends. Other measures of chain size have been reviewed by Tompa (4).

6. Reality and the Freely Orienting Chain

Let us consider a very long linear polymer chain. No matter what the structure of this chain may be, as long as there is no means of long-range interaction along the chain, the chain may be replaced by an equivalent "freely orienting" chain for the purposes of computation in this chapter. This substitution may be described as follows.

The freely orienting chain assumes only that the chain may be split into N equivalent "bonds," each of length a. These "bonds" are to be freely orienting; that is, the direction of the end-to-end distance of one "bond" should not depend upon the orientation of the two adjacent "bonds." Obviously, if a chain is long enough to appear relatively flexible, it may be split into subchains that are also flexible. The direction of the end-to-end length of any of these subchains will not be dependent upon the orientation of the adjacent subchains. Consequently, the "bonds" of the freely orienting chain can be identified with these subchains. A real molecule that has been arbitrarily divided into N subchains, each subchain having an average end-to-end length a, will be fully equivalent to the freely orienting chain used for the computations in this chapter (5).

Subject only to the restriction that N should be large and yet not so large that a subchain will be so short as to appear stiff, the values of N and a are purely arbitrary. It is necessary to set the additional restriction that the observed value of R for the real chain must be related to that computed for the freely orienting model in Eq. (1.7), namely, $R^2 = Na^2$. This condition can be satisfied by many values of N and a. An additional restriction is needed if definite values are to be assigned to N and a. Very often the further restriction is given that the fully extended length Na of the freely orienting chain must equal the fully extended length L of the real chain it is to represent. Hence,

$$R^2_{\text{expt}} = Na^2 \qquad L_{\text{real}} = Na \qquad (1.19)$$

These two conditions may be solved simultaneously for both N and a in terms of R and L; thus N and a can be assigned values in terms of experimentally measurable quantities.

It should not be supposed, however, that the values assigned to N and a by this procedure have any easily interpreted meaning. By definition, a is the average end-to-end length of a subchain. There is no reason to think that, when all these subchains (each in its average configuration) are placed end to end along a straight line, they should total the fully extended length of the real chain. In fact, there is every reason to think that this length will be much smaller than the contour or extended length of the real chain, since the length a consists of at least several real chain bonds in a more or less random configuration. It is therefore misleading to give any quantitative physical significance to the values of a and N obtained by this procedure.

Nevertheless, the representation of a real polymer chain by an equivalent freely orienting chain does have real value. In particular, if one uses the conditions in Eq. (1.19), the value of a for a given polymer in similar circumstances will be a constant independent of molecular weight, designated M, provided only that M is large. In addition, N will be directly proportional to M under the same conditions. Therefore, all the relations obtained in this chapter through use of the freely orienting model will remain meaningful for comparisons between chains of the same polymer under similar conditions. These values will not be expected to hold true for a very stiff chain when the temperature is raised considerably, since the chain will probably become appreciably more flexible at higher temperatures. This could change the value of R for the chain, and consequently a and N would change. Similarly, comparison of a and N values for chemically different chains will in general be of little quantitative significance.

7. Dimensions of Branched Molecules

The dimensions of branched molecules can be obtained by using the same methods applied to linear molecules in this chapter. These computations depend, of course, upon the particular branched molecule under consideration. Calculations for the radius of gyration of various branched molecules can be found in the pertinent literature (6,7). The distribution function for the chain segments in various other branched molecules has also been computed (8).

8. Excluded Volume Effects

The computations given in this chapter have all assumed that distant parts of the same molecule do not interfere with each other and thereby influence the various chain configurations. This would not be true if the chain had charges or mutually repulsive groups along its length, since these charges or groups would repel each other, and the chain would tend to avoid curled-up configurations. In fact, since the molecular segments have volume, more than one of them cannot occupy the same space at the same time; hence many chain configurations will be impossible, since they would require two chain segments to be in the same place. This effect obviously is most important for the highly coiled configurations of the molecule. These effects are serious for isolated polymer molecules in dilute solution. It is only in a so-called "theta" solvent that the polymer chains will assume their random configurations. In such a solvent, the internal chain repulsions and exclusions are balanced by the fact that the solvent is a poor one for the chain.

In a solid polymer or its concentrated solution (i.e., above perhaps 10 per cent polymer), a given polymer segment is unable to distinguish between segments from its own chain and those from other chains, since the overlap is essentially total. Hence the chain has no reason to assume one configuration in preference to another because of repulsions or exclusions resulting from distant segments within the same molecule. For this reason, the calculations in this chapter apply equally well to dilute polymer solutions in a theta solvent and to pure polymers and concentrated solutions thereof in any solvent.

9. Measured Polymer Sizes

Typical measured values of $(R^2/M)^{1/2}$ for various polymers are given in Table 2, where M is the polymer molecular weight. Also included are the computed values, assuming each chain backbone atom to be free to move without steric hindrance while maintaining the proper valence angles with its closest neighbors. For simple carbon-carbon backbone chains, these values are given by Eq. (A1.8) in Appendix 1. More complicated chain backbones have been treated (1) by using obvious extensions of the methods of Appendix 1.

It is assumed that the experimental values of $(R^2/M)^{1/2}$ were obtained on molecules sufficiently long so that $R^2 = Na^2$ applies.

If that were true, the ratio $(R^2/M)^{1/2}$ would be independent of molecular weight. This is actually the case for most of the molecules listed in Table 2; however, there is some doubt as to whether the cellulose molecules were flexible enough at 30°C to justify this assumption (9).

TABLE 2

Size of Various Polymers in a Theta Solvent [*from Flory* (1)]

Polymer	Temperature, °C	$(R^2/M)^{1/2}_{expt}$, Angstroms	$(R^2/M)^{1/2}_{eq}$, Angstroms	Ratio
Polyisobutylene	24	0.795	0.412	1.93
Polyisobutylene	95	0.757	0.412	1.84
Polystyrene	25	0.735	0.302	2.44
Polystyrene	70	0.710	0.302	2.35
Polymethyl methacrylate	30	0.680	0.310	2.19
Polyacrylic acid	30	0.710	0.363	1.96
Natural rubber	0–60	0.830	0.485	1.71
Gutta-percha	60	1.030	0.703	1.46
Polydimethylsiloxane	20	0.730	0.456	1.60
Cellulose tributyrate	90	0.845	0.408	2.07
Cellulose tributyrate	130	0.730	0.408	1.80
Cellulose tributyrate†	30	(2.0)	0.408	4.9

† Although the molecule used for this measurement had a molecular weight of 220,000, its size indicates it was essentially rodlike and so it cannot be expected to act like a random coil (9).

It is clear that the sizes of some of the molecules listed in Table 2 are somewhat temperature-sensitive. This results from the fact that steric hindrance to free rotation of the bonds on the valence-angle cone is of less consequence at high than at low temperatures. It may be assumed that the larger thermal energy resident in the chain at high temperatures causes the chain to more nearly approach the ideal of free rotation. Of course, the mere fact that all these molecules are considerably larger than their free rotation values indicates that steric hindrance is decidedly of importance at these temperatures.

APPENDIX 1
R for Special Chains

To compute the size of a polymer molecule, one must evaluate Eq. (1.6) of the foregoing text:

$$R^2 = Na^2 + (1/q) \sum_{j=1}^{q} [\mathbf{a}_1 \cdot \mathbf{a}_2 + \mathbf{a}_1 \cdot \mathbf{a}_3 + \cdots + \mathbf{a}_{N-1} \cdot \mathbf{a}_N]_j$$

$$(A1.1)$$

where the term $\mathbf{a}_1 \cdot \mathbf{a}_2$ means $a_1 a_2 \cos \theta$, with θ being the angle between a_1 and a_2. This expression will be evaluated for two types of model chains.

1. RESTRICTED 90°-BOND-ANGLE CHAIN

Consider a chain for which the first bond points in the $+x$ direction. The second is taken to point in either the $\pm y$ direction; the third points in either the $\pm z$ direction; the fourth points in either the $\pm x$ direction; and so on. There are N bonds in all, and each has a length a.

In general, for this model $\mathbf{a}_{n+1}$ and $\mathbf{a}_{n+2}$ are perpendicular to $\mathbf{a}_n$; therefore $\mathbf{a}_n \cdot \mathbf{a}_{n+1}$ and $\mathbf{a}_n \cdot \mathbf{a}_{n+2}$ are zero. In addition, all other segments of the chain are perpendicular to $\mathbf{a}_n$ except segment $\mathbf{a}_{n+3}$, $\mathbf{a}_{n+6}$, etc., and therefore do not contribute to the sum in Eq. (A1.1). The remaining terms typified by $\mathbf{a}_n \cdot \mathbf{a}_{n+6}$ will have values of $\pm a^2$ with equal probability. For this reason they will tend to cancel each other, and the average value of the sum for a large number of molecules will be essentially zero. Hence the last term of Eq. (A1.1) is zero, with the final result being

$$R^2 = Na^2 \qquad (A1.2)$$

2. FREELY ROTATING TETRAHEDRAL CHAIN (10,11)

This chain consists of a number of carbon atoms joined together as shown in Figure A.1 and is typical of many linear polymers.

In order to simplify the problem, it is assumed that each chain bond can rotate freely on the valence cone illustrated in the figure. Now Eq. (A1.1) must be evaluated for this model. To accomplish this, it is convenient to consider taking a time average of a given molecule rather than taking the average value at a given instant over a large number of molecules. This may be done by obtaining the time average of all such products as $\mathbf{a}_n \cdot \mathbf{a}_m$ and substituting these average values in Eq. (A1.1).

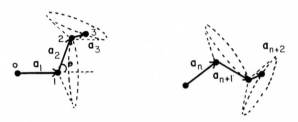

Figure A.1.   Typical segments along a freely rotating tetrahedral chain. Notice that each bond is restricted to maintain an angle θ with the adjacent bond but is free to rotate on the valence cone as indicated.

In Figure A.1 consider the bond $\mathbf{a}_{n+2}$, which is able to rotate on its valence cone without disturbing the lower-numbered bonds in the chain. Obviously, as it alone rotates, its average value over a long period of time will be a vector of magnitude $a \cos \theta$ pointing along vector $\mathbf{a}_{n+1}$. Therefore,

$$\langle \mathbf{a}_{n+1} \cdot \mathbf{a}_{n+2} \rangle_{av} = \langle \mathbf{a}_{n+1} \cdot \mathbf{a}_{n+1} \cos \theta \rangle = a^2 \cos \theta \qquad (A1.3)$$

Similarly, the average value of the vector $\mathbf{a}_{n+1}$ will be $\mathbf{a}_n \cos \theta$. From which it follows that

$$\langle \mathbf{a}_n \cdot \mathbf{a}_{n+2} \rangle = \langle \mathbf{a}_n \cdot \mathbf{a}_{n+1} \cos \theta \rangle = \langle \mathbf{a}_n \cdot \mathbf{a}_n \cos^2 \theta \rangle = a^2 \cos^2 \theta$$
$$(A1.4)$$

Hence, in general,

$$\langle \mathbf{a}_n \cdot \mathbf{a}_{n+P} \rangle = a^2 \cos^P \theta \qquad (A1.5)$$

Substitution of these values in Eq. (A1.1) leads to the result that

$$R^2 = Na^2 + a^2(\cos \theta + \cos^2 \theta + \cos^3 \theta + \cdots + \cos^N \theta$$
$$+ \cos \theta + \cos \theta + \cos^2 \theta + \cdots + \cos^{N-1} \theta$$
$$+ \cos^2 \theta + \cos \theta + \cos \theta + \cdots + \cos^{N-2} \theta \qquad (A1.6)$$
$$+ \cdots\cdots\cdots\cdots\cdots\cdots\cdots\cdots\cdots\cdots\cdots$$
$$+ \cos^N \theta + \cos^{N-1} \theta + \cos^{N-2} \theta + \cdots + \cos \theta)$$

or

$$R^2 = Na^2 + a^2[2(N - 1) \cos \theta + 2(N - 2) \cos^2 \theta$$
$$+ 2(N - 3) \cos^3 \theta + \cdots + 2 \cos^N \theta]$$
$$= Na^2 + 2Na^2(\cos \theta + \cos^2 \theta + \cdots + \cos^N \theta)$$
$$- 2a^2(\cos \theta + 2 \cos^2 \theta + \cdots + N \cos^N \theta)$$

$$R^2 = Na^2 + 2Na^2 \left(\frac{1 - \cos^N \theta}{1 - \cos \theta} \right) \cos \theta$$
$$- 2a^2 \cos \theta \left[\frac{1 - \cos^N \theta}{(1 - \cos \theta)^2} \right] \qquad (A1.7)$$

If N is large and $\cos \theta$ is not too close to unity, the above relation may be simplified to yield

$$R^2 \simeq \frac{1 + \cos \theta}{1 - \cos \theta} Na^2 \qquad (A1.8)$$

Since $\cos \theta = \frac{1}{3}$ for a tetrahedral chain, $R^2 = 2Na^2$.

3. OTHER MODEL CHAINS

Many observers have refined the free-rotation tetrahedral model to take account of various steric hindrances to free rotation (1,4). Unfortunately, it appears that such refinements are not especially significant, since they usually only take account of nearest neighbor interactions along the chain. Molecular models of most polymers reveal that chain atoms further removed along the chain are also of importance in hindering the free rotation of the chain bonds. For this reason it is advisable to assign only qualitative significance to such computations.

APPENDIX 2

Radius of Gyration

The definition of the radius of gyration of a polymer molecule is given by Eq. (1.9) of this chapter. If m is the same for each bond, this equation may be written as

$$S^2 = (1/N)\left\langle \sum_{i=1}^{N} s_i^2 \right\rangle \tag{A2.1}$$

This equation will be evaluated with the freely orienting chain as a model. As pointed out in Sec. 1.6, the computation making use of this model will also apply to any real chain that has a high molecular weight.

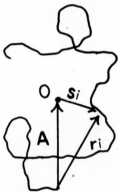

Figure A.2.   A diagram indicating the position of vectors used in Appendix. The center of mass of the molecule is at point O.

Let us consider the chain shown in Figure A.2. The point O represents the center of mass of the chain. $\mathbf{A}$, $\mathbf{r}_i$, and $\mathbf{s}_i$ are the vector distances shown, and the vector $\mathbf{r}_i$ starts on segment 1 and reaches to segment i. By inspection of the diagram

$$\mathbf{A} + \mathbf{s}_i = \mathbf{r}_i \tag{A2.2}$$

By definition, the center of mass is chosen such that $\Sigma\, \mathbf{s}_i = 0$, and thus the sum of Eq. (A2.2) over all elements in the chain can be written

$$\sum_{i=1}^{N} \mathbf{r}_i = N\mathbf{A} \tag{A2.3}$$

This relation is of importance in evaluating Eq. (A2.1), since

$$\sum_{i=1}^{N} \mathbf{s}_i^2 = \sum_{i=1}^{N} (\mathbf{r}_i - \mathbf{A})^2$$

$$= \sum_{i=1}^{N} (r_i^2 - 2\mathbf{A} \cdot \mathbf{r}_i + A^2)$$

$$= \sum_{i=1}^{N} r_i^2 - 2NA^2 + NA^2$$

from which

$$\sum_{i=1}^{N} \mathbf{s}_i^2 = \sum_{i=1}^{N} r_i^2 - (1/N)\left(\sum_{i=1}^{N} \mathbf{r}_i\right)\left(\sum_{j=1}^{N} \mathbf{r}_j\right) \tag{A2.4}$$

Evaluating the first term on the right-hand side of Eq. (A2.4),

$$\sum_{i=1}^{N} r_i^2 = \sum_{i=1}^{N} (\mathbf{a}_1 + \mathbf{a}_2 + \cdots + \mathbf{a}_i)^2 \tag{A2.5}$$

The average value of this product is easily found, since for a freely orienting chain the average of such terms as $\mathbf{a}_n \cdot \mathbf{a}_m$ is zero; hence,

$$\left\langle \sum_{1}^{N} r_i^2 \right\rangle = \sum_{1}^{N} ia^2$$

or

$$\left\langle \sum_{1}^{N} r_i^2 \right\rangle = N^2 a^2/2 \tag{A2.6}$$

A procedure similar to that employed in evaluating the first term may be used to evaluate the second term on the right-hand side of Eq. (A2.4). After considerable manipulation, it is found that

$$(1/N)\langle \Sigma\, r_i\, \Sigma\, r_j \rangle = (1/N) \sum_{i=1}^{N} \left[\sum_{j=1}^{i} ja^2 + a^2 i(N - i) \right]$$

$$\cong (1/N) \sum_{i=1}^{N} (a^2 Ni - a^2 i^2/2)$$

$$\cong N^2 a^2/3 \tag{A2.7}$$

where it has been assumed that $N \gg 1$.

By use of Eqs. (A2.1), (A2.4), (A2.6), and (A2.7), one derives

$$S^2 = Na^2/6 \qquad (A2.8)$$

which is the desired expression for the radius of gyration of the chain.

It is also useful to know the value of $\langle s_i^2 \rangle$. From Eqs. (A2.2) and (A2.3), this is evaluated as

$$\langle s_i^2 \rangle = \langle r_i^2 \rangle + (1/N^2)\langle \Sigma \, \mathbf{r}_i \, \Sigma \, \mathbf{r}_j \rangle - (2/N)\langle \mathbf{r}_i \, \Sigma \, \mathbf{r}_j \rangle$$

This expression may then be evaluated by the procedure used above, with the result that

$$\langle s_i^2 \rangle = (a^2 N/3)[u^3 + (1 - u)^3] \qquad (A2.9)$$

where $u \equiv i/N$.

APPENDIX 3

Chain-end Distribution Function

The computation of the chain-end distribution function is of great importance in polymer physics. Not only is the end result valuable in itself, but its computation may be used to illustrate three fundamental techniques applicable to polymer computation. For this reason, the distribution function will be obtained by three different methods.

1. METHOD 1: FREELY ORIENTING CHAIN, STATISTICAL PROCEDURE (13)

Let us consider a freely orienting chain bond. It will, on the average, have an x component that is zero. The root mean square value of the x component will not be zero, however. It is given by

$$\langle a_x^2 \rangle = \int_0^{\pi/2} a^2 \cos^2 \phi (2\pi a \sin\phi \, a \, d\phi) \bigg/ \int_0^{\pi/2} (2\pi a \sin \phi a \, d\phi)$$

from which

$$\langle a_x^2 \rangle = a^2/3 \qquad (A3.1)$$

The freely orienting chain will therefore act like a chain whose bonds can, on the average, have components in the x, y, and z directions of $\pm a/\sqrt{3}$.

First, let us compute the probability that the x component of the chain end-to-end distance is $n(a/\sqrt{3})$ where $N \gg n$. From Eq. (A3.1) it is evident that this is equivalent to seeking the probability that "heads" will come up n times more than "tails" in N tosses of a coin. This probability is expressed as

$$P(n) = (1/2)^N N! / [(N - n)/2]! [(N + n)/2]! \quad (A3.2)$$

This expression can be reduced by using Sterling's approximation for the factorials. If the assumption is then made that $(n/N) \ll 1$, replacing n^2 by $3x^2/a^2$ gives

$$P(x) = (3/2\pi Na^2)^{1/2} \exp(-3x^2/2Na^2) \quad (A3.3)$$

The probability that the components of the distance between chain ends will be x, y, and z is given by a product of three such factors; hence,

$$P(x,y,z) = (3/2\pi Na^2)^{3/2} \exp[-3(x^2 + y^2 + z^2)/2Na^2] \quad (A3.4)$$

2. METHOD 2: DIFFUSION EQUATION (14)

For a chain with n freely orienting segments, each of length a, the end-to-end distribution function can be written as $P(\mathbf{r},n)$, where $\mathbf{r}$ is the vector end-to-end distance. The new distribution function for a chain containing one more segment will be $P(\mathbf{r}, n + 1)$. But since this has been obtained by adding a vector length $\mathbf{a}$—i.e., one segment—to the previous chain,

$$\langle P(\mathbf{r}, n + 1) \rangle = \langle P(\mathbf{r} + \mathbf{a}, n) \rangle \quad (A3.5)$$

The expression $P(\mathbf{r} + \mathbf{a}, n)$ is now expanded to give

$$P(\mathbf{r} + \mathbf{a}, n) = P(\mathbf{r},n) + \left(\frac{\partial P}{\partial x} a_x + \frac{\partial P}{\partial y} a_y + \frac{\partial P}{\partial z} a_z \right)$$

$$+ (1/2!)\left[\frac{\partial^2 P}{\partial x^2} a_x^2 + \frac{\partial^2 P}{\partial y^2} a_y^2 + \frac{\partial^2 P}{\partial z^2} a_z^2 + \frac{2\partial^2 P}{\partial x \, \partial y} a_x a_y + \cdots \right]$$

$$+ \text{higher terms} \quad (A3.6)$$

As usual with the freely orienting chain, the cross-product terms and the a_x, a_y, and a_z terms will average out to zero. If the higher-order terms are discounted, then

$$\langle P(\mathbf{r} + \mathbf{a}, n) \rangle = \langle P(\mathbf{r}, n + 1) \rangle = \langle P(\mathbf{r},n) \rangle$$

$$+ \frac{a^2}{6} \left(\frac{\partial^2 P}{\partial x^2} + \frac{\partial^2 P}{\partial y^2} + \frac{\partial^2 P}{\partial z^2} \right)$$

or
$$\frac{\partial P}{\partial n} = \frac{a^2}{6} \left(\frac{\partial^2 P}{\partial x^2} + \frac{\partial^2 P}{\partial y^2} + \frac{\partial^2 P}{\partial z^2} \right) \qquad (A3.7)$$

This equation is the partial-differential equation for diffusion; its solutions are well known. In the present instance, the solution is

$$P(\mathbf{r}) = (3/2\pi Na^2)^{3/2} \exp(-3r^2/2Na^2) \qquad (A3.8)$$

Although the approximations made in obtaining Eq. (A3.8) were not obvious in the consequences, the equation must be subject to the same restriction as stipulated for Eq. (A3.4); hence the above result will be valid only if $r \ll Na$.

3. METHOD 3: DELTA-FUNCTION SUBCHAIN MODEL

The third method here presented for the calculation of the chain-end distance distribution function is sometimes more easily extended to other problems than are the previous two methods. First, the chain is assumed to be made up of N freely orienting segments of nonfixed bond length. The probability that the end of the $n + 1$ segment is at x, y, and z distances ξ, η, and ν from the end of the nth segment will be taken as proportional to

$$\exp[-(3/2a^2)(\xi^2 + \eta^2 + \nu^2)] \qquad (A3.9)$$

From Eq. (A3.4) it is apparent that in effect a segment is for our purposes defined as a connected group of individual bonds whose number is large enough for the end-to-end distance of this segment to be governed by the distribution function for a chain. That is to say, the actual chain is split into Z subchains, each of average length a. Clearly, from the form of Eq. (A3.9), these segments have only a negligible (i.e., $\sim 10^{-7}$) chance of being longer than $5a$.

The probability that the Z chain segments are such that the chain configuration is characterized by segment coordinates $\xi_1, \xi_2, \ldots, \xi_z$ and $\eta_1, \eta_2, \ldots, \eta_z$ and $\nu_1, \nu_2, \ldots, \nu_z$ is found by taking the product of the independent probabilities for the N segments:

$$\prod_{i=1}^{N} \exp\left[-(3/2a^2)(\xi_i^2 + \eta_i^2 + \nu_i^2)\right] \tag{A3.10}$$

If probabilities such as Eq. (A3.10) could then be added for all configurations of the chain that result in a chain-end separation characterized by X, Y, and Z, the probability for that particular chain-end separation would be the result, and the problem would be solved.

Such a computation can be carried out by integrating the expression in Eq. (A3.10) over all values of ξ, η, and ν, provided we first multiply by a function Δ which is unity when

$$\xi_1 + \xi_2 + \cdots + \xi_z = X \qquad \eta_1 + \eta_2 + \cdots + \eta_z = Y$$

and $\nu_1 + \nu_2 + \cdots + \nu_z = Z$ and zero otherwise. Such a function does exist and is called a "delta function." One of several possible representations for it is

$$\Delta = \iiint_{-\infty}^{\infty} \exp\left[jt_x(\Sigma\,\xi_i - X) + jt_y(\Sigma\,\eta_i - Y)\right.$$
$$\left. + jt_z(\Sigma\,\nu_i - Z)\right] dt_x\, dt_y\, dt_z \tag{A3.11}$$

where $j = \sqrt{-1}$ and the sums extend over $1 < i < N$.

Following the procedure outlined above,

$$P(r) \sim \iiint_{\xi\eta\nu} \Delta \prod \exp\left[-(3/2a^2)(\xi_i^2 + \eta_i^2 + \nu_i^2)\right] d\xi_1$$
$$\cdots d\xi_z\, d\eta_1 \cdots d\eta_z\, d\nu_1 \cdots d\nu_z \tag{A3.12}$$

with the limits ranging from $-\infty$ to ∞.

For mathematical reasons involving the validity of Eq. (A3.11) for the delta function, it is best always to integrate over t_x, t_y, and t_z last. The integrals in Eq. (A3.12) can be carried out by completing the square in the exponential for each variable. After the integration has been carried through and the probability normalized, it is found that

$$P(r) = (3/2\pi Na^2)^{3/2} \exp\left[-(3/2Na^2)r^2\right] \qquad (A3.13)$$

which is identical with the results found previously. Once again the result is obviously restricted to long chains at elongations that are not too large.

APPENDIX 4

Mass Distribution Function (16,17)

The distribution of chain segments about the center of mass of a molecule may be computed by using method 3 of Appendix 3. Referring to Figure A.2, one lets $\mathbf{r}_i = \mathbf{X}_i + \mathbf{Y}_i + \mathbf{Z}_i$ and $\mathbf{A} = \mathbf{A}_x + \mathbf{A}_y + \mathbf{A}_z$. Utilizing the procedure of Appendix 3, the expression for the probability that $\mathbf{r}_i = \mathbf{X}_i + \mathbf{Y}_i + \mathbf{Z}_i$ is as follows:

$$P(s_i) = P(X_i)P(Y_i)P(Z_i)$$

where

$$P(X_i) \sim \int \cdots \int \exp\left[-(3/2a^2) \sum_1^N \xi_n^2 + 2\pi j t_x(\xi_1 + \cdots \right.$$
$$\left. + \xi_i - X_i - A_x)\right] d\xi_1 \cdots d\xi_N \, dt_x \qquad (A4.1)$$

There are similar expressions for $P(Y_i)$ and $P(Z_i)$.

As in Appendix 3, the summation is taken over all configurations, but only those for which

$$-A_x + \xi_1 + \xi_2 + \cdots + \xi_i = X_i$$

are selected. That is to say, only those configurations are counted in which the end of the chain is at $-A_x$ and the i'th segment is at X_i.

An examination of Figure A.2 leads to the relation

$$A_x = (1/N) \sum_{n=1}^N \sum_{q=1}^n \xi_q = (1/N) \sum_{p=1}^N (Z + 1 - p)\xi_p \qquad (A4.2)$$

as well as similar expressions for A_y and A_z. These values may be substituted in expressions such as Eq. (A4.1), and after the integrations have been carried out and the probability normalized,

$$P(s_i) = (\phi/\pi)^{3/2} \exp (-\phi s_i^2) \qquad (A4.3)$$

where

$$\phi = 9N^2/\{2a^2[i^3 + (N - i)^3]\}$$

In order to obtain the density of segments at a given distance from the center of mass of the molecule, $P(s_i)$ must be summed over all values of i, while s_i remains equal to a constant value s. This integration has not been carried out in closed form, but series solutions are known (16). The theoretical curve in Figure 3 has been evaluated with the aid of these series.

PROBLEMS

1. Compute the rms end-to-end length R for a linear polystyrene molecule having a molecular weight of 10^6. Assume free rotation on the valence cone. Compare this value with that obtained from the data of Table 2.

2. If molecule A containing p freely orienting segments is joined to molecule B containing q segments by attaching one end of molecule B to the central segment of molecule A, how large are the rms distances between one end of molecule A and the other two ends of the branched molecule?

3. Write out Eq. (1.6) in detail for a molecule having 6 bonds.

4. Starting from Eq. (1.6), find the rms distance between the centers of the terminal carbon atoms in the propane molecule. Check your answer merely by substituting from Eq. (1.2) into Eq. (1.1). Express the distance in angstroms, assuming the proper values for the bond lengths and angles.

5. Starting from Eq. (1.6), find the rms distance between the centers of the terminal carbon atoms in the n-butane molecule. Repeat for isobutane. (Assume free rotation on the valence cone.)

6. How true is the saying that "a polymer molecule of high molecular weight is essentially spherical"? What is meant by the term "high molecular weight" in this expression?

7. A linear molecule having p freely orienting segments is to be compared with the same molecule after q short chain branches have been added to it. Without doing any computation, what can one say about the mean square

end-to-end length, radius of gyration, and distribution of segments for the branched molecule as compared to the original molecule?

8. A certain polymer chain has an rms end-to-end length of 10^3 Å. Find the chain-end separations for this molecule which are only $\frac{1}{20}$ as probable as the separation of 10^3 Å.

9. Show in detail how the first of Eqs. (A2.7) is obtained for the second term on the right-hand side of Eq. (A2.4). Also show how this equation leads to the last of Eqs. (A2.7).

10. Show how one obtains Eq. (A2.9).

11. If the end-to-end separation of a linear freely orienting chain having N segments is b at some instant, what is the chance that the center segment of the chain is within a very small volume Δv at a distance A from one end and B from the other. $(A + B > b)$. [Hint: The probability of finding the central segment at a distance r from one particular end of the chain is proportional to $\exp\left(-3r^2/Na^2\right)$.]

Chapter 2

RUBBER ELASTICITY

1. Elasticity of a Chain

Let us consider a linear polymer molecule maintained at absolute temperature T, which will possess thermal energy of vibration, rotation, and translation. In addition, suppose that the temperature is high enough for the molecule to be able to move about and change its over-all configuration without much difficulty. Now examine the movement of the two ends of the chain.

The separation of the chain ends will be constantly changing as the molecule squirms about. Suppose one were to measure the distance r between the two chain ends at various randomly selected times. If one now examines the data and records the number of times the molecule had chain-end separations given by $0 < r < 0.10R$ and the number of times $0.10R < r < 0.20R$ and so on, these numbers could be plotted at the points $0.05R$, $0.15R$, etc., on a graph that relates the number of observed molecules to the chain-end separation. The result would be a graph similar to Figure 2; hence this graph represents the frequency with which a molecule will assume a given end-to-end length if it is allowed to move at random under thermal motion. It is, of course, merely a plot of $4\pi r^2 P(r)$, where $P(r)$ is the chain-end-separation distribution function.

Suppose that the chain ends were to be held at some fixed separation r. It is obvious that if one tried to clamp the chain ends quite far apart, the chain would exert an average pull on the clamps toward smaller values of r. This does not mean that

37

the pull will always be in the direction of smaller r, since the chain from time to time will seek under thermal motion a more highly extended configuration than the clamps will allow. On the average, however, since the clamps hold the chain in a rather extended configuration, the force on the clamps will be such as to pull them together. In fact, it is easily seen that for any separation of the clamps larger than zero, the average force on them will be such as to pull them toward each other. This observation follows from the fact that under random thermal motion one end of the chain will be found on the left side of the other end as much as it is on the right side. That is to say, the average vector distance between the chain ends is zero; consequently, it is only when the chain ends are both clamped at the same place that the average force on the clamps will be zero.

Therefore it appears that, qualitatively at least, a polymer chain will behave like a spring which has zero equilibrium length. If it is to be held in extended configurations such that the ends of the chain are a distance r apart, the chain will act like a stretched spring and try to decrease r to zero. The force, or tension, in the chain will apparently be larger for larger values of r. The molecule does not, however, exert a constant pull on the clamps; indeed, sometimes it tries to push the clamps apart even though r may be quite large. The average force on the clamp is nevertheless always in such a direction as to contract the molecule.

It is possible to compute the average chain-end separation for a chain subjected to a stretching force F applied to the chain ends (2,18). Notice that in this computation the chain is permitted to move about under a combination of thermal motion and the applied tensile force F. The chain ends are not fixed at any one separation. The freely orienting chain is used as a chain model, since this model will give realistic results for actual chains of high molecular weight.

A segment of length a in a freely orienting chain will usually have no preferred direction or orientation. When the chain is subjected to a tension F, however, the segment will have different potential energies as it is aligned in various directions. In order to make the problem definite, let us suppose the tension is in the x direction and equivalent to F. As a result of this tension, it will require an average energy $2aF$ to move a segment from a position parallel to the x direction to a position that is antiparallel. If the segment is assumed to have zero potential energy when it has no component of its length in the x direction, its potential energy is therefore

$$V = -Fa \cos \theta \tag{2.1}$$

where θ is the angle between the x axis and $\mathbf{a}$.

According to the Boltzmann distribution law, the probability that the segment makes an angle θ with the x axis is proportional to

$$\exp\left(-V/kT\right) \tag{2.2}$$

Hence, the average value of the x component of a as it undergoes thermal motion will be

$$\langle a_x \rangle = \frac{\int_0^\pi (a \cos \theta)(2\pi a^2 \sin \theta \, d\theta) \exp\left[Fa \cos \theta / kT\right]}{\int_0^\pi (2\pi a^2 \sin \theta \, d\theta) \exp\left[Fa \cos \theta / kT\right]}$$

or

$$\langle a_x \rangle = a[\coth (aF/kT) - (kT/aF)] \tag{2.3}$$

The function in brackets in the right-hand term of Eq. (2.3) is usually referred to as the "Langevin function," encountered by Langevin in his theory of the ordering of magnetic dipoles in a magnetic field. The function is usually represented by the symbol $\mathscr{L}\,(aF/kT)$.

Since $\langle a_x \rangle$ is the average x component of a typical chain segment, the average x separation of the chain ends will be N times as large. Therefore,

$$\langle r_x \rangle = Na\mathscr{L}(aF/kT) \tag{2.4}$$

The subscript for r is not essential, since the average value of r_y and r_z will be zero because there is no tension in these directions. Solving Eq. (2.4) for F gives, symbolically at least,

$$F = (kT/a)\,\mathcal{L}^*(r/Na) \tag{2.5}$$

where $\mathcal{L}^*(r/Na)$ is called the "inverse Langevin function" of r/Na. This equation gives the force F needed to maintain the chain at an average elongation r.

The inverse Langevin function can be written in series form thus:

$$F = (kT/a)\,[3(r/Na) + (9/5)(r/Na)^3$$
$$+ (297/175)(r/Na)^5 + \cdots] \tag{2.6}$$

which for $r \ll Na$ becomes

$$F \cong (3kT/Na^2)r \tag{2.7}$$

Equation (2.7) confirms the supposition made earlier concerning the springlike character of a polymer molecule. It states that the average elongation of the molecule (i.e., the average increase in chain-end-separation distance) is proportional to the applied tension. The spring constant for the molecule is $3kT/Na^2$. In this regard, it is interesting to notice that the molecular spring is stiffer at higher temperatures. This condition is reasonable, since at higher temperatures the chain segments will be undergoing much more violent motion and will be harder to align. Also, the larger N becomes, the softer the spring becomes. This correspondence is merely a reflection of the fact that for a given elongation each chain segment will be less highly oriented if N is larger. Although Eq. (2.7) is a good approximation for small elongations of the molecule, it is about 7 per cent in error when r/Na has increased to a value of $\frac{1}{3}$. At still greater elongations, according to Eq. (2.5), the value of F increases quite rapidly, and it becomes infinite when $r = Na$. This fact is in accord with the freely orienting chain model, since this model supposes each segment to have a fixed length a. When $r = Na$ the chain is fully elongated, and if the chain were infinitely strong, the tension F would become infinite. The variation of r/Na with F as predicted by Eq. (2.5) is shown in Figure 4.

The result given in Eq. (2.5) can be used to find the chain-end distribution function over the whole range of chain-end separations (see Appendix 5). It is found that the distribution previously given [Eq. (1.13)], the so-called "gaussian distribution," is accurate up to quite high elongations.

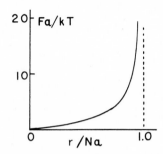

Figure 4.   The force-extension curve for a freely orienting chain.

2. Elasticity of a Network; Tensile Stress

The result found in the previous section for the force needed to stretch a polymer chain may be used to compute the force needed to elongate a rubber network. For the purposes of this calculation, it is assumed that the network consists of ν polymer chains per unit volume, each chain being composed of N freely orienting segments. As pointed out in Chapter 1, this chain model will give valid results provided that the chains are sufficiently long. Furthermore, it is assumed that each chain end is tied to other chains in the network and that the chains possess random configurations so that the ordinary chain-end distribution function of Eq. (1.13) applies.

In brief outline, the computation will be carried out as follows. First, the work done in stretching an arbitrary single chain is computed. This result is then averaged over all the chains in unit volume and multiplied by ν, the number of chains in unit volume, to obtain the energy stored in unit volume of rubber. Since the small amount of work done on a piece of rubber when it is stretched a small distance is simply the product of the applied force and the small distance, the applied force is found by differentiation of the stored energy. These computations are carried out in detail below.

Consider a unit volume of rubber to which an x-directed tensile force is applied. The rubber, assumed incompressible, will take on new dimensions. Its x length will increase to α, while its y and z dimensions will be reduced to $1/\sqrt{\alpha}$. The sample still has unit volume, of course.

A primary assumption will now be made with regard to the way the individual chains elongate. If the three components of the chain-end separation for an arbitrary molecule are x_0, y_0, and z_0 before deformation, it is assumed that the deformed dimensions are αx_0, $y_0/\sqrt{\alpha}$, and $z_0/\sqrt{\alpha}$. This relationship constitutes what is called an "affine deformation," namely, that each element in the volume distorts in the same way as does the volume as a whole. It appears quite likely that this assumption is valid except for highly stressed chains. In any case, attempts to remove this qualification produce results that indicate the error incurred by this assumption is negligible for the present purposes (22).

The work done in deforming the chain is merely the integral of the applied force throughout the deformation distance. That is,

$$\text{Work per chain} = \int_{x_0}^{\alpha x_0} F_x \, dx + \int_{y_0}^{y_0/\sqrt{\alpha}} F_y \, dy + \int_{z_0}^{z_0/\sqrt{\alpha}} F_z \, dz \qquad (2.8)$$

But from Eq. (2.7), the force needed to hold a chain at an elongation x is equivalent to $x(3kT/Na^2)$, with similar expressions for the y and z forces. These values may accordingly be substituted in Eq. (2.8), which gives

Work per chain

$$= (3kT/2Na^2)[(\alpha^2 - \alpha^{-1})x_0^2 + (\alpha^{-1} - 1)r_0^2] \qquad (2.9)$$

where

$$r_0^2 = x_0^2 + y_0^2 + z_0^2$$

The average work per chain may be obtained by multiplying

Eq. (2.9) by the distribution function of Eq. (1.12) and integrating over all values of x_0, y_0, and z_0. The answer to this integration is already known, however, since it will merely consist in finding the average value of r_0^2 and x_0^2. The former value is R^2 and the latter is $R^2/3$, where R^2 is equal to Na^2 for this model. Therefore,

Average energy per chain

$$= (3kT/2)[(\tfrac{1}{3})(\alpha^2 - \alpha^{-1}) + (\alpha^{-1} - 1)] \qquad (2.10)$$

To obtain the total energy stored in unit volume of the rubber, Eq. (2.10) must then be multiplied by the number of chains per unit volume ν, with the result that

W = stored energy per unit volume

$$= (\nu kT/2)[(\alpha^2 - \alpha^{-1}) + 3(\alpha^{-1} - 1)] \qquad (2.11)$$

Since the stored energy W is the result of the work done by the tensile stress σ applied to the unit volume,

$$W = \int_{\alpha=1}^{\alpha} \sigma \, d\alpha$$

from which

$$\sigma = \partial W/\partial \alpha$$

Carrying out the indicated differentiation of Eq. (2.11)

$$\sigma = \nu kT(\alpha - \alpha^{-2}) \qquad (2.12)$$

This is the classical expression for the tensile stress needed to deform a rubber to an extension ratio α. Its form is shown in Figure 5. Equation (2.12) was first derived in somewhat variant ways by Kuhn (19), Wall (11), James and Guth (18), Treloar (20), and Flory and Rehner (21). Equation (2.12) is based upon several assumptions, which include:

1. The rubber is incompressible.
2. The chains are properly represented by the freely orienting model.
3. All chains have the same molecular weight.
4. The chains deform in an affine manner.

5. The deformation is small enough for the gaussian distribution function for chain ends to be valid.

6. No energy is stored in stretched, distorted, or broken bonds, chemical or otherwise.

7. The rubber was crosslinked in the unstretched state.

8. All chains were tied to the network at both ends.

The first of these assumptions is almost invariably true. In those cases where it does fail, one of the other assumptions listed above is obviously wrong. For this reason, the error proceeding from this approximation is nearly always negligible.

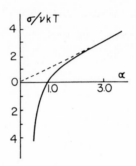

Figure 5.   The stress-strain relation for the ideal rubber represented by Eq. (2.12).

As pointed out in Chapter 1, assumption 2 is valid provided that the network chains are long enough to contain a large number of freely orienting segments. This approximation has been dealt with in detail by Treloar (22), who demonstrates that the approximation is valid for rubbery materials within the range of crosslinking usually found in practice.

An examination of the development of Eq. (2.12) shows that assumption 3 concerning the uniformity of molecular weight is of no consequence. This is easily seen from Eq. (2.10), where it is clear that the average energy stored in a chain is independent of the chain's molecular weight. Hence, the computation would yield the same result even if a distribution of molecular weights were assumed.

The assumption made concerning the affine deformation of the chains has been investigated quite thoroughly (22). Later, in Eq. (6.14), it will be shown that the numerical constant in Eq. (2.12) is altered when network-junction motion is taken into consideration. The present computation can be extended to the region of high deformations. This amplification is carried out in Appendix 6 of this chapter, where the range of validity of Eq. (2.12) is discussed further.

Experimentally, it becomes evident that assumption 6 is valid for most common rubberlike materials. Exceptions occur in special cases where weak chemical or association bonds along the chain act as temporary crosslinks during the stretching process. Of course, if the rubber begins to crystallize upon stretching, this condition will not remain true, and Eq. (2.12) will not be valid.

Sometimes a polymer network is formed in a swollen or stressed system of chains. If the polymer is then dried or if the stress is removed, the network chains will no longer be in a random set of configurations. For this reason Eq. (1.12), and consequently Eq. (2.12), will not be valid. The proper result for cases such as these has been obtained by Flory (1).

3. Chain-end Correction

Frequently, assumption 8 of the preceding section is not satisfied. Since the polymer network is usually formed by crosslinking a set of primary chains that originally had a number average molecular weight M_n, these original chain ends will usually be left dangling. The exact correction for this effect is rather complex and will not be given here. For most purposes, however, the quantity can be replaced by an effective number of chains ν_e, which is given approximately (1,23,24) by

$$\nu_e = (\rho \mathbf{N}/M_c)[1 - (2M_c/M_n)] \qquad (2.13)$$

In this expression ρ is the density of the polymer, M_c is the average molecular weight of a network chain, and $\mathbf{N}$ is Avogadro's number. If the primary number-average molecular weight of the molecules M_n is very large compared with the molecular weight of the network chains M_c, then ν_e is very nearly equal to the number of chains per unit volume, namely, $\rho N/M_c$.

4. Other Types of Deformation

The computation leading to Eq. (2.12) assumed the rubber to be subjected to a simple tensile elongation. This restriction was established when the limits of integration were chosen for Eq. (2.8). Other types of deformation could also be satisfactorily treated merely by substituting appropriate limits of integration in that equation. Perhaps the second most important type of deformation is the case of simple shear. The appropriate limits placed in Eq. (2.8) then lead to the result that

$$\sigma = \nu k T \gamma \qquad \text{(simple shear)} \qquad (2.14)$$

where γ is the shear strain. It will be noticed that, as long as the gaussian chain distribution is valid, the shear stress is proportional to the shear strain. Hence, the rubber obeys Hooke's law in *shear*, even though it does not do so for moderate *tensile* deformations.

Other types of deformation may also be treated by the methods used here. These will not be examined in detail, however, and the reader is therefore referred to the excellent treatment of various other deformations given by Treloar (22).

5. Effect of Fillers on Modulus

It is customary in many cases to add inert, nonrubbery filler to a rubber. Such fillers often impart extra strength and abrasion resistance to the rubber. In this section, however, only the effect of filler on the modulus (σ/strain) will be considered.

Many types of fillers have been used in practice, ranging from such crude materials as sawdust through carbonates, silicates, and carbon blacks. These materials are introduced into the rubber in the form of a fine powder, and it is hoped that the mixing procedure will disperse the filler as very small particles in a rubber matrix. This aim is very often difficult to achieve. In any event, the fillers are commonly classified in two groups, reinforcing and nonreinforcing fillers. This classification is not completely satisfactory, since no general agreement has been reached as to what one means by the word "reinforcing." Basically, a filler which raises the modulus while still maintaining the rubberlike qualities of the base material and which at the same time increases the strength of low-strength rubbers would be classified as a reinforcing filler.

The assumption usually made is that nonreinforcing fillers do not interact with the rubber; that is to say, even though the rubber might wet the filler surface, there is no molecular bonding between filler and rubber. In such a case the filler can be treated as particulate matter suspended in a viscous, elastic material. When the rubber is crosslinked, the viscous effect is negligible for slow deformations, and it may be shown from the classical theory for spheres immersed in an elastic matrix that

$$\sigma = vkT(\alpha - \alpha^{-2})(1 + 2.5v + 14.1v^2 + \cdots) \qquad (2.15)$$

where v is the volume fraction of filler (25).

If the filler particles are not assumed to be spherical, Eq. (2.15) must be modified somewhat. Each term beyond the first in the series must be multiplied by a shape factor that is usually greater than unity (25). This modification is seldom used, however, since most departures from Eq. (2.15) observed experimentally are much larger than reasonable shape factors can explain.

Whether or not a given filler is reinforcing depends to a certain extent upon the rubber base material. Other complications arise from the fact that it is often impossible to duplicate the degree of dispersion of the same or various fillers in different rubbers. For this reason, the mass of data on the action of fillers in rubbers is very difficult to correlate in orderly, concise fashion. It has been shown, however, that Eq. (2.15) can be applied reasonably well in several simple cases. Typical of such data are the results achieved by Cohan through using a calcium carbonate filler in SBR synthetic rubber (26). His data indicate that Eq. (2.15) applies to this combination, and hence calcium carbonate can be classed as a nonreinforcing filler for SBR.

In general, there are very few substances that can be classified as practical reinforcing fillers. Paramount among these are the various carbon blacks and, to a lesser extent, certain specially prepared silicas. These suitable materials have two things in common. They can both be highly dispersed in rubber, with particle diameters reaching as low as 100 Å. In addition, the surface of each is chemically active and can undergo direct molecular bonding with the rubber. Whether these bonds are chemical or physical has not yet been completely settled, but indications encourage the probability that the bonds important in reinforcement are rather strong (27,28).

These strong bonds between the rubber molecules and the filler surface act much differently than might be expected for a surface merely wetted by the rubber. This deviation results from the fact that a chain attachment at the filler surface in reality acts as a network crosslink point. Its effects on the rubber are felt at points far away from the filler surface: for example, a vulcanized natural rubber sample might commonly have a molecular weight between crosslinks of $M_c = 6 \times 10^3$. From Table 2 it is found that R for this network chain would be about 60 Å. Therefore, when the rubber is stretched, the attachment at the filler surface will pull directly on a network junction some 60 Å away from the surface. Since this distance is comparable to the distance between filler particles, the filler-rubber bonds will give rise to relatively long-range forces within the rubber.

From these considerations it is evident that the addition of an interacting filler to a rubber will cause two effects. First, it will increase the modulus by a small amount as a result of the effect basic to Eq. (2.15). Second, and usually much more important, the filler surface will crosslink the rubber to itself, thereby increasing ν and, consequently, the modulus. This latter action of the filler has far-reaching consequences with regard to the tensile strength of the rubber. The interpretation of this effect will be discussed in Chapter 10.

Obviously, the number of crosslinks introduced into the rubber by the filler depends directly on the filler surface area exposed to the rubber. Hence, high reinforcement will be possible only if the filler is highly dispersed. For a given volume fraction of filler, the surface area available is proportional to the reciprocal of the particle radius. Since carbon black particles usually have radii of about 60 Å and since the calcium carbonate particles used by Cohan to test Eq. (2.15) had radii of about 500 Å, on this basis alone it might be expected that the carbonate would be about one-tenth as effective as the carbon black. There is little doubt in this particular case that the surface of the nonreinforcing filler is much less highly interacting than a carbon black surface. However, it is not safe to assume in general that a nonreinforcing filler behaves as it does because of lack of filler-rubber bonding, for the dispersion of the filler is also of great importance.

6. The Mullins Effect (27)

Rubbers that contain reinforcing fillers display a curious effect, the "Mullins effect," which gives considerable information concerning the modulus reinforcing action of the filler. It may be described best by reference to the stress-strain curve shown in Figure 6.

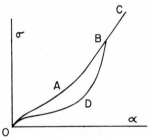

Figure 6. A typical stress-strain curve for a rubber containing carbon black. The rubber was first stretched from O through A to B. On the second stretch it follows curve ODBC.

If a vulcanized rubber filled with carbon black is stretched slowly for the first time, it gives a stress-strain curve somewhat like curve $OABC$ of Figure 6. Suppose that a particular rubber is only stretched to B on this curve during the first stretching cycle. If the sample is now relaxed and perhaps swollen in a solvent so as to facilitate complete recovery, the dried rubber will follow curve $ODBC$ in the next stretching cycle. Obviously, although the curves do not differ much at very small elongations, the rubber has been softened by the first stretching process. Actually, the intermediate portion of the second stretch cycle is not too greatly different from what might be expected for a rubber containing no filler, a so-called "gum stock."

A possible explanation of this Mullins softening effect is as follows (27). If we examine the chains connecting the surfaces of two adjacent filler particles, some of these chains will be rather highly elongated, while others will be very loosely coiled since they must conform to the gaussian distribution of chain-end lengths. This condition is illustrated in Figure 7. If the rubber

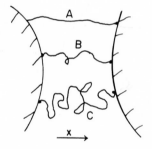

Figure 7.   Three typical chains attached to two adjacent filler particles.

is now stretched in the x direction, the filler particles will almost certainly separate in proportion to the over-all elongation of the rubber. Obviously, chain A must break at a relatively small elongation. Before breaking, nevertheless, it and similar chains will hold an enormous load and will give rise to a high modulus. On the second stretch, however, these chains, being broken, will not be holding any load; consequently, the modulus will be lower.

The softened rubber shows interesting recovery effects at high temperatures. In addition, the curves of Figure 6 may be interpreted in terms of degree of dispersion of the filler, energy of the attachment points, and number of rubber-filler attachments. The reader is referred to the pertinent literature for a further discussion of this effect (27).

7. Effect of Chain Entanglements

Equation (2.12) states that the tensile force needed to stretch a rubber is proportional to the number of network chains in unit volume. It was further shown that a correction is necessary to account for loose chain ends in the rubber, and this correction is given by Eq. (2.13). In this section, still another correction for the value of ν used in Eq. (2.12) is discussed, a correction resulting from entanglements of the polymer chains.

Consider the portion of a rubber network illustrated in Figure 8. Two chains are entangled at the point E, and this entangle-

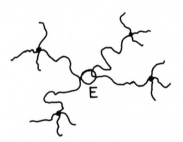

Figure 8. The two network chains shown form an entanglement crosslink at E.

ment cannot be loosed without breaking a chain in the network. Consequently, it will act in many respects as if it were a true chemical crosslink. As will be seen in Chapter 3, the molecular weight between entanglements in natural rubber is about 9,000.

Hence, if M_c is near 9,000, a large portion of the effective network chains will be the result of entanglement-type crosslinks.

The exact contribution of entanglements to the total number of effective network chains is not simple to determine. In general, it may be said that the entanglements cannot act as permanent crosslinks unless they are held in place by adjacent chemical crosslinks, as shown in Figure 8. Hence, if a true-equilibrium modulus is measured, the effect of entanglements will increase with the degree of crosslinking at small values of crosslinking, i.e., at small ν. At large values of crosslinking, however, where M_c is smaller than the average molecular weight between entanglements, nearly all the entanglement crosslinks will be effective, and their number should not increase further with increasing crosslinking.

Although the exact variation of total number of network chains (ν) with increasing number of chemically crosslinked chains (ν_{Ch}) will be quite complicated for small ν, the effect at large ν is more easily described. This results from the fact that the number of entanglement network chains (ν_E) should be constant at high degrees of crosslinking. Therefore,

$$\nu = \nu_{Ch} + \nu_E = \nu_{Ch} + \text{constant} \qquad (2.16)$$

for ν large.

Equation (2.16) predicts that a graph relating total number of network chains to number of chemical network chains should be a straight line of slope unity for large values of ν. Such a plot, taken from the work of Mullins on natural rubber (29), is shown in Figure 9. It is apparent that, even though the data do not extend to high enough degrees of crosslinking to prove the point, Eq. (2.16) applies at large ν. Since the intercept of the asymptotic line of unit slope is ν_E according to Eq. (2.16), from Figure 9 it is evident that $\nu_E \approx 9 \times 10^{-5}$ mole. This leads to the supposition that the molecular weight between entanglement points (M_e), which is equivalent to ρ/ν_E, will be about 11,000. Although this value is far from exact, it does not differ too greatly from the value found by other measurements, as will be shown in Chapter 3.

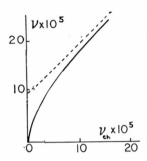

Figure 9.   The solid curve represents the data of Mullins (28) for natural rubber, showing the total number of network chains as a function of the number of chains predicted from the chemical vulcanization kinetics. The broken line has unit slope.

8. Experimental Tests of Theory

Experimental tests have been made to determine the applicability of Eqs. (2.12) and (2.13). Some of these investigations have neglected the effect of entanglements, and thus the predicted modulus vkT would not be verified by them. One of the few investigations that makes a proper correction for entanglements is that of Mullins mentioned above (29). He finds that the experimental modulus is accurately predicted by theory if the proper corrections are made, at least in the case of natural rubber.

Many investigators have found that the variation of effective network chains with degree of crosslinking and primary molecular weight follows the relation in Eq. (2.13) quite closely. Perhaps the most careful work testing this correspondence is that of Flory on butyl rubbers (30). Using fractionated rubbers of varying molecular weight, he introduced exactly the same number of crosslinks into each sample; hence, he had a series of rubber networks that had constant M_c but different known M_n. The stress-strain properties of these networks were shown to have the dependence on M_n predicted by Eqs. (2.12) and (2.13). These data, together with the theoretical work done on this problem, indicate strongly that Eq. (2.13) is a suitable representation of the effect of chain ends on network elasticity.

Until now it has been assumed that no difficulty exists in obtaining stress-strain data on rubbers, but such is not actually the case. Although it is quite true that most rubbers stretch comparatively rapidly under a fixed load to a point which appears to be an equilibrium elongation, careful measurements show that in most cases the rubber continues to elongate with time. Experimental and theoretical treatment of this effect is left until Chapter 6. However, it is obvious that, since an equilibrium elongation is often not reached, it is difficult to decide what value of α applies in Eq. (2.12) for a given value of σ.

Many investigators ignore this effect and measure the elongation at any "reasonable" time after the load is applied. They find in general that their experimental data are better represented by a relation of form

$$\sigma = 2C_1(\alpha - \alpha^{-2}) + 2C_2(1 - \alpha^{-3}) \qquad (2.17)$$

the so-called "Mooney-Rivlin equation." This relation agrees with the theoretical relation of Eq. (2.12), provided $2C_1$ is set equal to $\nu k T$ and C_2 is zero.

Careful experimental work by Ciferri and Flory (31) has indicated that the experimental value of C_2 in Eq. (2.17) will be zero if great care is taken to allow the rubber network to reach equilibrium before measuring α. In practice, this was accomplished by going to high temperatures and/or by swelling the rubber to facilitate the approach to an equilibrium elongation. It therefore appears that, even though Eq. (2.17) may fit the stress-strain curve for a rubber under practical testing conditions, Eq. (2.12) is valid for a rubber network at equilibrium under an applied load.

It may therefore be stated that the theory of rubber elasticity is firmly founded in experiment, for Eqs. (2.12) and (2.13) are well verified. These relations will not apply, of course, when the value of M_c becomes so small that the network chains can no longer be considered as freely orienting chains. Although the behavior of the rubber stress-strain curve at extremely high elongations is fairly well known from theory, as pointed out in Appendix 6 of this chapter, in many cases additional difficulties become important in this region as a result of crystallization of the rubber. Some aspects of this problem will be discussed in Chapters 10 and 13 in connection with tensile strength.

APPENDIX 5

Exact Chain Distribution Function (2,18)

According to Eq. (2.5), the tension in a chain that has been extended to an end-to-end separation r is given by

$$F = (kT/a)\mathcal{L}^*(r/Na) \qquad (A5.1)$$

The energy stored in such a chain will be equivalent to the work done in stretching it, namely,

$$V = \int_0^r F\, dr = (kT/a) \int_0^r \mathcal{L}^*(r/Na)\, dr \qquad (A5.2)$$

According to Boltzmann's distribution law, the probability that a chain would have an end-to-end distance r *when no force is applied* to the chain ends is

$$P(r) = (\text{constant}) \exp\left[-V/kT\right]$$

or

$$P(r) = (\text{constant}) \exp\left[-\phi(r/Na)\right] \qquad (A5.3)$$

where

$$\phi(r/Na) = \int_0^r \mathcal{L}^*(r/Na)\, dr/a$$

The quantity $\phi(r/Na)$ is not a simple function, but it can be expanded in series form to give

$$\phi(r/Na) = (3N/2)[\beta^2 + (\tfrac{3}{10})\beta^4 + (\tfrac{33}{175})\beta^6 + \cdots] \qquad (A5.4)$$

where $\beta = r/Na$. For small values of β, the first term in the series is the only one of importance, and Eq. (A5.3) goes over into Eq. (1.13). If β is $\frac{1}{3}$, the neglect of higher terms gives rise to only about a 4 per cent error.

APPENDIX 6

High Elongations

The stress σ needed to maintain a rubber network at a very high elongation may be obtained in much the same way as the moderate elongation problem was solved in the text of this chapter. Equation (2.8) will hold true at both small and large elongations. Since the external force applied to the rubber is exerting a tensile stress in the x direction, the rubber will actually be compressed in the y and z directions; hence the low-elongation forms for F_y and F_z may still be used in Eq. (2.8). However, the value given for F_x by Eq. (2.5) must now be used instead of the approximate form given in Eq. (2.7). Substitution in Eq. (2.8) gives

$$W/\nu = (3kT/2Na^2)(y_0^2 + z_0^2)(\alpha^{-1} - 1)$$
$$+ (kT/a) \int_{x_0}^{\alpha x_0} \mathcal{L}^*(x/Na)\, dx \qquad \text{(A6.1)}$$

This expression should now be averaged over all chains in the configurations they had before the tensile force was applied; that is, the equation should be averaged for all values of x_0, y_0, and z_0. To do this, multiply by the distribution function of Eq. (1.12) and integrate over all x_0, y_0, and z_0. The result is

$$\langle W \rangle/\nu = (3kT/2Na^2)(2R^2/3)(\alpha^{-1} - 1)$$
$$+ (kT/a) \int_{x_0=0}^{\infty} \int_{x_0}^{\alpha x_0} \mathcal{L}^*(x/Na)\, dx\, P(x_0)\, dx_0 \qquad \text{(A6.2)}$$

It is convenient to delay the actual evaluation of the integral in Eq. (A6.2) until after the next step. To find the stress σ, the derivative of W is calculated with respect to α. The following expression is then found:

$$\sigma/\nu k T = -\alpha^{-2} + (1/a) \int_{x_0=0}^{\infty} x_0 \mathcal{L}^*(\alpha x_0/Na) P(x_0)\, dx_0 \qquad (A6.3)$$

The integral in Eq. (A6.3) is best evaluated by first writing the inverse Langevin function in series form thus:

$$\mathcal{L}^*(\alpha x_0/Na) = 3\beta x_0 + (\tfrac{9}{5})\beta^3 x_0^3$$
$$+ (\tfrac{297}{175})\beta^5 x_0^5 + \cdots \qquad (A6.4)$$

where $\beta = \alpha/Na$. After inserting this expression in Eq. (A6.3) and carrying out the integrations,

$$\sigma/\nu k T = -\alpha^{-2} + (1/a)\{3\beta\langle x_0^2\rangle + (\tfrac{9}{5})\beta^3\langle x_0^4\rangle$$
$$+ (\tfrac{297}{175})\beta^5\langle x_0^6\rangle + \cdots\} \qquad (A6.5)$$

where

$$\langle x_0^{2n}\rangle = (3/2\pi Na^2)^{1/2} \int_{-\infty}^{\infty} x_0^{2n} \exp(-3x_0^2/2Na^2)\, dx_0$$

or

$$\langle x_0^{2n}\rangle = (R^2/3)^n[1 \cdot 3 \cdot 5 \cdots (2n-1)]$$

Substitution of these values into Eq. (A6.5) gives

$$\sigma/\nu k T = -\alpha^{-2} + (\tfrac{1}{3})(N)^{1/2}[3(\alpha/\sqrt{N}) + (\tfrac{9}{5})(\alpha/\sqrt{N})^3$$
$$+ (\tfrac{297}{175})(\alpha/\sqrt{N})^5(\tfrac{5}{3}) + \cdots] \qquad (A6.6)$$

The expression in brackets in Eq. (A6.6) is nearly the same as $\mathcal{L}^*(\alpha/\sqrt{N})$. The first two terms of the series are exactly correct; but the third term is a factor $\tfrac{5}{3}$ too large, and the next term will be $(5 \cdot 7)/3^2$ (or $\tfrac{35}{9}$) too large. Hence, to a fair approximation,

$$\sigma/\nu k T = (\tfrac{1}{3})(N)^{1/2}\mathcal{L}^*(\alpha/\sqrt{N}) - \alpha^{-2} \qquad (A6.7)$$

This approximate expression agrees with the result frequently quoted (1,22). It is believed, however, that the result of Eq. (A6.6) is more correct. Nevertheless, the distinction between Eq. (A6.6) and Eq. (A6.7) is trivial, in view of the fact that this method of computation assumes an affine deformation of the chains. This will certainly not be the case at such high elongations, with their consequent extreme stresses. A procedure has been derived by Treloar for including the effects of a nonaffine deformation (22,32). His result is compared with Eq. (A6.7) in Figure A.3. Unfortunately, the more correct force-extension curve found by Treloar and shown in Figure A.3 cannot be ex-

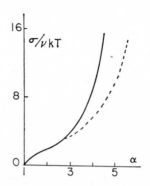

Figure A3. Comparison of the stress-strain curve found from Eq. (A6.7) (solid curve) with that found by Treloar (22) without assuming an affine deformation (broken curve).

pressed in simple mathematical form. For most purposes, however, Eq. (A6.7) will be accurate enough, even though it does predict a maximum elongation for the network that is somewhat too small.

PROBLEMS

1. Suppose a freely orienting chain with 1000 segments each of length 7 Å is subjected to a force on its ends of 10^{-6} dyne. What will be the average separation of the chain ends? Compare this value with the extended length of the chain. Repeat for a force of 10^{-5} dyne.

2. How large a force is needed to elongate the following piece of rubber to a length of 10 in.? (Express your answer in both psi and kg/cm².)

Original length = 4 in.
Area of cross section = 0.0400 in.²
M_n = 30,000 M_c = 6000
Density = 0.90 gm/cc

3. Consider a rubber for which the potential energy resulting from attractive forces between the chains decreases markedly as the chains are oriented. What

can one say about the effect of these forces upon the equilibrium stress-strain curve for the vulcanized rubber?

4. Suppose it were possible to eliminate all viscous forces so that an equilibrium stress-strain curve could be plotted for a freely orienting polymer molecule at absolute zero. What would the curve look like?

5. Carry out the integrals of Eq. (2.3) in detail and show that the result is as given there.

6. A fallacious argument sometimes heard goes as follows: "A polymer chain acts like a spring whose most probable and average end-to-end lengths are zero (see Fig. 1). Hence, a polymer network consisting of such chains would collapse, since the average distance between chain ends, and between junction points, would be zero. It does not collapse because it is essentially swollen by the actual mass of the chains." What is wrong with this argument? Does it have any validity at all?

7. The computations of Chapter 2 for the elasticity of rubber networks assumed long chains. Describe qualitatively what would happen to the stress-strain curve for the rubber as the number of crosslinks is increased to a very high value. What would the material be like when there is about one crosslink for each chain atom? To what common substance is this question relevant?

8. A strong rubber that has an ultimate elongation of $\alpha = 5$ may be swollen in a good solvent until the volume fraction of rubber in the swollen sample is only about 0.2. Are the chains very highly extended in such a swollen rubber? Explain.

9. Derive Eq. (2.14), the stress-strain relation in simple shear, by the method of Chapter 2. [*Hint:* The shear strain $\gamma = \alpha - (1/\alpha)$.]

10. Mooney and Rivlin have given a more general (but empirical) form for the stored energy function of Eq. (2.11):

$$W = C_1[\alpha^2 + (2/\alpha) - 3] + C_2[(1/\alpha^2) + 2\alpha - 3]$$

Find the stress-strain relation equivalent to Eq. (2.12) as predicted by this relation. Compare the two relations, showing in what ways they agree and in what ways they differ. A so-called "Mooney-Rivlin plot" is a plot of $\sigma/(\alpha - \alpha^2)$ vs. $1/\alpha$. What should such a plot look like if the above relation is valid? Interpret the features of the plot.

11. Suppose an isolated polymer chain carried equal charges of $+Q$ on each of its two ends. What would be the general form for the chain-end separation distribution function in such a case? (Do not attempt to normalize the function.) About how large would Q have to be if the chain were to be nearly fully elongated under the action of these charges? (Take $N = 10^2$ and $a = 5 \times 10^{-8}$ cm.)

12. Given an SBR rubber that has a primary number-average molecular weight of 30,000, how large will be the small-elongation tensile modulus if $M_c = 10,000$? If $M_c = 5,000$? Assume the kinetic theory to be correct and

ignore entanglements. Express your answer in both psi and kg/cm². How large would the shear modulus be in each case?

13. Solid propellants used in rockets often consist of filled rubbers, with about 80 per cent of the material being solid, nearly spherical filler particles and the remainder being vulcanized rubber. What would you predict for the stress-strain curves of these materials as a function of rubber-filler adhesion? Only a qualitative answer is expected, but the reasons for your conclusions should be given.

14. Using the method of the text, derive the stress-strain relation for a swollen vulcanized rubber. Show that the tension based on the original unswollen sample cross-section is given by $\sigma = (\nu k T / V_p^{1/3})(\alpha - 1/\alpha^2)$, where V_p is the volume fraction of polymer. Assume the rubber to have been vulcanized in the unswollen state.

Chapter 3

DIFFUSION AND VISCOSITY

1. Diffusion of a Particle

Let us consider a liquid composed of a large number of small molecules arranged somewhat as shown in Figure 10. These molecules will be vibrating with frequencies on the order of 10^{12} to 10^{13} vibrations per sec because of their thermal energy. Since the molecules are confined to a rather well-defined cage or cell by the surrounding molecules in the local liquid structure, a molecule such as A may be said to have a fairly well-defined average position for its mass center. A given molecule will usu-

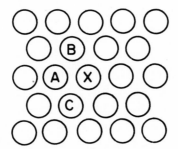

Figure 10.   A schematic diagram of molecules in a liquid.

ally have very many vibrations during the time that the average position of its center of mass requires to move a distance of one molecular diameter. For this reason it is convenient to ignore the vibrational motion of the mass center and speak only of its average position over a large number of vibrations.

61

A molecule such as A in Figure 10 can undergo translational motion relative to its neighbors in one of several ways. For example, if molecule X in Figure 10 is missing from the liquid lattice structure, a hole will exist adjacent to A. If A acquires enough thermal energy and moves in the proper direction at just the right time, it can squeeze out from its own cell and take up a new position in the hole. Although it is possible for it eventually to move back into its old position, where a hole now exists, there is a good chance that an adjacent molecule might supplant A in the hole it left behind; thus A's new position would become more or less permanent. In this event, it is convenient to say that molecule A has "jumped" to a new position. Its "jump distance" will be designated by δ and is defined as the average change in position of the center of mass resulting from such a jump.

There are many other ways in which molecule A can move to a new equilibrium position. For example, molecules C, A, B, and X could move cooperatively in a circular pattern so as to displace C to A, A to B, etc. This motion would require considerable looseness of packing in this region of the liquid, or else the molecules would be unable to squeeze past their neighbors to execute the projected motion. It is often convenient to classify this empty space between molecules as "free volume," which will be discussed more fully in the next chapter. In any event, there are many possible ways in which a small molecule in a liquid may move to a new equilibrium position. On the average a molecule will change its equilibrium position ϕ times per sec. It will make ϕ jumps per sec, where ϕ is the so-called "jump frequency." The average distance a molecule moves when it jumps is the jump distance δ.

Once ϕ and δ are known, it is possible to compute the diffusion constant for the molecule. It follows from the definition of the diffusion constant D that

$$D = \langle X^2 \rangle / 2t \tag{3.1}$$

where $\langle X^2 \rangle$ is the mean square value of the X displacement that the particle undergoes in time t. It is a simple matter to compute $\langle X^2 \rangle$, since it amounts to the same mathematical problem as finding the mean square distance from the beginning to the end of a freely orienting chain of $N = \phi t$ segments, each of length δ. This was done in Chapter 1, with the result [Eq. (1.7)] that

$$R^2 = Na^2$$

or

$$3\langle X^2 \rangle = \phi t\, \delta^2 \tag{3.2}$$

The multiple 3 arises from the fact that $R^2 = \langle X^2 \rangle + \langle Y^2 \rangle + \langle Z^2 \rangle$. Substitution of this value in Eq. (3.1) gives

$$D = \phi\, \delta^2/6 \tag{3.3}$$

This relation is of value because it states explicitly what factors determine the diffusion rate of small molecules. It is quite general and can be applied to the diffusion of small molecules in a liquid consisting of like molecules, or it can also be applied to the diffusion of small molecules through a liquid composed of polymer molecules. Since δ will not vary greatly from material to material, the diffusion constant will vary chiefly as a result of changes in the jump frequency ϕ.

2. Diffusion of Polymer Molecules: No Entanglements

The method used in the previous section to derive the diffusion constant for small molecules can easily be extended to polymer molecules (33). It cannot, of course, be said that a polymer molecule moves as a single unit; instead, a small portion of a chain will jump from one position to another, and this motion will not involve the motion of distant parts of the chain.

Consider the usual freely orienting chain consisting of N freely orienting segments, each of length a. If a small section of a freely orienting segment jumps to a new position and if its jump distance is δ', the center of mass of the segment will be moved a distance δ. From the definition of center of mass, δ will be smaller than δ' by the ratio of the mass of the small section to the mass of the freely orienting segment. Therefore, the center of mass of a freely orienting segment may be considered to undergo a jumplike motion ϕ times per sec, each jump being of length δ.

When a freely orienting segment of the chain jumps a distance δ, the center of mass of the molecule will move a distance δ/N in the same direction. It should be noted that the motion of the center of mass of the molecule does not imply that the molecule moves as a unit. The motion of the center of mass arises from the fact that it is defined as the mass center of the molecule, and whenever a portion of the molecule moves, the mass center of the molecule must move also.

Since there are N segments in the molecule, each of which jumps ϕ times per sec, the center of mass of the molecule will make $N\phi$ jumps per sec. The jump distance for the center of mass is δ/N. Therefore the center of mass of a polymer molecule makes $N\phi t$ jumps in time t, each jump of length δ/N; and the equation analogous to Eq. (3.2) for the motion of the center of mass of a polymer molecule is

$$3\langle X^2 \rangle = (N\phi t)(\delta/N)^2 \tag{3.4}$$

This value, when substituted in Eq. (3.1), yields

$$D = \phi\,\delta^2/6N \quad \text{(no entanglements)} \tag{3.5}$$

for the diffusion constant of the whole molecule.

It should be noticed that ϕ is the jump frequency of a small portion of a freely orienting segment and δ is the distance the center of mass of the segment moves when a portion of the segment jumps. It is not known a priori just how large the jumping unit is. There are indications that it is much smaller than a freely orienting segment, but this question is not easily settled. In any event, since the center of mass of the freely orienting segment will move each time a portion of it jumps, ϕ can be considered the jump frequency of the freely orienting segment as well.

3. Effect of Entanglements

The preceding computation leading to Eq. (3.5) is valid provided that a molecule is not constrained to move in a certain way by external forces. It assumes that the molecule is free to move by itself without dragging other molecules along with it. This assumption cannot be correct if the molecule is very long and is imbedded in a matrix composed of other molecules. In this case the molecules will ordinarily be entangled with each other as shown in Figure 11, where the entanglement at point E of the

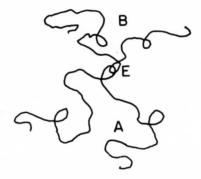

Figure 11.   The two molecules A and B are entangled at point E.

figure binds molecules A and B together. To a certain extent at least, molecule A must drag molecule B along with it if it is to move over any sizable distance.

If one traces the steps leading to Eq. (3.5), it is possible to show that the derivation breaks down when entanglements are considered. This is most easily seen by considering first the simpler case of a chain, such as A in Figure 11, tied solidly at some fixed point E in space. Although the chain can undergo considerable thermal motion about this point, the motion will not be entirely random, since the center of mass of the chain cannot move more than a fixed distance from point E. Similarly, a chain that is more or less tightly entangled with another is constrained, and its motion will not be completely random.

On the other hand, if two chains, each N segments long, are tightly entangled with each other but with no others, their *combined* center of mass will move at random. Hence, the chains will act in many ways like a single chain with $2N$ segments. It therefore appears that Eq. (3.5) will apply even to entangled chains, provided N is replaced by a larger number N^* that will correct for the dragging action of the entangled chains. This application will be shown to be true in the ensuing discussion.

4. Molecular Friction Factor: No Entanglements

An expression for the diffusion constant D may be obtained in a second way. This method is based upon the fact that it may be shown quite generally for large particles (34) that

$$D = kT/(\text{molecular friction constant}) \qquad (3.6)$$

The "molecular friction constant" is defined as the force needed to pull the undeformed molecule through its surroundings at unit speed. It is this quantity which will reflect the effects of entanglements.

Consider first the usual freely orienting chain that is not entangled with other chains. Suppose a force f_0 is required to pull a single freely orienting segment through its surroundings at unit speed. It will then require a force Nf_0 to pull the whole molecule through its surroundings with unit speed. Hence, the molecular friction constant for a nonentangled molecule is Nf_0, where f_0 is called the "segmental friction factor." Substitution of this value in Eq. (3.6) yields

$$D = kT/f_0 N \qquad \text{(no entanglements)} \qquad (3.7)$$

If Eqs. (3.5) and (3.7) are compared, it is found that $\phi\delta^2/6$ must equal kT/f_0. Solving for f_0 gives the following expression for the segmental friction factor:

$$f_0 = 6kT/\phi\delta^2 \qquad (3.8)$$

Since the quantity N that will contain the effect of entanglements cancels out, it appears that Eq. (3.8) will be true whether or not entanglements are present. Later it will be seen that such is actually the case.

5. Molecular Friction Factor: Entanglements Present (33)

If a polymer molecule is entangled with other polymer molecules, it will require a force larger than Nf_0 to pull the molecule through its surroundings with unit velocity. In principle, the computation of the molecular friction constant in the presence of entanglements is quite straightforward. It will be assumed that all polymer molecules are identical and that entanglements exist along a molecule at uniform intervals. The molecular weight between entanglement points will be designated M_e, and this molecular weight will contain N_e freely orienting segments.

If a given molecule, the primary molecule, is pulled along with unit speed, its own segments require a force Nf_0 to make them move through the surrounding material. In addition, there will be a number of molecules entangled with this primary molecule in such a way as to impede its motion. But since these molecules are not firmly tied to the primary molecule, they will slip somewhat as the primary molecule moves along. Hence, rather than moving with unit velocity as does the primary molecule, they will move with a velocity that is some fraction s as large as the velocity of the primary molecule. This quantity s is called the "slippage factor." It is unity for chemically cross-linked molecules and is zero for a molecule that is not pulled along at all.

In turn, the molecules entangled with the primary molecule will pull along still other molecules. These molecules will pull along still more, and so on. The net effect of these entangled chains is to necessitate the application of a force much larger than Nf_0 if the primary molecule is to be pulled through its surroundings with unit velocity. Although the exact computation of this effect presents a very difficult problem, an approximate solution has been obtained (33). In Appendix 7 of this chapter it is shown that, for reasonable values of the slippage constant s, the molecular friction factor for an entangled molecule can be approximated as follows:

$$N^* f_0 = N f_0 \qquad \text{for } M < 2M_e \qquad (3.9)$$

and

$$N^* f_0 = (N f_0)(\rho \mathbf{N}/48)(M/M_e)^2 M^{1/2}(R^2/M)^{3/2} \sum_{n=1}^{\infty} s^n (2n-1)^{3/2}$$

$$\text{for } M > 2M_e \qquad (3.10)$$

where ρ is the density of the polymer, and the other symbols have their usual meaning.

Equations (3.9) and (3.10) show that $N^* f_0$ should be proportional to the molecular weight M, provided that $M < 2M_e$. For molecular weights above $2M_e$, $N^* f_0$ should be proportional to $M^{3.5}$. Hence, a plot of log N^* vs. log M should consist of two intersecting straight lines: at low molecular weights, a straight line of unit slope; at high molecular weights, a straight line of slope 3.5. The point of intersection of the two lines, together with the actual slope of the curves near the intersection point, is somewhat influenced by the value chosen for the slippage factor s. This behavior is shown in Figure 12, where the more exact

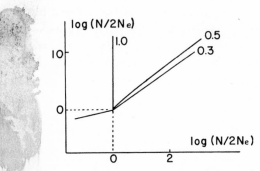

Figure 12.   The variation of the effective number of chain segments (or, alternately, viscosity) with molecular weight is shown for the slippage factors indicated on each curve.

equation given in Appendix 7 has been plotted for various values of s, using reasonable values for ρ, M_e, and R^2/M. As pointed out in Appendix 7, these values are not critical.

It is perhaps surprising that the value of N^* approaches infinity when $N = 2N_e$ and $s = 1$. The explanation of this is quite simple, however. If s is taken as unity, the case does not involve slipping entanglements but fixed crosslinks instead. When $N = 2N_e$, the condition for infinite network formation is present, and at this point a molecule must pull along an infinite number of other molecules if it is to move. Therefore, the friction constant N^*f_0 must become exceedingly large, as the graph shows.

Of course, in the case of entangled molecules it is obvious that s will not be unity. Its exact value is exceedingly difficult to compute and is unknown at the present time; however, comparison of the curves in Figure 12 with experimental data on viscosity cited later in this chapter indicates that s should be between 0.2 and 0.3. Values of s in this range give numbers of order unity for the sum of Eq. (3.10). For such values the intersection of the two straight lines of Figure 12 occurs at $M_b \cong 2M_e$. This is not an exact relation, but it is unlikely that most polymers will depart far from this value of the molecular weight at M_b, the molecular weight at the break between the two straight lines.

6. Diffusion of Entangled Polymer Molecules

Starting with the basic relation given in Eq. (3.6) between the diffusion constant and the molecular friction factor, one has at once

$$D = kT/N^*f_0 \qquad (3.11)$$

The quantity N^*f_0 is given by Eq. (3.10) for $M > M_b$ and by Eq. (3.9) for $M < M_b$, where $M_b \cong 2M_e$. If one now compares Eq. (3.11) with Eq. (3.5) and associates N^* with N, an equation for f_0 is obtained that is identical to the result given in Eq. (3.8), namely,

$$f_0 = 6kT/\phi \, \delta^2$$

This equation is of value since it provides a crossover relation between two ways of looking at the process of molecular motion.

One point of view pictures the freely orienting segment as rubbing against its neighbors with a friction factor f_0, while the other viewpoint considers the segment to jump from place to place with frequency ϕ. The two conceptions are essentially equivalent for most purposes, and Eq. (3.8) connects the one with the other.

7. Viscosity of Polymer Solutions and Melts: Theory (33,35)

Consider a unit cube of polymer such as that shown in Figure 13. If a force F is applied uniformly to the top of the cube as

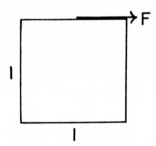

Figure 13.   A diagram showing the action of a shearing force F on a unit cube.

shown and this force displaces the top surface with respect to the bottom surface at a very small uniform velocity v, then by definition the viscosity of the polymer is

$$\eta = F/v \qquad (3.12)$$

This assumes the velocity to be small enough so that the cube will not be much distorted during the measurement. Equation (3.12) can be rearranged to give

$$\eta = Fv/v^2$$

and since Fv is the energy expended per second on the cube,

$$\eta = (\text{energy loss per sec in unit volume})/\dot{\gamma}^2 \qquad (3.13)$$

The quantity $\dot{\gamma}$ is the shear rate and is the same as v in this instance. In general, it is the change in liquid velocity per unit length in a given direction, i.e., the velocity gradient.

It is now apparent that the computation of the viscosity for a system of molecules amounts to finding the energy loss in unit volume as a result of a given shear rate. This loss of energy is obviously caused by the rubbing together of the molecules as the liquid layers flow past each other. If the amount of friction work done on a single molecule of the liquid can be computed, the viscosity can be found by multiplying this energy loss by the number of molecules per unit volume.

Consider the polymer molecule shown in Figure 14. As a result of the shearing force illustrated in Figure 13, the material in which the molecule is imbedded will move relative to the

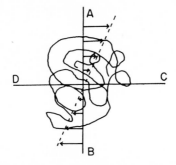

Figure 14.   The action of the sheared fluid represented by the arrows is to cause the molecule to rotate clockwise.

center of mass of the molecule. Since a single molecule will not seriously distort the flow lines in a concentrated polymer solution or melt, the relative velocity of the matrix material through the polymer molecule will be as indicated by the arrows in Figure 14. As this liquid flows through the molecule, it will cause the molecule to rotate in a clockwise direction.

Even though the liquid flow at A and B will tend to make the molecule rotate clockwise, however, the stationary liquid at D and C will tend to oppose any motion of the molecule. Hence, the molecule will move more slowly than the matrix liquid at A and B while moving more swiftly than the liquid at C and D. The consequent viscous rubbing action between the polymer and the surrounding liquid will give rise to frictional energy losses. It is shown in Appendix 8 of this chapter that the rate of energy loss for such a molecule in a shear gradient $\dot{\gamma}$ is

$$\dot{W} = (\dot{\gamma}^2/36)(Nf_0)R^2 \qquad (3.14)$$

Multiplying Eq. (3.14) by the number of molecules per unit volume ($\mathbf{N}\rho/M$) gives the rate of energy loss per unit volume. This value may then be substituted into Eq. (3.13) to obtain the following expression for the shear viscosity:

$$\eta = (\rho\mathbf{N}/36)(R^2/M)Nf_0 \qquad \text{(no entanglements)} \qquad (3.15)$$

If the molecules are entangled, the energy loss per molecule will be much larger than is given by Eq. (3.14). It is possible to replace the molecular friction factor Nf_0 in Eq. (3.14) by a larger value N^*f_0 if entanglements are considered. Although a rigorous proof has never been given that the N^* applicable to the molecular motion envisaged in connection with viscous effects should be exactly equal to the N^* computed in Sec. 3.6 for translational motion, qualitative considerations indicate that they should be essentially the same. Hence, in the case of any concentrated polymer solution or for a polymer melt,

$$\eta = (\rho\mathbf{N}/36)(R^2/M)N^*f_0 \qquad (3.16)$$

where N^*f_0 is given by Eqs. (3.9) and (3.10).

8. Relation between D and η

It is possible to combine Eq. (3.16) with Eq. (3.11) to obtain an interesting result. Multiplying D by η gives

$$D\eta = (\rho\mathbf{N}/36)(R^2/M)kT \qquad (3.17)$$

Since all the quantities in this relation are relatively easily measured, it can be used to check the theoretical reasoning used above.

From a practical standpoint, Eq. (3.17) is of value since it relates D to η through the quantity R^2/M. Because η and R^2/M are easily measured or estimated, Eq. (3.17) can be used to find the more difficult quantity to measure, namely, D.

9. Variation of M_e with ρ

The molecular weight between entanglement points along a molecule (M_e) will vary as ρ, the mass of polymer in unit volume, varies. That this relation is true becomes obvious when one considers that, if a highly entangled group of polymer chains is diluted with diluent, the value of ρ can be decreased to the point where the molecules no longer overlap and no entanglements will be present. Accordingly, one would expect M_e to increase as ρ decreases.

Let us now consider a long molecule contorted in such a way that it has several loops along its length which would act as entanglements if another chain passed through them in just the right way. The number of chains passing through such a loop will be proportional to the total number of chains per unit volume, i.e., to ρ. Hence, the chance that a given loop in a chain is entangled with another chain is proportional to ρ. Since M_e equals the molecular weight of a chain divided by the number of entanglements, it follows that $M_e \sim 1/\rho$. Therefore, there results the important relation

$$M_e\rho = \text{constant} \tag{3.18}$$

Equation (3.18) is based upon the assumption that a given chain in the polymer has more possible places along its length where entanglements could occur if there were more chains present per unit volume. In other words, since M_e is assumed to have reached no asymptotic value even at the highest possible value of ρ, this is equivalent to assuming that there are still other places along the chain where entanglements could occur. Although this is not a necessary assumption in the derivation of any of the previous equations except Eq. (3.18), there appears to be no experimental evidence to show that Eq. (3.18) does not hold true. However, it is not inconceivable that Eq. (3.18) will be found untrue for some exceptionally rigid chain.

10. Experimental Evidence: High Molecular Weights

Many experimental data are available for the viscosity of polymer melts and their concentrated solutions. These data (36), without exception, follow a relation of form

$$\eta = KM^{3.5} \tag{3.19}$$

for M greater than some critical molecular weight M_b as predicted by Eqs. (3.16) and (3.10). Data for two typical pure polymers, polystyrene and polyisobutylene (37), are shown in Figures 15 and 16.

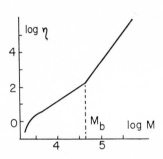

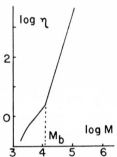

Figure 15. Variation of melt viscosity of polystyrene (37) as a function of molecular weight at 217°C. The line for M greater than M_b has a slope of 3.5.

Figure 16. Variation of melt viscosity of polyisobutylene (37) as a function of molecular weight at 217°C. The line for M greater than M_b has a slope of 3.5.

Not only do pure polymer melts obey Eq. (3.19) above the break at M_b, but similar behavior is also noticed for concentrated solutions of polymers. This is shown by the data for 25 per cent solutions of polymethyl methacrylate in diethyl phthalate (38) given in Figure 17. Similar studies have been made on concentrated solutions of polystyrene, polyvinyl acetate, and polyisobutylene (39). All these investigations indicate that the molecular weight at which the break in the viscosity curve occurs (M_b) is related to the polymer concentration by the value

$$M_b \rho = \text{constant} \tag{3.20}$$

at least within experimental error. Since it was shown in Sec. 3.5 that M_e/M_b is essentially a constant, Eq. (3.18) predicts the validity of Eq. (3.20).

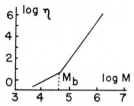

Figure 17. Variation of melt viscosity of polymethyl methacrylate (38) plasticized with 75 per cent diethyl phthalate at 60°C.

Because of the existence of the experimental relations stated in Eqs. (3.19) and (3.20), the theoretical considerations leading to Eqs. (3.10) and (3.16) appear well founded. Further confirmation of theory is obtained by experimental checks of Eq. (3.17). These checks have been made by measuring both D and η and seeing if they conform to Eq. (3.17). Three polymer systems have been used: poly-n-butyl acrylate (33), polystyrene (33), and polymethylene (40). In some cases, plasticizer content has also been varied. Although the experimental errors involved in measuring D are usually quite large, the validity of Eq. (3.17) has been confirmed by all these measurements.

Since a large number of polymers have now been characterized with regard to their melt viscosity, it is interesting to compare $\rho M_b/M_0$ for these polymers where M_0 is the monomer molecule weight. This number should be approximately equal to ρ times twice the number of monomer units between chain entanglements in the pure polymer. A tabulation of these values is given in Table 3.

The values for the number of monomer units between entanglements in the pure polymer appear to defy interpretation at this time. For example, comparing the values for polyethylene, polymethyl methacrylate, and polystyrene shows that polarity is not the sole determining factor. Comparison of polystyrene and polymethyl methacrylate shows that glass temperature is

TABLE 3
Entanglement Spacings†

Polymer	$_f M_b / M_0$	M_b	Method
Polystyrene	380	40,000	Viscosity
Polymethyl methacrylate	100	10,000	Viscosity
Polyisobutylene	310	17,000	Viscosity
Polydimethylsiloxane	500	37,000	Viscosity
Polyvinyl acetate	260	22,000	Viscosity
Polyethylene	80	2,000	Viscosity
Natural rubber	240	17,000	Compliance
Polyethylene oxide	140	6,000	Compliance

† These are average values from the literature and should only be considered approximate.

not the controlling factor. At the present time, there appears to be no satisfactory way for predicting M_b from polymer structure, but various tentative suggestions have been made (41).

The constancy of M_b with temperature is still in doubt. Certain dynamic measurements to be discussed in Chapter 9 purport to measure M_e; they indicate a small increase in M_e with temperature at least in certain cases. However, the theoretical and experimental difficulties associated with such measurements leave appreciable doubt as to the validity of the small changes noted. Contrary to this, viscosity measurements have indicated that M_b is not much dependent upon temperature in the cases of several polymers. For this reason, it can only be concluded that if temperature variations in M_b and M_e occur they are not very large.

11. Experimental Evidence: Low Molecular Weights

The variation of viscosity with M at low molecular weights is shown in Figures 15, 16, and 17. Although relevant theory predicts, through Eqs. (3.9) and (3.16), that the data in this region should be represented by a straight line of unit slope in these figures, it is clear that this is not the case. Analysis of all data available concerning such variation indicates that the more highly diluted the polymer is, the more closely the data approximate the theoretical slope. The data also agree more closely with theoretical predictions when the polymer is at a temperature far above its glass temperature.

This discrepancy between experiment and theory has the following basis (42,43). A polymer segment near a chain end will, on the average, have a higher jump frequency than the usual polymer segment. This phenomenon results from the fact that the chain end loosens the local liquid structure and thereby facilitates motion. Any segment, whether or not it is in the particular chain that supplies the chain end, will move more freely as a result of the chain end being near by. Hence, f_0 will decrease with molecular weight, and consequently the viscosity will change more than would be predicted from Eq. (3.16) with f_0 constant. In the next chapter it will be shown how this complication can be treated. When the variation of f_0 is compensated for, the experimental data below M_b appear to agree with theory also.

12. Non-Newtonian Viscosity

In this chapter it has been assumed that the viscosity of the polymer is Newtonian. In other words, the measured viscosity is assumed to be independent of the shear rate $\dot{\gamma}$ used for the measurement; however, such is not actually the case. The viscosity of concentrated polymer solutions and melts decreases at very high shear rates. This effect is most evident at high molecular weights; at very low rates of shear, the viscosity is constant. The measurements described in this chapter have been made at low shear rates. The molecular factors responsible for the apparent decrease in viscosity at high shear rates will be discussed in Chapter 9.

13. Effect of a Distribution of Molecular Weights

The equations for viscosity given in the previous sections are of form $\eta = KM^a$, where a is unity for low molecular weights and 3.5 for high molecular weights. These equations apply only in the case of a narrow molecular-weight distribution. It can be shown that similar equations apply even in the case of a heterogeneous polymer, provided a particular average value of M is used (44).

At low molecular weights, the effect of entanglements is negligible; thus the length of one chain does not influence the viscosity increase caused by another chain. This assumes, of course, that chain-end effects upon f_0 are negligible. If this is the case, then the viscosity will be the sum of the viscosities of each of the molecular-weight species present. That is,

$$\rho\eta = K_1 \Sigma \rho_i M_i \qquad (3.21)$$

where ρ_i is the concentration of the i'th species. But a comparison of the sum in Eq. (3.21) with the definition of the weight-average molecular weight given in the Introduction indicates that

$$\eta = K_1 M_w \qquad \text{(low } M) \qquad (3.22)$$

Therefore, if the effect of chain ends and entanglements upon the friction factor $N^* f_0$ can be neglected, the viscosity should depend upon the weight-average molecular weight in the same way as the viscosity of a fraction would depend upon its molecular weight.

The behavior of polymers at high molecular weight is not quite so simple. This complication results from the fact that the length of one molecule affects the viscosity contribution of other molecules because of entanglements. Hence, the addition of component viscosities cannot easily be carried out. There is convincing experimental data (42,44) showing that the proper relation at high molecular weights should be of the following form:

$$\eta = K_2 M_w{}^{3.5} \qquad \text{(high } M) \qquad (3.23)$$

This fact has been confirmed by theoretical treatment (45). However, the theory result predicts that, for very wide distributions in molecular weight, the proper average is not M_w but a value somewhere between M_w and M_z, the next higher average. The theory predicts that M_z will be a better approximation to the true average if $M_w/M_n > 2$. This condition depends upon the exact form of the distribution and cannot be stated precisely. An experimental confirmation of this prediction is still lacking.

APPENDIX 7

Molecular Friction Factor (33)

It has been shown that (33) the molecular friction factor N^*f_0 can be approximately expressed as

$$N^*f_0 = Nf_0[1 + (M/8M_e)]$$

$$\{1 + \sum_{n=1}^{\infty} (sM/2M_e)^n(1/B_n)[1 - \exp(-B_n)]\} \qquad (A7.1)$$

where

$$1/B_n = (\rho N/3)(R^2/M)(RM/2M_e)(2M_e/M)^n(2n - 1)^{3/2}$$

In this expression the symbols R and M have their usual meaning, while ρ is the density of polymer, N is Avogadro's number, and M_e is the molecular weight between chain entanglements.

The value for N^*f_0 simplifies greatly in the region of molecular weights where $M \ll 2M_e$ and becomes

$$N^*f_0 = Nf_0 \qquad \text{for } M \ll 2M_e \qquad (A7.2)$$

Also, at very large molecular weights one has

$$N^*f_0 = Nf_0(\rho N/48)(M/M_e)^2 M^{1/2}(R^2/M)^{3/2} \sum_{n=1}^{\infty} s^n(2n - 1)^{3/2}$$

$$\text{for } M \gg 2M_e \qquad (A7.3)$$

A graph showing the variation of N^*f_0 with chain molecular weight will therefore show N^*f_0 proportional to M for $M \ll 2M_e$. In the other limit, namely, $M \gg 2M_e$, N^*f_0 is found to be proportional to $M^{3.5}$. Furthermore, Eq. (A7.1) reveals a rather sharp break near $2M_e$; and thus Eq. (A7.2) is a rather good approximation to Eq. (A7.1) for $M < 2M_e$, while Eq. (A7.3) appears valid for $M > 2M_e$.

The exact value of the molecular weight M_b at which Eq. (A7.2) is to be replaced by Eq. (A7.3) is found by equating the two values for N^*f_0 and solving for M_b. The approximate value of M_b at which the friction constant changes from a first to a 3.5-power dependence on molecular weight is given by

$$M_b/M_e = (48/\mathbf{N}\beta)^{0.40}(M/R^2)^{0.60}(1/M_e\rho)^{0.20}(1/\rho)^{0.20} \qquad (A7.4)$$

where

$$\beta = \sum_{n=1}^{\infty} s^n(2n - 1)^{3/2}$$

For a given polymer, M/R^2 and $M_e\rho$ should be essentially constant even when considerable plasticizer is present. The near constancy of M/R^2 for polymers in bulk and concentrated solution is discussed in Chapter 1. It is shown in Sec. 3.10 why $M_e\rho$ can be considered a constant for a given polymer. If—as experimental data cited in this chapter indicate to be the case—s is between 0.1 and 0.3, the chains slip over each other quite freely at the entanglement points. Hence, s should not vary much, if any, from polymer to polymer. It thus appears that M_b/M_e will not vary much for a given polymer or even for different polymers.

If β is replaced by 0.60 and if a value of 2×10^{16} is used for M/R^2,

$$M_b/M_e = 12/(M_e\rho^2)^{0.20} \qquad (A7.5)$$

Since $M_e\rho$ is usually of order 10^4 and ρ is of order unity, Eq. (A7.5) gives M_b/M_e to be about 1.9. If ρ changes by a factor of 10, M_b/M_e will change by a factor of about 1.6. If M_e were to change by a factor of 10, with ρ remaining constant, the quantity M_b/M_e would again change by a factor of 1.6.

APPENDIX 8

Viscous Energy Loss (35)

Consider the molecule illustrated in Figure 14 earlier in this chapter. It will be, on the average, spherically symmetrical and will rotate with angular velocity ω about an axis through its center of mass. In Figure A.4, the Z axis will be the axis of rotation and the rotation will be clockwise. As a result of the shearing action, the velocity of the liquid at a height y above the x axis is $\dot{\gamma}y$.

The chain segment shown at point P in Figure A.4 is at a distance $(x^2 + y^2)^{1/2}$ from the axis of rotation. It will experience

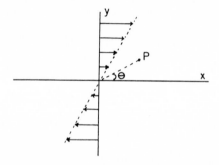

Figure A4.   Diagram illustrating the coordinate system and sheer gradient used to compute the viscous energy loss of a molecule.

a torque about the axis for two reasons. First, the shear gradient causes the surrounding liquid to flow past point P with a velocity $\dot{\gamma}y$. This causes a clockwise torque on the segment about the axis that has a value of $f_0(\dot{\gamma}y)(x^2 + y^2)^{1/2} \sin \theta$. Second, because the molecule is moving through the liquid with angular velocity ω, the segment experiences a counterclockwise torque equal to $\omega f_0(x^2 + y^2)$. Hence, the total torque on the segment about the Z axis is

$$\text{Torque} = f_0[(\dot{\gamma}y)(x^2 + y^2)^{1/2} \sin \theta - \omega(x^2 + y^2)] \qquad \text{(A8.1)}$$

which may be written as

$$\text{Torque} = f_0[\dot{\gamma}(x^2 + y^2)\sin^2\theta - \omega(x^2 + y^2)] \qquad \text{(A8.2)}$$

If all the segments of the molecule are located that lie at a distance $(x^2 + y^2)^{1/2} \pm \Delta r$ from the Z axis, they will lie within a cylindrical shell concentric with the Z axis with radius $(x^2 + y^2)^{1/2}$ and thickness $2\Delta r$. The average torque caused by the frictional forces on the segments in this cylindrical shell is obtained by averaging Eq. (A8.2) over all values of θ:

$$\text{Average torque} = f_0[\dot{\gamma}(x^2 + y^2)(\tfrac{1}{2}) - \omega(x^2 + y^2)] \qquad \text{(A8.3)}$$

However, under steady flow conditions and with a spherically symmetrical molecule, the molecule must rotate with constant angular velocity. This will be the case if the average torque on all possible cylindrical shells is zero. In that event, the torque of Eq. (A8.3) must be zero, and thus

$$\omega = \dot{\gamma}/2 \qquad \text{(A8.4)}$$

Hence, it is observed that the angular velocity of the molecule is one-half the shear gradient.

It is now possible to compute the frictional energy loss due to the motion of a single polymer segment in the fluid. The energy loss per second will be equal to the product of $f_0 v$, the frictional force, and v, the distance moved against the force in a second. Again, for the segment shown in Figure A.4, the i'th segment,

$$
\begin{aligned}
v_i^2 &= v_{ix}^2 + v_{iy}^2 \\
&= [y_i\dot{\gamma} - (x_i^2 + y_i^2)^{1/2}\omega\sin\theta_i]^2 + (x_i^2 + y_i^2)\omega^2\cos^2\theta_i \\
&= (\dot{\gamma}/2)^2(x_i^2 + y_i^2)\sin^2\theta_i + (\dot{\gamma}/2)^2(x_i^2 + y_i^2)\cos^2\theta_i
\end{aligned}
$$

or

$$v_i^2 = (\dot{\gamma}^2/4)(x_i^2 + y_i^2) \qquad \text{(A8.5)}$$

The energy loss per second for the i'th segment is then

$$\dot{W}_i = f_0(\dot{\gamma}^2/4)(x_i^2 + y_i^2) \qquad \text{(A8.6)}$$

and for the whole molecule is

$$\dot{W} = \Sigma\, \dot{W}_i = N f_0(\dot{\gamma}^2/4)(\langle x^2 \rangle + \langle y^2 \rangle) \qquad \text{(A8.7)}$$

But since the molecule is spherically symmetrical, the mean

square value of the x distance from the Z axis averaged over all segments in the molecule is simply $S^2/3$, where S^2 is the mean square segment distance from the center of mass of the molecule (found to be $R^2/6$ in Chapter 1).

Substitution of these values in Eq. (A8.7) gives the following expression for the average energy loss per second per molecule:

$$\dot{W} = (\dot{\gamma}^2/36)(Nf_0)(R^2) \qquad \qquad (A8.8)$$

PROBLEMS

1. Suppose a monomeric molecule moves in a jumplike fashion. Its jump distance is 2 Å, and its jump frequency is 10^6 sec^{-1}. What will be the rms distance the molecule will move in 10 min? How large is the diffusion constant?

2. Through what rms distance will a natural rubber molecule of 8×10^3 molecular weight diffuse in 10 min if the molecular weight of a segment is 80, the jump distance is 0.5 Å, and the jump frequency is 10^5? What is the diffusion constant in this case?

3. Consider the diffusion of a polystyrene molecule of molecular weight 10^4 through the polymer. Suppose the temperature is 150°C, which is high enough so that the polymer is far above its glassy state. Will the rate of diffusion of the chain depend upon whether or not it is linear or branched? Explain.

4. If the segments of the polystyrene molecules of problem 3 have a jump distance of 0.20 Å, a jump frequency of 10^4 sec^{-1}, and a molecular weight per segment of 150, how large a force must be applied to one of these molecules to move it through the matrix at a speed of 10^{-5} cm/sec? How large would f_0 be for such a molecule?

5. Compare the size of the molecular friction factor for a polystyrene molecule in polystyrene having $M = 10^6$ with the friction factor that would apply if no entanglements were present. Assume $\Sigma s^n(2n - 1)^{3/2} = 0.6$.

6. If the jump frequency and jump distance for the polymer in problem 5 are 10^4 sec^{-1} and 0.2 Å, respectively, how far will such a molecule diffuse in 10 min? How does this distance compare with the rms end-to-end length of the molecule?

7. Consider a polymer of unit density whose molecules contain 10^3 freely orienting segments each. The segmental jump distance is 0.50 Å. If the jump frequency is 10^6 sec^{-1}, what will be the viscosity of the polymer (a) if no entanglements exist? (b) if one entanglement point occurs for every 100 freely orienting segments and $\Sigma s^n(2n - 1)^{3/2} = 0.6$? Compare these values with the ones that would be observed at the glass temperature where the jump frequency would be about 10^{-1} sec^{-1}.

8. The computation of the viscous energy loss for a polymer without entanglements given in Appendix 8 assumed a linear chain. How would the result be changed if one considered a branched molecule of the same molecular weight for which S_b, the radius of gyration of the branched molecule, was a fraction K times as large as S of the linear polymer? How would the viscosity be changed?

9. Consider two polymers having the same density, chemical constitution, and molecular weight. One polymer contains long chain branches and the other is linear. Qualitatively, how would the log η vs. log M curves look for these two polymers? Be careful to show any shift of M_b for the two polymers. Explain your answer.

Chapter 4

SEGMENTAL MOTION AND THE
GLASS TEMPERATURE

1. The Jump Frequency ϕ

It was shown in Chapter 3 that the rate of diffusion of large
molecules composed of many segments is intimately related to
the jump frequency of a segment. The jump frequency ϕ was
defined as the number of times per second that a segment of a
polymer chain translated from one equilibrium position to another. Similarly, the viscosity of polymeric systems was shown
to be directly influenced by the jump frequency of the freely
orienting segments in the molecule. In addition, the jump frequency ϕ was shown to be related to the segmental friction
factor f_0 by Eq. (3.8). The purpose of this chapter is to show
how ϕ and f_0 depend upon temperature and polymer constitution.

Ideally one would start from a basic knowledge of intermolecular forces and compute the motion of the molecule in a liquid as
a problem in many-body dynamics. In reality, such an approach
is obviously out of the question, except perhaps for the simplest
types of small molecules. Even then, great difficulties arise in
carrying through an exact formulation; thus one must resort to
various simplifications if usable answers are to be obtained (46).

Polymer molecules in general are far too complicated to allow
an exact computation of the segmental motion. Two alterna-
tives present themselves: the problem can be formulated rigor-

ously and then mathematical approximations can be sought that will allow a solution to be found; or a simple approximate model for the molecular situation can be set up and the model system solved rigorously. Both approaches have been applied to the motion of small molecules in low-molecular-weight liquids and crystals. Each has yielded valuable results that have more or less complemented each other.

In the case of polymeric systems, however, the computation of molecular motion has been restricted to the use of more or less realistic model systems. No attempt has yet been made to carry through a rigorous solution for the motion of actual polymer segments. There appears to be little likelihood that such a computation will be feasible in the near future. With this fact in mind, a model system will be used in this chapter to describe the motion of molecules in low-molecular-weight materials. This model will then be extended to include the motion of polymer segments.

2. Motion of Small Molecules; Free Volume and Thermal Expansion

Consider a model of a liquid that consists of n rather small molecules contained in volume V. Each of these molecules will occupy a volume $v = V/n$ at some temperature T. This volume per molecule will consist partly of free space, since the molecules will be vibrating about their equilibrium position and will consequently exclude other molecules from taking up positions too close to them. In addition, there is the possibility that, under their random thermal motion, some of the molecules may pull apart in such a way as to open a void or hole in the liquid.

An average amount of free volume $v_f(= V_f/n)$ may be assigned to each of the n molecules. As a crude model, assume that each piece of free volume comes in a spherical shape of radius b and that the energy of the free volume is just a surface-tension energy $4\pi\epsilon b^2$. To a first approximation, ϵ may be considered the surface energy per unit area; numerically it would then equal the surface tension of the liquid.

According to the Boltzmann distribution law, the chance that a particular molecule will have associated with it a hole of radius b will be proportional to $\exp\left(-4\pi\epsilon b^2/kT\right)$. The average size of a hole in the liquid will therefore be obtained from the following expression:

$$v_f = \frac{\displaystyle\int_{b=0}^{\infty} (\tfrac{4}{3})\pi b^3 \exp\left(-4\pi\epsilon b^2/kT\right) db}{\displaystyle\int_{0}^{\infty} \exp\left(-4\pi\epsilon b^2/kT\right) db} \tag{4.1}$$

After the indicated operations are performed,

$$v_f = (1/6\pi)(kT/\epsilon)^{1.5} \tag{4.2}$$

This leads to the following expression for the volume of a liquid that has volume V_0 at $T = 0$:

$$\begin{aligned} V &= V_0 + V_f \\ &= V_0 + (n/6\pi)(k/\epsilon)^{1.5}T^{1.5} \end{aligned} \tag{4.3}$$

Since the volume coefficient of expansion of a liquid (α) is by definition $(1/V_0)(dV/dT)$,

$$\alpha \cong (n/4\pi)(k/\epsilon)^{1.5}T^{0.5} \tag{4.4}$$

where V_0 has been taken as unity, and variation of n with temperature has been neglected. Since the value α is usually regarded as essentially independent of T, Eq. (4.4) may seem in error because of the factor $T^{0.5}$; however, the value of α actually does increase with T for most liquids. In fact, the expansion of straight-chain paraffin hydrocarbons, to mention one instance, is far better represented by an α varying as in Eq. (4.4) than by a constant α. In addition, the numerical value given for α by Eq. (4.4) is not unreasonable.

For example, if one takes $n = 6 \times 10^{21}$ per cc and $\epsilon = 28$ ergs/cm^2, it turns out that α is given by Eq. (4.4) to be about

1.2×10^{-3} per °C at room temperature. This value is completely reasonable for a low-molecular-weight liquid. Of course, one should not give much quantitative significance to Eq. (4.4), since the model used for deriving it was grossly oversimplified.

3. Motion of Small Molecules; Jump Frequency at Large T

A molecule will be able to jump to a new equilibrium position provided: (1) there is enough free volume available to make such a jump possible; (2) the molecule has enough energy to break loose from its neighbors and move into the hole; and (3) the molecule is moving in the proper direction at just the right time to enter the hole. Of these three factors, only the first will be highly temperature-sensitive. Free volume can only be obtained by opening a void in the liquid. This will require considerable thermal energy to be localized in a small region of the liquid if the hole is to be of molecular dimensions.

The energy needed for the molecule to break loose from its neighbors and move into the hole will usually be only a small fraction of the energy needed to produce the hole; consequently, this factor should be a much less critical function of the temperature than is the first. Similarly, a molecule will ordinarily be vibrating in its equilibrium cell with such a high frequency that, if the first condition is satisfied and a hole is present, the molecule will eventually vibrate in the proper direction for entering the hole. Therefore, one may approximate the true situation by stating that the probability that a molecule will jump to a new equilibrium position is equal to a constant multiplied by the probability that a large hole is adjacent to the molecule. If the hole must have a volume v^* or larger if a molecule is to jump into it, the fraction of the total number (n) of holes having volumes larger than v^* must be found. Since the probability of finding a hole of radius b is proportional to $\exp\left(-4\pi\epsilon b^2/kT\right)$, the following expression results for the number of holes larger than v^* (assuming each hole to be independent):

$$\frac{n \int_{b*}^{\infty} \exp\left(-4\pi\epsilon b^2/kT\right) db}{\int_{0}^{\infty} \exp\left(-4\pi\epsilon b^2/kT\right) db} \tag{4.5}$$

This expression may be integrated in terms of the error function. Then, if the critical energy defined by

$$\epsilon^* = 4\pi\epsilon b^{*2}$$

is much greater than kT, as it ordinarily will be, Eq. (4.5) yields

$$n(\pi\epsilon^*/kT)^{1/2} \exp\left(-\epsilon^*/kT\right) \tag{4.6}$$

The jump frequency ϕ will be proportional to the quantity given by expression (4.6) and will also be proportional to the time required for the local liquid structure about a molecule to change its energy appreciably. This time will ordinarily be much shorter than the time between jumps, since it will depend primarily on the vibrational collisions of adjacent molecules. For this reason, it should not be highly temperature-sensitive. In addition, the jump frequency should depend upon various geometrical factors mentioned previously; hence,

$$\phi = \phi_0 \exp\left(-\epsilon^*/kT\right) \tag{4.7}$$

where the quantity ϕ_0 defined by Eq. (4.7) is far less temperature-sensitive than the exponential.

An order of magnitude for ϕ_0 can be obtained by noting that if the temperature is very high the exponential factor in Eq. (4.7) becomes unity, and thus ϕ_0 is equal to ϕ. In this limit, there should be a very large number of holes present; accordingly, the jump frequency ϕ should be very close to the reciprocal of the time necessary for the molecule to cross its cell. This value will be of the order of the vibration frequency of the molecule, which will be in the range 10^{12} to 10^{14}. Since ϕ is always much smaller than this, as will be shown later, it is clear that $\epsilon^* \gg kT$ at ordinary temperatures.

Equation (4.7) may be substituted in Eq. (3.3) to give the diffusion constant:

$$D = (\phi_0\delta^2/6) \exp(-\epsilon^*/kT) \qquad (4.8)$$

Also, Eq. (4.8) can be used in Eq. (3.6) in order to obtain the molecular friction factor for the molecule. In either case, the primary temperature dependence for motion of the molecule enters through the factor $\exp(-\epsilon^*/kT)$.

Notice that if the value of D has been measured over a range of temperatures Eq. (4.8) can be used to obtain ϵ^* as well as $\phi_0\delta^2$. This is accomplished by plotting $\ln D$ vs. $1/T$. According to Eq. (4.8), this plot should be a straight line with slope $-\epsilon^*/k$ and intercept $\ln(\phi_0\delta^2/6)$. Such plots, the so-called "Arrhenius plots," are reasonably linear for most liquids. The values of ϵ^* usually are found to lie between 5 and 15 Kcal/mole.

4. Motion of Polymer Molecule Segments at Large T

The preceding sections of this chapter are extremely pertinent for the behavior of polymer molecules. It is true that a small molecule and a polymer molecule cannot be considered to move in the same way; but as pointed out in the previous chapter, the jump-frequency concept may be applied to polymer segments, which in many ways behave like small molecules. For example, in order for a polymer segment to jump from one position to another, a critical amount of free volume (v^*) must be available. In addition, the jump frequency will be dependent upon rather complicated geometrical and vibrational factors. But, as was true in the case of small molecules, one would not expect these factors to be nearly as temperature-sensitive as the free-volume factor. Even in the case of polymer molecules, therefore, the computation of the jump frequency reduces primarily to computation of the probability that a piece of free volume is larger than the critical value for movement (v^*).

Reexamination of the computations in Secs. 4.2 and 4.3 shows that Eqs. (4.5), (4.6), and (4.7) are applicable to the case of polymer molecules as well as to small molecules. Of course, v^* and ϵ^* must now be interpreted as the critical free volume and energy for a polymer segment to jump.

Substitution of Eq. (4.7) in Eq. (3.8) yields the following expression for the segmental friction factor f_0:

$$f_0 = (6kT/\phi_0\delta^2) \exp (\epsilon^*/kT) \qquad (4.9)$$

This value can then be used in Eq. (3.11) to obtain the diffusion constant of a polymer molecule:

$$D = (\phi_0\delta^2/6N^*) \exp (-\epsilon^*/kT) \qquad (4.10)$$

Again it may be seen that an Arrhenius plot can be used to find ϵ^*, provided Eq. (4.10) is valid. Later in this chapter it will be seen that Eq. (4.10) is often a poor approximation for polymers unless ϵ^* is allowed to vary. The reasons for this are related to the fact that the various pieces of free volume, that is, the holes, were assumed to act independently of each other when Eq. (4.5) was derived.

Similarly, Eq. (4.9) can be substituted into Eq. (3.16) to obtain an expression for the viscosity of polymers:

$$\eta = (\rho \mathbf{N} kT/6\phi_0\delta^2)(R^2/M)N^* \exp (\epsilon^*/kT) \qquad (4.11)$$

This equation predicts that an Arrhenius plot of $\ln (\eta/T)$ vs. $(1/T)$ should give a straight line with slope ϵ^*/k. As in the case of Eq. (4.10), experimental data for polymers show Eq. (4.11) to be applicable only if ϵ^* is allowed to vary with temperature.

Typical Arrhenius plots for two polymers at various plasticizer contents are shown in Figures 18 and 19. The apparent value of ϵ^* at any temperature can be found from the slope of the curve at that temperature. Obviously, the slope and therefore ϵ^* increases as the temperature or the plasticizer content is lowered. At very high temperatures or with large plasticizer contents, the value of ϵ^* is close to 15 Kcal/mole for most polymers. The value of ϵ^* becomes very large at temperatures near the glass temperature, and values in excess of 200 Kcal/mole have been reported (38,48). Figure 20 shows the values for pure polymethyl methacrylate at various temperatures.

The nonconstancy of ϵ^* for polymers indicates that a basic error exists in the derivation and ideas leading to Eqs. (4.10) and (4.11). Experimental data for the diffusion constant and viscosity of low-molecular-weight liquids indicate that the apparent validity of Eq. (4.8) for monomeric liquids merely results from the fact that measurements are seldom taken at temperatures near the glass temperature for low-molecular-weight liquids

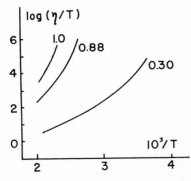

Figure 18.   The viscosity of polystyrene–dibenzyl ether solutions as a function of temperature at the weight fraction of polymer shown on the curves (42).

Figure 19.   The viscosity of a polyisobutylene of 134,000 molecular weight as a function of temperature (47).

(49). Since most liquids crystallize at temperatures far above their glass temperatures, the viscosity and D for these liquids is only available near the glass temperature if the liquid can be supercooled.

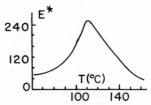

Figure 20.   Variation of ϵ^* (Kcal/mole) as a function of temperature for polymethyl methacrylate (38).

Measurements of η and D have been made on supercooled liquids of low molecular weight. It is found that these liquids also show that ϵ^* must increase rapidly as the glass temperature is approached. Deviations from Eq. (4.8) are fully as large for low-molecular-weight liquids as for the case of polymers when compared with Eq. (4.10); hence it is clear that the nonconstancy of ϵ^* has very little, if anything, to do with the polymeric nature of the liquid. The cause of the variation in ϵ^* is traceable to the assumption made in obtaining Eq. (4.4), namely, that each hole or piece of free volume acts independently. This assumption is discussed in the next section.

5. Segmental Motion near the Glass Temperature

The simple picture presented in the previous sections predicts that the rate of molecular motion will decrease in proportion to $\exp(-\epsilon^*/kT)$ as the temperature decreases. Since the model used to obtain this result implies that the energy ϵ^* is constant, the rate of molecular motion varies exponentially with $1/T$. It was seen in Sec. 4.4 that the rate of molecular motion actually changes much faster than exponentially at low temperatures. Apparently, the simple model used in the previous sections is in error, and the difficulty may be traced to the following cause. It was assumed that each packet of free volume, or hole, acted independently of every other hole. Such is not really the case, and two major sources of error are introduced by this assumption.

First, if two holes are adjacent to each other, they will actually have less surface energy than was calculated for them separately. This loss results from the fact that there will be no surface at their region of contact, and thus the surface energy will be decreased in proportion to this missing area. This effect will become more pronounced when the number of holes is large, since the number of contacts between holes will then be largest. Consequently, the distribution of hole sizes given by Eq. (4.5) will underestimate the number of small holes. There is no reason to think, however, that this effect will change the functional form of Eq. (4.7) in any serious way.

Second, if two holes are adjacent to each other, they will actually constitute a much larger hole than either will separately. As a result, even in a liquid that has no individual holes large enough to allow a molecular jump, two or more holes may coalesce to comprise a hole large enough for molecular motion to occur. This cooperation of free volume is an influential factor in determining the rate of segmental motion at low temperatures. The problem has been approached in several ways (49,50,51), but only one of the simplest methods will be given here.

Consider a liquid of volume V consisting of n molecules and free volume V_f. The proper approach would be to consider the free volume to be composed of an extremely large number (N) of small packets of free volume. These packets will be distributed in various ways among the n molecules, and each way of distribution will have a certain amount of free energy associated with it. This free energy will consist of an entropy term and an energy term. The entropy term can be determined from a consideration of the permutations and combinations of N balls distributed among n boxes. The energy term will be extremely complicated, since it will involve the surface energy associated with the various arrangements of the N holes.

There is good reason to believe that the energy term will not vary too much with the mode of arrangement of the N holes provided that N, and hence V_f, is held constant. This proceeds from the following considerations. The surface energy per unit volume of a hole, the energy density of a hole, will be $4\pi a^2\epsilon/(\tfrac{4}{3})\pi a^3$, or $3\epsilon/a$; thus it is evident that small holes have a higher energy density than large holes. However, it was indicated above that small holes have a greater tendency to share surfaces than do large holes, an effect that would lower the energy density for small holes. It is hoped that these and other similar effects will cancel each other, thereby resulting in the same energy density for all size combinations of the N holes. This assumption is actually made in the present approach to the problem; consequently, the energy term in the free energy is ignored.

For the present it will be assumed that the free volume V_f

consists of n packets, one for each molecule or segment. The correct treatment (51) does not assume these packets to be of equal size. For simplicity, however, it will be assumed here that each packet has the same size (v_f); consequently, $V_f = nv_f$.

The chance that a particular molecule (or segment, in the case of polymer chains) will have q packets associated with it is

$$p(q) = [1 - (1/n)]^{n-q}(1/n)^q\{n!/q!(n - q)!\} \qquad (4.12)$$

This expression is derived through the following reasoning. Consider n boxes into which one throws n balls at random. The chance that a given ball will go into a given box is $1/n$, while the chance that it will not go into this box is $1 - (1/n)$. Hence, the chance that a particular box will contain q balls is the product of the chance that q balls will go into the box, or $(1/n)^q$, and the chance that $(n - q)$ balls will not go into the box, or $[1 - (1/n)]^{n-q}$. But this only accounts for one way of obtaining q of the n balls in one box. There are $n!/(n - q)!q!$ ways of permuting n objects of which q are the same; therefore, the factor containing the factorials also enters into Eq. (4.12).

Since n will be a very large number that will be considered to be much larger than q,

$$[1 - (1/n)]^{n-q} \cong e^{-1} \qquad (4.13)$$

Also,

$$n!/q!(n - q)! = (n)(n - 1) \cdots (n - q + 1)/q!$$

$$\cong n^q/q! \qquad (4.14)$$

Hence,

$$p(q) \cong e^{-1}(1/q!) \qquad (4.15)$$

If q is not too small (and it will be seen later that it is of order 40 or larger), by Sterling's approximation for the factorial,

$$p(q) \cong (1/2\pi q)^{1/2} \exp\left[-q\left(\ln q - 1\right) - 1\right] \qquad (4.16)$$

But since $q = v_f'/v_f$, where v_f' is the actual amount of free volume associated with the molecule, one has the following for the probability that a molecule has a free volume v_f' associated with it:

$$p(v_f') = (v_f/2\pi v_f')^{1/2} \exp\left[-\beta v_f'/v_f\right] \qquad (4.17)$$

where $\beta = (\ln q - 1)$ and unity has been neglected in comparison to q.

For a molecule or segment to jump to a new position, more than a critical amount of free volume (v^*) must be associated with it. Therefore, the probability that a molecule can jump to a new position will be proportional to the integral of $p(v'_f)$ over $v^* < v'_f < \infty$. As will be seen later, v'_f/v_f is much larger than unity in this range; and since β is a slowly varying function of v'_f, as is the term in front of the exponential,

$$\int p(v'_f)\, dv'_f \cong (\text{constant}) \exp\left[-\beta^* v^*/v_f\right] \qquad (4.18)$$

Proceeding as in Sec. 4 of this chapter, one has the following value for the jump frequency of the segment or molecule:

$$\phi = \phi_0 \exp\left[-\beta^* v^*/v_f\right] \qquad (4.19)$$

where

$$\beta^* \equiv \ln\left(v^*/v_f\right) - 1$$

It should be noticed that β^* will not be too far from unity for reasonable values of the ratio v^*/v_f. Since v^* itself is not well known, the quantity β^* may for many purposes be considered as unity.

A more exact treatment which does not assume uniform size of the free-volume packets but which neglects surface-energy effects has been carried through by Cohen and Turnbull (51). Their result is essentially the same as Eq. (4.18), but with a somewhat different value for β^*. Therefore Eq. (4.19) may be used with confidence, provided that β^* is considered to be a constant approximately equal to unity.

Equation (4.19) can be substituted in Eq. (3.3) to obtain the diffusion constant for small molecules, with the result that

$$D = (\phi_0 \delta^2/6) \exp\left(-\beta^* v^*/v_f\right) \qquad (\text{small molecules}) \qquad (4.20)$$

This equation has been tested for various small-molecule liquids and found to give reasonable results even at low temperatures.

Similarly, Eq. (4.19) can be used in Eqs. (3.8), (3.11), and (3.16) to give the following expressions applicable to polymer molecules:

$$f_0 = (6kT/\phi_0\delta^2) \exp (\beta^*v^*/v_f) \qquad\qquad\qquad (4.21)$$
$$D = (\phi_0\delta^2/6N^*) \exp (-\beta^*v^*/v_f) \quad\Big\} \text{ (polymers) } (4.22)$$
$$\eta = (\rho\mathbf{N}kT/6\phi_0\delta^2)(R^2/M)N^* \exp (\beta^*v^*/v_f) \qquad (4.23)$$

In these equations, the quantities ϕ_0, δ, v^*, and v_f refer to polymer segments, not to the molecule as a whole, of course. A discussion of the applicability of these equations to actual experimental results will be deferred until after a consideration of the glass temperature.

6. The Glass Temperature

Liquids that do not crystallize readily, whether polymeric or otherwise, exhibit a so-called "glass transition." The phenomena constituting this "transition" may be best described by considering a simple experiment. Suppose a liquid such as molten polystyrene to be slowly cooled. If one measures the amount of force required to push a needle into the polymer at a reproducible rate as a function of temperature, data such as plotted in Figure 21 will be obtained.

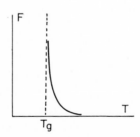

Figure 21. The force needed to push a needle into a molten polymer as a function of temperature.

From Figure 21 it becomes apparent that the polystyrene is a soft material at high temperatures but also that it gets extremely hard below a certain temperature. Although the transition from hard to soft occurs over a temperature range of at least several degrees, there is a reasonably well-defined temperature above which the polymer is soft and below which it is hard. The hard polymer is well known and is a glasslike material. The soft polymer varies from a rubbery material for very high molecular weights to an oil for very low molecular weights. In any event, there exists a rather small temperature range in which the polymer changes from a liquid to a glass. This is the transition referred to as the "glass transition."

Another qualitative method for detecting the glass transition range is to employ a polymer in the form of a sheet. If the material has a high molecular weight, and therefore a high viscosity, it will not lose its shape very rapidly even though it is soft. When soft, it can easily be folded provided that it is not too thick a sheet. However, when the temperature is lowered to the region where the polymer sheet becomes glasslike, the sheet will no longer fold, for it will be brittle and will break rather than fold. Measurements of this general type give rise to the concept of a so-called "brittle temperature," the temperature at which the material changes from soft to hard. This temperature is fairly well defined for a given material, but it will obviously depend upon the thickness of the sheet and the exact way in which it is flexed. Nevertheless, different investigators using different modifications of this technique will usually agree within a few degrees as to the brittle temperature for a given material.

These two tests are too qualitative to define a precise temperature for the glass transition. Ideally, one would like to use techniques similar to those used for the determination of melting points of crystals. Since glasses, unlike crystals, show no distinct change in X-ray diffraction pattern in the range of the transition, this method cannot be used. There is no latent heat, similar to the latent heat of fusion, observed as the material passes through the glass transition. Unlike with the melting of crystals, there is no large change in volume as the polymer changes from glass to liquid. In fact, all the abrupt changes in thermodynamic parameters that occur at a first-order phase transition are missing from the behavior of the material in the glass transition (52).

Fortunately, several properties associated with the volume expansion of these materials exhibit somewhat unique behavior in the glass transition region. This is shown in Figure 22, where the volume expansion curve for polystyrene is plotted as a function

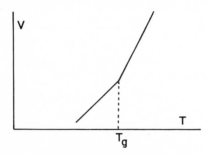

Figure 22.   The specific volume of a polymer such as polystyrene as a function of temperature.

of temperature (53). It is found that the thermal expansion coefficient for the polymer is larger above the glass transition than below it. Although the magnitude of this change differs from polymer to polymer, it is roughly true that the thermal expansion coefficient for the glass (α_g) is about ½ the value for the liquid (α_l). The intersection of the two lines in Figure 22 is readily obtained to within a degree of accuracy; hence this type of measurement permits definition of a more or less distinctive temperature called the "glass temperature" (T_g). It is usually found to be within a few degrees of the much less precisely defined "brittle temperature." Any other property of the polymer that is closely related to thermal expansion will also show a similar change in behavior at the glass temperature. For example, a plot of refractive index of the polymer versus temperature leads to a set of intersecting lines such as those shown in Figure 23 (54). Of course, T_g determined from index of refraction measurements will agree with the value found through volume expansion if the conditions of the tests are comparable.

Even with these measurements, a fundamental difficulty arises when one attempts to define T_g. Careful investigation reveals that the point of intersection of the two curves in Figures 22 and 23 varies, depending upon the speed with which the polymer is warmed or cooled during the measurement (53,38,55). For example, with polystyrene of high molecular weight, if the data for Figure 22 are taken as the sample is cooled at a rate of 1°C/min, T_g is found to be about 105°C; however, if the rate is 1°C/day, $T_g = 100°C$. Although different investigators disagree somewhat as to the exact magnitude of this time effect, the above-mentioned values are at least qualitatively correct.

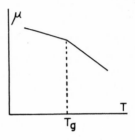

Figure 23.   Variation of refractive index of a polymer with temperature. For a typical polymer, the index would change by about 0.0001 unit per °C below the glass temperature (54).

In summary, the glass transition is the temperature region within which a noncrystallizing liquid, polymeric or otherwise, changes from a soft material to a hard, brittle material. Because this change occurs over a relatively small temperature range, any reasonable measurement that attempts to define the temperature at which the material becomes brittle will give a fair indication of the glass temperature. The exact value of the glass temperature is usually defined as the temperature at which the volume expansion coefficient shows an abrupt change. Even this definition of T_g is not without ambiguity, however, because T_g so defined is found to be somewhat lower for a slowly cooled material than for a rapidly cooled material. It appears to be a quite general rule that the faster the test method used to measure either T_g or the brittle point, then the higher the value obtained for T_g.

7. Glass Temperature and Molecular Motion

The glass transition temperature is that temperature at which the molten polymer changes to a hard glass. Actually, this transformation occurs over a temperature range that includes the glass temperature T_g. What is really meant by this statement is that there is a small temperature region about T_g in which the polymer viscosity varies rapidly with temperature from a very high viscosity characteristic of a glass to a low viscosity characteristic of a more or less viscous liquid. This is shown in Figure 24, where the viscosity of polymethyl methacrylate is plotted as a function of temperature.

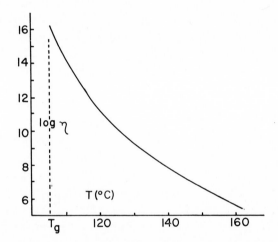

Figure 24. A plot of the variation of viscosity with temperature for a polymethyl methacrylate (38) having $M = 63,000$.

If one refers to Eq. (4.23), it is observed that the viscosity of a polymer depends upon many factors; but only one of these would appear to be very temperature-sensitive. That temperature-sensitive factor is the segmental jump frequency ϕ. Similarly, Eq. (4.20) for the rate of diffusion of molecules in low-molecular-weight liquids contains only one highly temperature-sensitive factor, the molecular jump frequency ϕ. It would therefore appear that the primary molecular quantity responsible for the change from liquid to glass is the jump frequency.

When the jump frequency is large, the molecules can move easily under the action of an external force, and the material will appear soft. On the other hand, if the jump frequency is extremely low, the molecules will appear to be frozen in place, and the substance will act like a hard, brittle material. Apparently, then, the jump frequency is high at a temperature somewhat above T_g, but it rapidly decreases to an almost negligible value as the temperature is reduced below T_g.

With this interpretation in mind, it is a simple matter to explain the variation in T_g observed for different test methods. Consider the following two methods of test. In the first method, a standard pinlike indentor is pressed into the test material with application of a fixed force. If the indentor penetrates at least 0.10 in. in 100 sec, the material is said to be soft, and consequently it is above its "brittle point." When the material becomes hard enough so that the penetration is less than 0.10 in. in 100 sec, it will be said to be hard and will be considered below its "brittle point." The brittle point is obviously the temperature at which the molecules are moving exactly fast enough to allow the indentor to satisfy the above condition.

The second method will be regarded as identical with the first except that the criterion for the "brittle temperature" will be that the indentor penetrate the required distance in a time of 0.10 sec instead of 100 sec. In this case the molecules will be moving much faster at the "brittle temperature" than they were in the first test method. Consequently, the second "brittle temperature" must actually be a higher temperature than would be found by using the first method. It is not surprising therefore that various test methods give different values for the "brittle temperature." As pointed out above, fast test methods will give higher "brittle temperatures" than do slow test methods.

The cause of the volume expansion anomaly at T_g is perhaps not so obvious as the above interpretation of the hardness. Consider a polymer or a low-molecular-weight liquid at a temperature far above T_g. It contains a large amount of free volume. When it is cooled, the material contracts and the free volume decreases. This decrease in free volume is a necessary consequence of the fact that more free volume represents a higher energy state of the material, and the material will seek the lower energy states at lower temperatures. This fact was shown quite explicitly in Sec. 4.2, where Eq. (4.2) was derived for the free-volume dependence upon temperature.

When the molecules of the solid readjust to new equilibrium positions at lower temperatures with a consequent loss of free volume, it necessarily follows that molecular motion is involved. Some free volume can be lost merely by a decrease in the amplitude of vibration of the segments about their equilibrium position. Of course, only minor, short-range adjustments in free volume are possible by means of this mechanism, but these adjustments will occur almost instantaneously as the temperature is decreased. This is the so-called "van der Waals' contraction" of the material, which gives rise to the thermal expansion and contraction of solids.

As pointed out in Sec. 4.5, however, there are packets of free volume, or holes, too large to be lost by the mere decrease in vibration amplitude of the molecules. If these holes are to be modified so as to conform to the equilibrium state of the material when the temperature is lowered, molecules or molecular segments must move over fairly long distances in order to accomplish this. If the jump frequency is large, this rearrangement will be almost instantaneous, and the material will assume its new equilibrium volume soon after the temperature is changed. If the jump frequency is very small, it will require a very long time for the material to contract to its true equilibrium value.

Hence it is evident that the expansion coefficient for the liquid (α_l) is large, because the material contracts at once as the temperature is lowered. In the glassy state, however, α_g is small because only the van der Waals' contraction is observed as the temperature is lowered. The jump frequency is too low to allow equilibration of the sizable holes during the time of the test.

Obviously the transition from glass to liquid depends upon the time allowed for the sample to reach equilibrium. The glass temperature, the temperature at which the expansion coefficient changes from α_l to α_g, is dependent upon the rate of test. A fast rate of test will give a higher value for T_g.

In order to conform with the experimental fact that the transition occurs over a limited temperature range, it must be true that ϕ varies extremely rapidly with temperature near T_g. A functional form for ϕ was derived in Sec. 4.5, and that value was then used to obtain explicit equations for the temperature variation of the diffusion constant for small molecules, Eq. (4.20), and the viscosity of polymer molecules, Eq. (4.23). Since both of these quantities are easily measured, a test of these equations is possible. This procedure is discussed in the next section.

8. The WLF Equation (49)

The variation of viscosity or diffusion constant with temperature for glass-forming liquids has been widely investigated. Since the viscosities of liquids at any given temperature depend seriously upon the molecular structure of the liquid, it is customary to restrict such investigations to a single liquid and express the results as ratios of viscosities at two temperatures. For this reason, the present discussion of the temperature variation of the viscosity and diffusion of liquids will be couched in terms of ratios of viscosities or diffusion constants.

Consider first Eq. (4.23) for the viscosity of a polymeric liquid. All the factors except the quantity $(T/\phi_0)\exp(\beta^* v^*/v_f)$ are essentially independent of temperature. Even the factor T/ϕ_0 will be relatively constant in comparison to the large changes usually observed for viscosity as a function of temperature. Consequently, for a given polymer system and to a good approximation,

$$\eta = B\exp(\beta^* v^*/v_f) \tag{4.24}$$

A similar relation may be derived for liquids composed of small molecules.

Equation (4.24) has been known for some time to be an exceptionally good representation for the viscosity of molten paraffins as well as many other liquids (56,57). It is often called the "Doolittle equation," since it was Doolittle who first proposed it as an empirical representation. Of course, its use depends upon the proper choice of free volume v_f, which will now be investigated.

Consider the viscosities of a liquid at two different temperatures, T_1 and T_2. From Eq. (4.24),

$$\eta_1/\eta_2 = \exp\left[(\beta^* v^*/v_{f1}) - (\beta^* v^*/v_{f2})\right] \tag{4.25}$$

Or after taking logarithms of each side,

$$\ln(\eta_1/\eta_2) = (\beta^* v^*)\left[(1/v_{f1}) - (1/v_{f2})\right] \tag{4.26}$$

If a molecule or chain segment has a total volume v_1 associated with it at T_1, it is reasonable to define the free volume at T_2 by the following relation (53):

$$v_{f2} = v_{f1} + \alpha v_1 (T_2 - T_1) \tag{4.27}$$

where α is the expansion coefficient for the gross liquid minus the expansion coefficient for the glass; that is, $\alpha = \alpha_l - \alpha_g$. This merely says that the free volume increase as the temperature is raised from T_1 to T_2 is equal to the thermal expansion in excess of the van der Waals' expansion of the glass. Hence it is assumed that the free volume effective in promoting molecular motion is only that portion which is in large enough packets so that it does not equilibrate readily at low temperatures. The reason for taking α as being $\alpha_l - \alpha_g$ rather than α_l will become apparent when the results for the variation of glass temperature with molecular weight are discussed in the next chapter.

In any event, if Eq. (4.27) is substituted into Eq. (4.26), one has after some rearrangement,

$$\ln(\eta_1/\eta_2) = (\beta^* v^*/v_{f1})(T_2 - T_1)/\left[(v_{f1}/v_1\alpha) + (T_2 - T_1)\right]$$

$$\tag{4.28}$$

This relation is very interesting because it is of the same form as a semiempirical relation proposed by Williams, Landel, and

Ferry (the so-called "WLF equation") to explain the temperature dependence of viscosity and other rate processes in glass-forming liquids (49). They found that, if T_1 is taken to be the glass temperature of the material, then Eq. (4.28) agrees with experiment in the temperature range $T_g < T < T_g + 120$, provided that

$$(\beta^* v^*/v_{f1}) = 40 \qquad \text{and} \qquad (v_{f1}/v_1\alpha) = 52 \qquad (4.29)$$

One therefore has the following equation, denoted the WLF equation,

$$\ln (\eta_g/\eta) = 40(T - T_g)/[52 + (T - T_g)] \qquad (4.30)$$

where η_g is the viscosity at the glass temperature. This equation has been tested against data for many noncrystalline polymers, as well as for other glass-forming liquids. Typical of these are silicates, boron trioxide, n-propanol, glycerol, and many others (49). They all appear to obey Eq. (4.30) very well within the range $T_g < T < T_g + 120$; therefore it may be concluded that the molecular ideas leading to Eq. (4.28) are probably valid.

It is interesting to examine the meaning of the relation in Eq. (4.29). If one takes $\beta^* = 1$, then $v_{fg} = v^*/40$; or, approximately 40 times as much free volume is needed for a segment or molecule to jump as is found on the average for each segment at the glass temperature. Hence, great aggregation of free volume must occur at low temperatures if a segment or molecule is to be able to move. Also, from Eq. (4.29), $v_{fg} = (52)(v_g\alpha)$. Since $\alpha = \alpha_l - \alpha_g$ is about 5×10^{-4} per °C in the case of most liquids, $v_{fg} = v_g/40$. In other words, about $\frac{1}{40}$ of the volume at the glass temperature is free volume. It should also be noticed that since v_{fg} was shown above to be about $v^*/40$, it appears that the hole needed for a molecule or segment to jump must be about equal to the size of the molecule or segment itself. This observation is entirely reasonable, of course.

Although Eq. (4.30) is nearly universal for glass-forming liquids, discrepancies do arise. First, the equation begins to depart from experiment if the temperature is raised too far above T_g. Each liquid behaves somewhat differently at these high temperatures. Such deviations are not unexpected, since the relations of Eq. (4.29) cannot be expected to be completely temperature-insensitive. It is well known that the expansion co-efficient of a liquid will vary with temperature; accordingly, α—and hence the quantity 52—will change at high temperatures. Also, there is no absolute assurance that $\beta^* v^*$ will be rigidly constant as a function of temperature. In addition, the quantity preceding the exponential in Eq. (4.24) is certainly not fully constant as assumed.

There are also indications that some materials would agree better with Eq. (4.29) if slightly different constants were used. This modification is not completely unreasonable from a theoretical standpoint; however, the difficulty of making measurements at temperatures near T_g still leaves much doubt as to whether or not these constants should change somewhat. Since a $10°$ temperature change near T_g can cause the viscosity to change by a factor of several hundred, experimental difficulties become quite influential near T_g. Also, as will be seen later, small amounts of impurity greatly influence the exact value measured for T_g.

Since measurements near T_g are difficult to make, Williams, Landel, and Ferry suggest that a different reference temperature be taken (49). They take as reference a temperature T_s that is roughly $50°C$ above T_g. In terms of this new reference temperature Eq. (4.30) becomes

$$\ln (\eta_s/\eta) = (20.4)(T - T_s)/[102 + (T - T_s)] \qquad (4.31)$$

They further suggest that T_s be obtained empirically by fitting the equation to the experimental data. However, if T_g is known, it would appear that the relation $T_s = T_g + 50$ will be accurate enough for most purposes.

Before concluding this section, it should be pointed out that Eq. (4.26) has been tested for several monomeric liquids that are not ordinarily regarded as glass-forming systems (51). Molten metals, for example, are found to conform reasonably well with Eq. (4.26). In addition, a simple extension of Eq. (4.26) can be used to predict accurately the variation of molecular motion as a function of pressure. Hence, one is led to believe that Eq. (4.26) is of great importance and has general validity.

9. Factors Influencing the Glass Temperature

The glass temperature is that temperature below which the molecular movement is so slow that the liquid appears hard or glasslike. An estimate of the rate of molecular or segmental jumping at T_g can be obtained in several ways. A rough estimate can be made from the measured viscosity of a polymer (34). This is most easily done for a polymer of low molecular weight, for which the entanglement factor will be inconsequential.

Experimental work by Fox and Flory (53) indicates that at T_g a polystyrene of 30,000 molecular weight will have a viscosity of 10^{11}. Since Eq. (4.23) may be written as

$$\eta = (\rho \mathbf{N} k T / 6\delta^2)(R^2/M)N^*\phi \qquad (4.32)$$

the jump frequency at T_g may be estimated by assuming reasonable values for N^* and δ. At this molecular weight $N^* = N$, and a value of 300 is not unreasonable for this quantity. If δ^2 is taken to be 3×10^{-15} cm and if a reasonable value is used for R^2/M, then ϕ is found to be 0.3 jumps per sec. This means that a chain segment in polystyrene makes a jump about once every 3 sec when $T = T_g$.

Other methods for estimating the jump frequency exist. The most reliable way, which is related to the dielectric response of dipoles fastened stiffly to the polymer chain, will be described in Chapter 12. All these methods lead to a similar result, however, that the jump frequency at the glass temperature is of the order of 10^{-1} per sec. It appears that the segmental jump frequency is essentially the same for all materials at their glass temperatures. Such a result is quite consistent with the nature of the glass transition as discussed in previous sections.

If it is considered that $\beta^* v^* / v_{f_g}$ is shown to be a constant by Eq. (4.29), it is possible to obtain considerable information concerning the glass temperature. Since $\beta^* v^*$ is likely to be very close to the size of the moving unit in any liquid, it is immediately apparent that the ratio of free volume per segment to the size of a segment is constant at the glass temperature. This fact leads to the following conclusions concerning the dependence of glass temperature upon polymer structure.

First, a polymer that consists of a stiff chain backbone with tightly held bulky side groups will have a high glass temperature. This follows from the fact that the moving segment is necessarily large for such a chain. Since the moving segment is large, the free volume per segment must be correspondingly large at T_g; hence one must go to rather high temperatures before the polymer has acquired enough free volume to allow fast movement of the segments, and T_g will accordingly be high. In this respect it is seen from Table 4 that the very flexible polymer—polyethylene—has a low T_g; whereas polystyrene, having bulky side groups, and polymethyl methacrylate, having a stiff backbone, have high glass temperatures. (Compare also polymethyl methacrylate with polymethyl acrylate.)

Second, a polymer which has high attraction forces between the chains will expand less readily than a noninteracting polymer; therefore such a polymer must be heated to a higher temperature before the free volume becomes as large as required at the glass temperature. This trend is easily seen by reference to Table 4. Notice in particular the large thermal expansion coefficient of silicone rubber as compared with all other polymers.

Third, loose dangling side groups on a polymer chain will tend to loosen the polymer structure, that is, increase the free volume. Hence, polymethyl methacrylate would be expected to show a higher glass temperature than poly-n-butyl methacrylate. Indeed, Table 4 shows the methacrylate series to behave in exactly the way predicted from such reasoning.

In general, then, it may be said that any structural factor which tends to lower the thermal expansion coefficient or which increases the stiffness and size of the moving segments will necessarily increase the value of the glass temperature. It should not be implied by this generalization, however, that the prediction

TABLE 4

T_g, T_m, and α_l for Selected Polymers[†]

Polymer	T_g, °C	T_m, °C	$\alpha_l \times 10^4/C°$	T_g/T_m, °K
Silicone rubber	−123	−58	12	0.70
Polybutadiene	−85		7.8	
Polyisobutylene	−70		5.9	
Polyisoprene				
(natural rubber)	−70	28	6.2	0.67
Poly-n-butyl acrylate	−56		6.0	
Polyvinylidene fluoride	−39	210		0.48
Polyethyl acrylate	−22		6.1	
Polymethyl acrylate	5		5.6	
Poly-n-butyl methacrylate	22		6.3	
Polyvinyl acetate	30		6.0	
Polyethyl methacrylate	65		5.4	
Polyvinyl chloride	82	180	5.2	0.78
Polystyrene	100	(230)	5.5	0.75
Polymethyl methacrylate	105		5.0	
Polyethylene	−110	135		0.50
Polypropylene	−18	176		0.57
Nylon 6	47	225		0.64

† These are average values from the literature and should only be considered approximate (59,60).

of glass temperatures is a simple matter. It is much easier to explain a glass temperature once it has been measured than it is to predict the value of T_g from a knowledge of structure only. Nevertheless, there is a rough rule that can be used to find the glass temperature for a polymer which crystallizes to some extent. In Table 4 there is tabulated the ratio of the glass temperature to the melting temperature, or T_g/T_m, using the absolute temperature scale, of course. It is seen that this ratio generally lies between 0.50 and 0.75. A more detailed examination shows that usually the ratio is close to 0.5 for symmetrical polymers such as polyethylene. The ratio is near 0.7 for the unsymmetrical polymers such as polystyrene and polyisoprene. These relationships between T_g and T_m are usually referred to as the Boyer-Beaman rule (58,59).

PROBLEMS

1. Assuming Eq. (4.2) to be correct, how large is the average hole size in benzene at 27°C?

2. Show that Eq. (4.6) follows from (4.5).

3. If the critical hole radius b^* is taken as 4 Å for a certain liquid that has a surface tension of 30 ergs/cm², and if ϕ_0 is taken to be 10^{13} sec^{-1}, what is the jump frequency at 27°C according to Eq. (4.7)?

4. If a particular sample of pure polystyrene has a viscosity of 10^3 poise at 160°C, what would you predict its viscosity to be at its glass temperature, 100°C? At 120°C?

5. Suppose the volume compressibility of a raw rubber to be 2×10^{-11} cm²/dyne. Furthermore, suppose that when a rubber is compressed, the volume loss is all due to a loss of free volume. (a) Find the change in free volume as the pressure is increased from atmospheric to 21 times atmospheric. (b) If β^*v^* is 10^{-21} cm³ and v_f was 5×10^{-23} cm³ under atmospheric pressure, by what factor will the viscosity change when the pressure is increased to the value given above?

6. A very crude test to determine brittle point is to pound a nail into the material in question with a hard blow of a hammer. If the material cracks, it is said to be below its brittle point. What can you say about the result of this test method in comparison to the glass temperature and to the brittle point determined by other means?

Chapter 5

EFFECTS OF DILUENT, CHAIN ENDS,
AND COPOLYMERIZATION

1. Methods for Changing T_g

It was pointed out in the last chapter that the glass temperature T_g appears to represent an iso-free volume state for the polymer; that is to say, at the glass temperature, about $\frac{1}{40}$ of the total volume of the material consists of free volume. This condition is apparently true for all glass-forming substances.

If this is actually the case, it follows that the value of T_g for a polymer can be changed by altering its free volume at a given temperature. For example, if the polymer is put under very high pressure while in the liquid state, some of the free volume will be lost by the compression. Hence, this polymer will exhibit a higher T_g than the noncompressed polymer, because it will have less free volume at any given temperature than does the uncompressed polymer. Such behavior has actually been observed (51,61,62).

Another possible method for lowering the T_g of a polymer would be to mix with it a miscible liquid that contains more free volume than the pure polymer. If one assumes additivity of free volume, the diluent-polymer solution will contain more free volume at any given temperature than would the polymer alone; consequently the plasticized polymer must be cooled to a lower temperature in order to reduce its free volume to the amount always present at the glass temperature. It is well known, of

112

course, that the value of T_g can be lowered by the addition of a compatible plasticizer. This effect will be treated in detail later in this chapter.

A polymer can be plasticized by copolymerization as well as by adding a low-molecular-weight diluent. If two different types of monomer units are placed in the same chain in such a way that the two chemical units do not separate into different phases, then the free-volume contribution of each will unite to constitute the free volume of the polymer. For example, if butadiene is co-polymerized with styrene, the resultant polymer will have a free volume intermediate between the high value found in poly-butadiene and the low value found in polystyrene; hence, T_g for this copolymer will be between the values for the homopolymers. To a first approximation at least, the free volume of the co-polymer can be considered as being composed of the sum of the free volumes furnished by an equivalent combination of the homopolymers. The limitations of this approach will be dis-cussed later.

A third important way in which T_g may be altered is the result of the action of chain ends. Since each chain end will necessarily possess more free volume than if it were chemically bound within a continuous chain, the presence of chain ends will increase the amount of free volume in the polymer at any given temperature. Hence, polymers with very low molecular weight will have a lower value for T_g than will a chemically identical polymer of higher molecular weight. This effect can become very large, as indicated by the fact (53) that a polystyrene with $M = 3000$ has a T_g of 43°C as compared with 99°C for $M = 300,000$.

2. Effect of Molecular Weight on T_g (53,63)

In the preceding section it was pointed out that a polymer chain end will contribute a certain amount of free volume to the system merely because it is not chemically bound within the central portion of the chain. If the free volume contributed by a chain end is designated θ, the following relation expresses the total amount of free volume per cubic centimeter contributed by chain ends:

$$\text{Chain-end free volume per cc} = (\theta)(2\rho\mathbf{N}/M) \qquad (5.1)$$

This follows from the fact that there are $2\rho\mathbf{N}/M$ chain ends per cc, where ρ is the polymer density and $\mathbf{N}$ is Avogadro's number.

Equation (5.1) gives the extra amount of free volume that a polymer of molecular weight M contains when compared with a polymer of infinite molecular weight. Such a polymer of finite molecular weight will have a glass temperature T_g that is not the same as the glass temperature of the infinite molecular weight polymer $(T_{g\infty})$. The finite-molecular-weight polymer must be cooled below $T_{g\infty}$, so that the additional thermal contraction will just compensate for the free volume contributed by the chain ends. Hence,

$$\theta(2\rho\mathbf{N}/M) = \alpha(T_{g\infty} - T_g) \qquad (5.2)$$

or

$$T_g = T_{g\infty} - (2\rho\mathbf{N}\theta/\alpha)(1/M) \qquad (5.3)$$

Equation (5.3) is of the form

$$T_g = T_{g\infty} - K/M \qquad (5.4)$$

which states that a straight line will result if T_g is plotted against M^{-1}. This proves to be true, as is shown in Figure 25, where T_g versus M^{-1} is plotted for polystyrene (53,62,64).

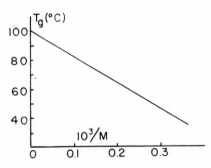

Figure 25.   Variation of the glass temperature of polystyrene as a function of molecular weight (53).

From the slope of the line in Figure 25, the quantity $(2\rho N\theta/\alpha)$ in Eq. (5.3) can be computed, since this is equivalent to K in Eq. (5.4). Since ρ, N, and α are known, θ can be computed and is found to be about 80 $Å^3$. This result means that each polystyrene chain end contributes a total free volume which is about half the size of a styrene unit. Such a value is not at all unreasonable and lends credence to the idea that the depression of T_g is the result of the free volume associated with chain ends.

Insight into the nature of free volume can also be obtained from an examination of the specific volume of polymers of various molecular weights as a function of temperature. Data illustrating this point are shown in Figure 26. Notice that

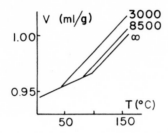

Figure 26.   The specific volume of polystyrene as a function of temperature for the molecular weights indicated on the curves (53).

polystyrenes of all molecular weights have the same specific volume in the glassy state. Also, note that the specific volume of polymers of different molecular weights is not the same at the glass temperature for each. Instead, the specific volume difference between two polymers at their respective glass temperatures, T_{g1} and T_{g2}, is equal to the glasslike expansion that takes place between these two temperatures, namely, $\alpha_g(T_{g2} - T_{g1})$.

However, all experimental data available indicate that the glass temperature is fixed at a constant-volume fraction of free volume, namely, 0.025. The only reasonable way to reconcile this fact with the difference in specific volume of polymers of various molecular weights at the glass temperature is to assume that the glasslike expansion does not constitute additional free volume in the sense used in these discussions. It was for this reason that the α used in the WLF equation was taken to be $\alpha_l - \alpha_g$. In other words, free volume as used in this and previous chapters refers only to packets of free volume that are too large to reach nearly instantaneous equilibrium at temperatures which are below T_g.

3. Effect of Diluent on T_g

If one accepts the conclusion reached in Chapter 4 that $\frac{1}{40}$, or 0.025, of the total volume of a liquid is free volume at T_g, in general the free-volume fraction is

$$V_f = 0.025 + \alpha(T - T_g) \tag{5.5}$$

This relation apparently applies equally well both to polymers and low-molecular-weight liquids, provided that $\alpha = \alpha_l - \alpha_g$. Equation (5.5) allows one to compute the free volume in any liquid or polymer at a given temperature T if α and T_g are known. Actually, the value of α for most polymers is very close to 4.8×10^{-4} per °C, and it is customary to use this value when the true value is not known.

Suppose V_p is the volume fraction of polymer and V_d is the volume fraction of diluent in a plasticized polymer. If the free volumes of each constituent are assumed to be additive, it is at once apparent that the free-volume fraction is

$$V_f = [0.025 + \alpha_p(T - T_{gp})]V_p$$
$$+ [0.025 + \alpha_d(T - T_{gd})]V_d \tag{5.6}$$

where the subscripts p and d refer to polymer and diluent, respectively. Upon simplification,

$$V_f = 0.025 + \alpha_p(T - T_{gp})V_p + \alpha_d(T - T_{gd})V_d \tag{5.7}$$

This relation may be used as follows to find the glass temperature of the plasticized polymer.

At the glass temperature of the plasticized system, it is found that $T = T_g$ and $V_f = 0.025$. Substitution of these values in

Eq. (5.7) yields the following expression for the glass temperature of a polymer diluent system:

$$T_g = [\alpha_p V_p T_{gp} + \alpha_d(1 - V_p) T_{gd}]/[\alpha_p V_p + \alpha_d(1 - V_p)] \quad (5.8)$$

This relation has been tested for several polymer-diluent systems and has been found to be reasonably accurate (63). Since T_{gd}, the glass temperature of the diluent, is not easy to determine in most cases, its value is often unknown. The same is often true of α_d. However, reasonable agreement with experimental data can be obtained by setting $\alpha_d = 10^{-3}$ per °C and obtaining an approximate value of T_{gd} from the glass temperature of one polymer-diluent combination.

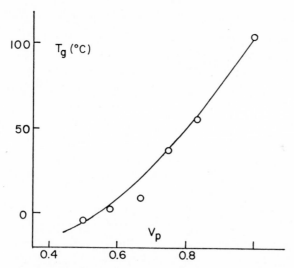

Figure 27.   Lowering of the glass temperature of polymethyl methacrylate by diethyl phthalate as predicted by Eq. (5.8) (solid line) and as found by experiment (63).

Typical agreement between Eq. (5.8) and experiment is shown in Figure 27 for the system polymethyl methacrylate–diethyl phthalate. A value of $T_{gd} = -65°C$ was used together with $\alpha_d = 10^{-3}$ per °C. The value for T_{gd} is the measured value, and

α_d is merely estimated. Since the exact value used for α_d is not too critical and since T_{gd} is known to be about $-65°C$ for this diluent, the agreement shown in Figure 27 is quite satisfactory.

4. Effect of Diluent on Viscosity

An expression for the viscosity of pure polymers and their concentrated solutions was found in Chapter 3. From Eqs. (3.9), (3.10), (3.16), and (4.21) the viscosity is given by

$$\eta = B'\rho M \exp (\beta^* v^*/v_f) \qquad M < 2M_e \qquad (5.9)$$

and

$$\eta = B\rho^4 M^{3.5} \exp (\beta^* v^*/v_f) \qquad M > 2M_e \qquad (5.10)$$

The quantities B and B' are essentially constant for a given polymer-diluent system, and ρ is the concentration of polymer in grams per cubic centimeter. Equation (5.9) applies in the region of low molecular weights, where the viscosity varies as M to the first power, while Eq. (5.10) applies in the high-molecular-weight region, where $\eta \sim M^{3.5}$. Since the free volume v_f is seriously dependent upon molecular weight at low molecular weights, where the number of chain ends becomes large, Eq. (5.9) indicates that η will not be directly proportional to M at very low values of M. This effect has been investigated, and it appears that after correcting for the effect of chain ends η is proportional to M even at very low molecular weights (43).

The present discussion will be restricted to the variation of η with polymer concentration. In that regard, it should be noted that the molecular-weight ranges over which Eqs. (5.9) and (5.10) are valid vary with concentration. This is a result of the fact that the point of transition between the two forms for η occurs at $M_b \cong 2M_e$, which is dependent upon ρ. If ρ_0 is the density of the pure polymer, it was shown in Eq. (3.18) that $M_e = M_{e0}\rho_0/\rho$, where the subscript zero refers to the pure polymer. In any event, the ratio of the viscosity of the pure polymer to the viscosity of the plasticized polymer is given by

$$\eta_0/\eta = (\rho_0/\rho)^4 \exp [(\beta^* v^*/v_{f0}) - (\beta^* v^*/v_f)] \qquad (5.11)$$

This relation, since it is based upon Eq. (5.10), applies only in the region $M > 2M_e$. A similar relation applies in the low-molecular-weight range, but ρ_0/ρ would appear to the first power in it.

Taking logarithms of each side of Eq. (5.11),

$$\ln (\rho^4\eta_0/\rho_0^4\eta) = \beta^*v^*[(1/v_{f0}) - (1/v_f)] \qquad (5.12)$$

But if one assumes additivity of free volume,

$$v_f/v_{f0} = V_p[0.025 + \alpha_p(T - T_{gp})]$$
$$+ (1 - V_p)[0.025 + \alpha_d(T - T_{gd})] \qquad (5.13)$$

with

$$v_{f0} = v[0.025 + \alpha_p(T - T_{gp})]$$

Upon substituting Eq. (5.13) in Eq. (5.12) and after replacing β^*v^*/v by unity as in Chapter 4, one finds

$$\ln \frac{\rho^4\eta_0}{\rho_0^4\eta} = \frac{(1 - V_p)[\alpha_d(T - T_{gd}) - \alpha_p(T - T_{gp})]}{[0.025 + \alpha_p(T - T_{gp})][0.025 + V_p\alpha_p(T - T_{gp}) + (1 - V_p)\alpha_d(T - T_{gd})]}$$

$$(5.14)$$

Equation (5.14) allows prediction of the variation of viscosity with diluent concentration. The viscosity predicted for the system polystyrene in diethyl benzene by Eq. (5.14) is given in Figure 28; the actual values found by experiment are shown by the points. Other systems have also been examined with respect to Eq. (5.14), and similar agreement between theory and experiment has been found (63).

Although Eq. (5.14) appears to describe the variation of viscosity with diluent reasonably well, it should be noticed that T_{gd} is usually considered an adjustable parameter since its experimental value is usually unknown. Hence, agreement between theory and experiment may be somewhat fortuitous. Certainly the additivity of free volume cannot be a correct assumption for highly interacting polymer-diluent systems. Caution must therefore be used in the application of Eq. (5.14) to such systems until the consequences of strong interactions

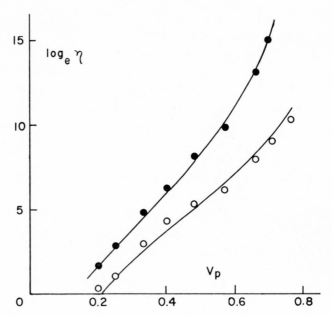

Figure 28.   Variation of the viscosity of polystyrene as a function of diethyl benzene concentration as predicted by Eq. (5.14) (solid lines) and as found from experiment (63).

have been more fully investigated from an experimental standpoint. The above type of reasoning has also been applied to the effect of pressure and tensile stress on glass temperature, and reasonable agreement has been found (65).

5. Effects of Copolymerization on T_g

There are two broad classifications of copolymer types. One classification includes all those polymers which exist in two or more phases in the melt. Since two different chemical types of polymers that are mutually soluble are rarely found, this classification includes most nonuniform copolymers. For example, graft copolymers (which consist of one polymer chain attached to the backbone of a different type of chemical chain) fall into this classification. Block copolymers (in which the backbone consists of alternating long sequences of two chemically different polymers) also fit into this category.

In these heterogeneous polymers, the polymer melt usually consists of chain sequences of one chain constituent precipitated as droplets in a matrix of the other constituent. If the blocks or grafts are extremely short, the phase separation may not occur. The size of the precipitated droplets will depend upon the lengths of the blocks and grafts, as well as upon the interaction energy between the chemical constituents. Such two-phase systems will show physical properties analogous to mechanical mixtures of two different polymers (66,67). Each phase will show its normal, or near-normal, glass temperature. For this reason, one cannot usually speak of the glass temperature for a block or graft copolymer, for it will often evidence two glass transitions.

Consider a graft copolymer between polyisoprene and polymethyl methacrylate (PMMA). One cannot state a priori which polymer will be the one precipitated in droplet form (68). If the polymer is prepared by casting from a solvent for the polyisoprene, which is not a solvent for PMMA, then the system will consist of droplets of PMMA in a rubber matrix. At room temperature, this system will behave like a filled rubber with the hard PMMA droplets acting as filler particles. At very low temperatures, below T_g for polyisoprene, the material will be a glass. The behavior at temperatures above T_g for PMMA will also be different from that at room temperature, since now the filler will have softened. On the other hand, if the copolymer is precipitated from a solvent for PMMA that is not a solvent for the rubber, a hard material will result at room temperature. It will consist of rubber droplets in a hard PMMA matrix. If properly prepared, such a polymer displays highly desirable impact properties. The material will become soft above T_g for PMMA; and it will be completely glasslike below T_g for the rubber phase.

The other category of copolymers consists of all those systems in which the chemical constituents alternate more or less randomly along the polymer chain. Phase separation does not occur in these copolymers, and thus one deals with an intimate molecular dispersion of the various monomer molecules making up the copolymer. Essentially, then, a new type of polymer unlike either of the polymers composed of the separate monomers has been produced.

It is tempting to speculate that the free volume contributed to the copolymer by a given monomer will be the same as the free volume it contributes to the homopolymer. Nonetheless, such a general assumption is obviously wrong. The free volume associated with a given chain unit is not a function of the chemical nature of that unit alone. Steric and energetic relations with the adjacent units along the chain backbone will also influence the amount of free volume that it contributes. Although this effect should not be overwhelming in most instances, it will nevertheless affect the quantitative relations involved.

If it is assumed that the amount of free volume contributed by a monomer unit is identical whether one is concerned with the copolymer or homopolymer, the value of T_g for the copolymer will be given by Eq. (5.8). This equation was actually derived for a polymer-diluent system. Since it does not matter whether the chain unit is in the homopolymer or copolymer if the assumption of constancy of free volume is made, the total free volume will be the same for a mixture of homopolymers as for the copolymer. Of course, α_d and T_{gd} in Eq. (5.8) will refer to one of the polymer components in this case. Equation (5.8) may be rewritten as

$$T_g = [T_{g1} + (KT_{g2} - T_{g1})V_2]/[1 + (K - 1)V_2] \qquad (5.15)$$

where the two subscripts refer to the two polymer constituents. The constant K is equal to (α_2/α_1). It should be noticed that Eq. (5.15) predicts the correct value of T_g for the homopolymers irrespective of the value chosen for K. If the proper value of K is not (α_2/α_1), this error will not be serious for copolymers consisting of a small amount of one monomer copolymerized with a large amount of another monomer. The variation of T_g with V_2 for various values of K is shown in Figure 29.

An equation similar to Eq. (5.15) has been derived by several people using different models and is often referred to as the Gordon-Taylor equation (69). Others, notably Fox (70) and Mandelkern, Martin, and Quinn (71), have arrived at similar results. This relation has been reviewed and compared with

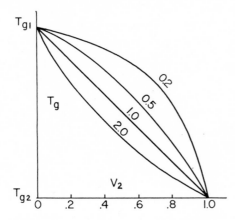

Figure 29. Variation of glass temperature with copolymer composition according to Eq. (5.15). The numbers on the curves are the values of α_2/α_1.

experiment by L. A. Wood (60). It is found that the functional form of Eq. (5.15) is correct, but the value of K cannot in general be taken as equal to α_2/α_1.

The fact that α_2/α_1 is not found to be the correct value for K is not surprising. As stated above, it is most unrealistic to assume that the free volume per unit is the same in the homopolymer and in the copolymer. If this had not been assumed, K would merely have been found to be proportional to α_2/α_1. It does not appear possible to predict the proportionality factor between K and α_2/α_1 at this time. In spite of this, Eq. (5.15) is still a useful relation that seems to agree with known experiments; however, the parameter K must be considered an experimental constant.

PROBLEMS

1. Suppose one is dealing with the rubber of problem 5, Chapter 4. If its glass temperature at atmospheric pressure is $-73°C$, what would you predict its glass temperature to be at a pressure of 21 atmospheres?

2. Suppose 20 gm of a polystyrene of molecular weight 50,000 is milled into 80 gm of natural rubber in the usual way on a rubber mill. Can a unique glass temperature be predicted for this mixture? What can be said about the behavior of this material?

3. Poly-n-butyl methacrylate has a glass temperature of 22°C. What would you predict would happen to T_g if the butyl group could be split so as to yield a true solution of polymethyl methacrylate in propane? Try to estimate reasonable values for the quantities in Eq. (5.8), giving reasons for your choices, and compute the resulting T_g. Is the answer reasonable? Explain.

4. Suppose a certain pure polymer of very high molecular weight has a viscosity of 10^6 poise at 127°C and has $T_g = 47°C$. It is then swollen with enough propylene glycol so that the volume fraction of polymer is 0.70. What is the viscosity of the plasticized polymer at 127°C? For simplicity, take the density of both pure materials to be unity and assume the additivity of free volume. T_g for the solvent is about $-113°C$.

5. What would you predict for the ability of the Gordon-Taylor equation, Eq. (5.15), to predict the glass temperature of a random copolymer of methyl methacrylate and n-butyl methacrylate? What about the random copolymer of methyl methacrylate and methyl acrylate? Explain.

6. Suppose a molten, moderate-molecular-weight polystyrene is subjected to a very high pressure and is cooled under pressure to 20°C. The cool material is placed in a dilatometer and heated at a rate of 0.1° per min to a temperature of 150°C. It is then cooled back down to room temperature at the same rate. Show on a rough graph what you would predict for the dilatometer readings during both the ascending and descending portions of the experiment. Defend your answer.

Chapter 6

THE DYNAMICS OF NETWORK
RESPONSE: CREEP

1. Network Response to Constant Load

Let us suppose a small tensile stress σ to be applied instantaneously to a crosslinked rubber. After some time, the rubber will reach an equilibrium elongation under this stress. The elongation will be given by Eq. (2.12), which was derived on the basis of a network at equilibrium. This final elongation will not be attained instantaneously, however. Although the time taken to reach the equilibrium state under the applied stress may be only a small fraction of a second for natural rubber at 20°C, this time becomes much longer at lower temperatures.

Typical response curves for crosslinked natural rubber at two temperatures, 10°C and −30°C, are shown in Figure 30 (72).

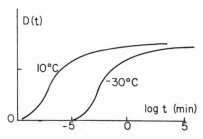

Figure 30.   Tensile creep of a natural rubber network at two different temperatures. The quantity $D(t)$, the compliance, is the relative elongation per unit stress.

Notice that these responses are plotted against the logarithm of time, and thus the curves will appear far different when plotted against time as in Figure 31. In any event, it is clear that the network elongates much more slowly at $-30°C$ than it does at $+10°C$. Although the shape of the response curve on the log plot of Figure 30 does not change with temperature, the position along the time scale is shifted by about four decades in time. More will be said about this shift later.

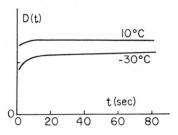

Figure 31.   The data of Figure 30 plotted on a linear time scale.

It is not difficult to interpret the effect of temperature on the response time of the network. To elongate a piece of rubber it is necessary to elongate the various chains between crosslink points in the rubber. In a single chain, for example, when the rubber is being stretched, essentially a stretching force is being applied to the two ends of the network chain. The chain will begin to elongate under this force; however, in doing so, the various segments of the chain must be displaced through the matrix of surrounding chains. Each segment will therefore experience a retarding viscous force equivalent to vf_0, where v is the velocity of the segment relative to its surroundings and f_0 is the segmental friction constant. As a result of this retarding friction force, the chain will only slowly elongate to its equilibrium elongation.

It was shown in Chapter 4 that f_0 was closely dependent upon temperature. As the temperature is lowered, the friction constant f_0 becomes larger; hence, at low temperatures it will be found that the network chains experience a very large viscous force retarding their elongation. Since the rubber as a whole elongates in the same way as do the chains comprising it, the rubber might reasonably be expected to elongate much less rapidly at low temperatures than it does when the rubber is warm. This condition is exactly what is demonstrated by experiment, as shown in Figures 30 and 31.

2. The Simple Voigt-Kelvin Model

Although the explanation given in the previous section for the time effects observed for network elongation must be qualitatively correct, it is desirable to obtain a quantitative model that represents the experimental data. One of the earliest mechanical models that it was hoped would represent the molecular motion is the Voigt-Kelvin model shown in Figure 32.

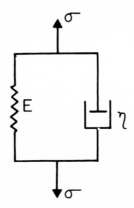

Figure 32.   The Voigt-Kelvin model. E is the spring constant and η is the viscous factor for the dashpot.

In this model the individual chain is considered to elongate much as a spring would elongate in a viscous medium. The solid rubber would then be represented by a spring of modulus or stiffness $E = 3\nu k T$ in parallel with a viscous element, a dashpot, which exhibits an internal viscosity η. This viscosity is not expected to be the same as the true viscosity of the rubber. If a stress σ is now applied to the model in Figure 32 and y is the spring elongation, the applied stress σ must equal the opposing tension in the spring (Ey) plus the viscous force $\eta(dy/dt)$; that is,

$$\sigma = Ey + \eta(dy/dt) \tag{6.1}$$

This differential equation has a solution of form

$$y = \sigma/E + A \exp\left[-(E/\eta)t\right] \tag{6.2}$$

Since $y = 0$ at time $t = 0$, the constant of integration A must equal $-\sigma/E$. Hence,

$$y = (\sigma/E)[1 - \exp(-t/\tau)] \tag{6.3}$$

where $\tau = \eta/E$, and this quantity is called the "retardation time" of the model. Notice that if the viscosity η is large, the retardation time is long. It is the time taken for the model to reach 0.632 of its equilibrium elongation $(0.632 = 1 - e^{-1})$.

It is now of interest to compare the response of the simple Voigt-Kelvin model as given by Eq. (6.3) with the observed elongation curve for the rubber shown in Figure 30. This comparison is made in Figure 33, where the value of τ has been

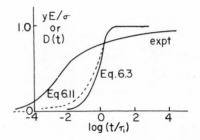

Figure 33.   The compliance curve for the rubber of Figure 30 (expt) compared with the response predicted from Eqs. (6.3) and (6.11).

chosen so as to make the curves assume the position shown on the time axis. Obviously the tensile stretching behavior of natural rubber networks does not correspond at all well to the deformation of a simple Voigt-Kelvin model. It should be noted that the values of τ and E do not influence the width of the response curve and that the values chosen for these constants are therefore of no consequence in this regard.

3. Dynamics of a Polymer Molecule (73)

Apparently one is not justified in replacing the actual polymer molecule by a simple Kelvin spring-dashpot model system. The lack of agreement between the response of the model and the real rubber network indicates that the elastic and viscous response of a true molecule must be examined more closely. A model of the polymer chain must still be considered, since the actual molecule is beyond present-day computational capabilities. However, a more realistic model than the Voigt-Kelvin system can certainly be devised.

A convenient model chain is the freely orienting chain used in previous chapters. The actual molecule is replaced by N freely orienting segments or, as they are sometimes called in this context, submolecules. It is further specified that these submolecules are still long enough for their individual end-to-end distances to behave in a way characteristic of a random chain. If the original molecule is quite long, it can always be split into submolecules for which this added condition will be true. However, since the length of a freely orienting chain segment has already been fully determined by the conditions set down in Chapter 1, it may not always be completely safe to associate a submolecule with a freely orienting segment. For the present at least, it will be assumed that the molecule has been split into N submolecules, each of which behaves as a gaussian coil.

As shown in Chapter 2, a gaussian coil behaves in many ways like a spring with spring constant $3kT/R^2$. [See Eq. (2.7), where R^2 is the mean square end-to-end distance.] Thus, if the mean square end-to-end length of a subchain is designated a^2, an applied force F_x will stretch the segment an equilibrium amount Δx, which is given by

$$F_x = (3kT/a^2)\,\Delta x \qquad (6.4)$$

During the time when the subchain is stretching immediately after the force has been applied, viscous and inertia forces will retard its motion. However, it will be seen later that the time taken for the small subchain to reach an equilibrium elongation under the force F_x will be almost negligibly small. For this reason the subchain is assumed to elongate instantaneously to the value given by Eq. (6.4).

In addition, the subchain can move as a unit over long distances through the polymer matrix. Because such long-range motions will take comparatively long times, they cannot be assumed instantaneous; therefore one must take account of the fact that, if the center of mass of a subchain moves through the liquid with speed v, the friction force retarding its motion is $f_0 v$. The quantity f_0 is the friction factor associated with the segment or subchain, and it has been discussed in detail in Chapter 3.

The mass of a subchain is M/N, which shall be denoted m. Since the internal structure of the subchain is being ignored in this discussion, it matters very little where the mass of the subchain is considered to be within the subchain; but for convenience, let us take the mass to be localized in a bead at the end of the subchain. This localization of mass is of no consequence so far as the final results are concerned, but it does help one to visualize the model being used. Such a model is shown, in part, in Figure 34.

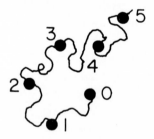

Figure 34.   A portion of the chain model used in the text. The sections between beads are gaussian submolecules.

Consider the portion of the model chain shown in Figure 34, and take this position to be the original configuration of the chain. Let x_0 be the component of the displacement of the 0'th bead. Similarly, let x_1 be the component of the distance through which the first bead has been displaced from *its* original position. In the same way, the x displacements from the positions shown in Figure 34 for the other beads will be x_2, x_3, etc.; in other words, the origins of the various x coordinates of the segments trace out the original configuration of the molecule.

The length $(x_1 - x_0)$ is the x component of the amount by which the first segment has been stretched. Similarly, the x distance which the i'th segment has been stretched is $x_i - x_{i-1}$. Hence, according to Eq. (6.4), the x component of the tension in this segment will be $e(x_i - x_{i-1})$, where e is defined as $3kT/a^2$.

Looking now at the i'th bead, one sees that the total x-directed force on it will be the difference between the x-component tensions in the i and $(i + 1)$ segments. Therefore the following expresses the net x-directed force on the i'th bead:

$$F_{xi} = e(x_{i+1} - x_i) - e(x_i - x_{i-1})$$

or

$$F_{xi} = ex_{i+1} - 2ex_i + ex_{i-1} \qquad (6.5)$$

with $e = 3kT/a^2$.

Notice that the y and z coordinates do not enter into the force equation, Eq. (6.5). Moreover, when the differential equation of motion of the segments is written, the x forces will give rise to velocities and accelerations in the x direction alone. It is apparent, then, that the y and z motions of the molecule need not be considered while treating the x motions. For visual purposes, the model chain of Figure 34 may therefore be replaced by the model of Figure 35. The two models will give identical results

Figure 35.   A chain model based upon the model of Figure 34. This simplified model is mathematically equivalent to the original model insofar as unidimensional motion is concerned.

as far as the x component of the chain motion is concerned. The linear model shown in Figure 35 has the great advantage that its motions can be easily pictured in terms of the so-called "normal modes" of vibration.

Figure 35 is an accurate model for a polymer chain as far as motion of the chain in the x direction is concerned, provided that any typical bead—say, the i'th—can be assumed to lie on either the right or left side of bead ($i - 1$). Furthermore, the lengths of the segments must conform to the gaussian distribution. With these restrictions, the model in Figure 35 is fully equivalent to the original freely orienting chain. It has no physical reality as far as the real molecule is concerned, except in the sense that its motion is mathematically equivalent to the x-direction motion of the freely orienting chain.

The great virtue of the model shown in Figure 35 is that its motion is easily described in terms of the longitudinal vibration of an elastic bar. It is well known that a series of identical masses separated by identical springs will vibrate in the same way as does a uniform bar, provided that the number of beads between vibration nodes is large (74). Since most polymer chains will contain very many freely orienting segments and since each bead in Figure 35 corresponds to one segment, the model should be much longer than shown. Although the exact solution for the motion of the model in Figure 35 is given in Appendix 9, its motion can be most easily visualized in terms of an elastic rod.

Consider now the longitudinal motion of an elastic rod and, for the present, neglect all viscous forces. It is known that such a rod has a large number of resonant frequencies. Depending upon how the rod is clamped or restrained and also upon how it is set in vibration, it may vibrate with one or a combination of many of these resonant frequencies. Each resonant frequency ω_n corresponds to a mode of motion of the bar. These modes of motion may be described with reference to Figure 36.

The simplest mode of motion consists of a pure translation of the bar in the x direction. Of course, the frequency for this mode of motion is zero, and hence $\omega_0 = 0$. This is not an important mode of motion in the present instance, since the molecule will be constrained in such a way that this motion is not possible. This pure translational mode is not shown in Figure 36.

A common mode of motion of a bar is illustrated in Figure 36a. This is the fundamental mode for a free-free bar and results when a bar that is clamped at its center is smoothly stroked along its length. It should be noted that amplitude plotted in

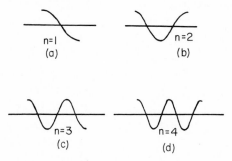

Figure 36.   Various resonant modes of motion of a chain.

this figure is the amplitude of vibration in the longitudinal or x direction. No transverse motion of the bar is considered since the discussion here is limited to motions under x-directed forces. There is only one node in this instance, and it is at the center of the bar. The resonant frequency for this mode is, in terms of the actual molecular parameters (see Appendix 9),

$$\omega_1 = (\pi/Na)(3kT/m)^{1/2} \qquad (6.6)$$

The second mode of motion is shown in Figure 36b. In this case the bar vibrates in three segments with two nodes. This vibration can easily be obtained if a bar is clamped at a point one-fourth of the way from its end. The frequency of this vibration is $2\omega_1$. Similarly, Figures 36c and d show the next two modes of vibration. In general, the resonant frequency of any mode is equal to $n\omega_1$, where n is the number of the mode. It should also be noticed that n is the number of nodes for the vibration under consideration.

As shown in Appendix 9, the very high resonance frequencies

for the model of Figure 35 depart somewhat from the values given by $\omega_n = n\omega_1$. In particular, the model of Figure 35 has a maximum possible frequency and is in that respect unlike the uniform bar, which can reach frequencies of order 10^{12} or higher. The limiting condition is that the uppermost mode has as many nodes as there are beads in the chain. For that mode, the resonant frequency is

$$
\begin{aligned}
\omega_N &= (2/a)(3kT/m)^{1/2} \\
&= (2N/\pi)\omega_1
\end{aligned} \tag{6.7}
$$

Hence, the maximum possible frequency is about N times as large as the fundamental.

Two features concerning the normal modes should be pointed out. First, the cut-off frequency ω_N is more or less an artifact. It has very little real meaning since it depends upon one of the unrealistic features of the model, the exact way in which its segments were selected. All that can be said in this regard is that, when modes of motion with frequencies near ω_N become important, the quantitative results obtained from this model will not be reliable. Fortunately, these very high modes of motion are usually of no consequence.

Second, it is well known that any possible motion of an elastic bar can be represented by a linear combination of the various modes of motion. That is to say, by taking all the possible figures such as those shown in Figure 36, the most complicated motion of the bar can be duplicated by multiplying each figure by an appropriate constant and adding all of them together. This is just another way of saying that a Fourier series of cosine terms can be used to represent the motion of an elastic bar. The same possibility holds true for the model of Figure 35.

4. Dynamics of a Polymer Molecule: Friction Effects (73)

The discussion in the preceding section assumed the model in Figure 35 to be perfectly free from all friction forces. In actuality, however, each bead experiences a viscous force proportional to the velocity of its motion through its surroundings. It is therefore necessary to consider what effect such forces have upon the model.

If one were to try to vibrate the molecule represented in Figure 35 by pulling on its ends in the x direction with a sinusoidal force, the molecule would show well-defined frequencies to which it would resonate. If a force of frequency $\omega_1/2$ was applied, the molecule would vibrate in a very complicated way but with very small amplitude. As the frequency of the force was increased, not much change would be noticed until the driving frequency became close to ω_1. At that time the molecule would begin to vibrate with very large amplitude and would be said to be resonating under the action of the force. Similar behavior would be noticed for applied forces with frequencies equal to any of the other resonant frequencies.

The above description applies only if the molecule does not experience friction forces. Without friction, the resonance frequencies are extremely sharp, and the amplitude at resonance is very large. If some friction is present, however, the vibration amplitude at resonance is much decreased, and the frequency range over which the molecule resonates spreads far to each side of the nondamped resonant frequency. In the case of real polymer molecules immersed in a viscous liquid, the damping is so large that the resonance frequencies cannot even be discerned. The resonance regions have lowered so much in amplitude, and the frequency range of resonance has become so large, that the resonances all blend together and produce the case of an overdamped spring system.

In spite of this complication resulting from the presence of viscous forces, the behavior of the model in Figure 35 can still be obtained. The general result for any type of applied force is given in Appendix 9. For the present instance, the case of creep, a constant force F is assumed to be applied to the ends of the polymer chain. The elongation of the chain as a function of time is then given by the following relation:

$$x_N - x_0 = (FNa^2/3kT)(8/\pi^2) \Sigma (1/n^2)[1 - \exp(-t/\tau_n)]$$
$$n = 1, 3, 5, \ldots, N \qquad (6.8)$$

where

$$\tau_n = f_0 N^2 a^2 / 3\pi^2 k T n^2$$

The meaning of this equation is as follows. When the tensile force F is applied to the ends of the molecule, all odd-numbered modes of vibration of the molecule are excited. These are the modes for which the chain ends move in opposite directions, as can be seen from Figure 36a and c. Since the applied force is *not* trying to move both ends of the molecule in the same direction, the even-numbered modes are not excited.

After a long time, the molecule will have reached an equilibrium elongation, and the exponentials in Eq. (6.8) will be zero. Each mode of response of the molecule will have contributed an amount proportional to $1/n^2$ to the elongation; hence it is clear that the first few modes of motion are by far the most important for this type of chain motion. For example, the fifth mode will contribute less than 4 per cent of the total elongation.

Another interesting fact brought out by Eq. (6.8) is that the response or retardation times (τ_n) for the various modes of motion are not at all uniform. In general, the higher modes of motion show the shorter retardation times. This characteristic is represented by the relation

$$\tau_n = (1/n^2)\tau_1 \qquad (6.9)$$

which means that the initial response of the chain just after the load has been applied will be chiefly the result of the response of the very high modes of motion. Notice also, from the definition of τ_1 in Eq. (6.8), that the retardation time is proportional to $f_0 N^2$. Consequently, the retardation times will be large for long chains in highly viscous surroundings.

Since the gross rubber sample must elongate in proportion to the individual chains, the final result is that

$$(\Delta L/L) = (\sigma/3\nu k T) \Sigma (8/\pi^2 n^2)[1 - \exp(-t/\tau_n)]$$
$$n = 1, 3, 5, \ldots, N \qquad (6.10)$$

where ν is the number of network chains in unit volume. Or, since the tensile compliance of the material $D(t)$ is merely $(\Delta L/L)/\sigma$,

$$3\nu kTD(t) = (8/\pi^2) \Sigma\, n^{-2}[1 - \exp(-t/\tau_n)]$$
$$n = 1, 3, 5, \ldots, N \qquad (6.11)$$

Equation (6.11) differs from the result obtained for the Kelvin spring-dashpot model in an easily visualized way. The result for the Kelvin model given by Eq. (6.3) is just a single term of Eq. (6.11). This means that the actual freely orienting chain does not behave like a single Kelvin element; instead, the chain

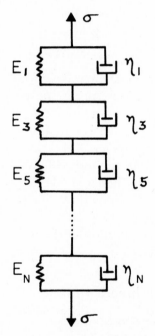

Figure 37.   A multiple Voigt-Kelvin model.

elongates like a series of many spring-dashpot elements. This can be seen to be true from a consideration of the series of Kelvin models shown in Figure 37.

According to Eq. (6.3), the model system in Figure 37 will

elongate in the following way, since each element is subject to the same stress and the elongations are additive:

$$y/\sigma = \Sigma\, E_n{}^{-1}[1 - \exp{(-t/\tau_n)}] \qquad n = 1, 3, 5, \ldots, N$$

$$(6.12)$$

with $\tau_n = \eta_n/E_n$. This equation for the compliance (y/σ) of the series of Kelvin models can be put in exactly the same form as Eq. (6.11) for the freely orienting chain model if the following replacements are made:

$$\eta_n/E_n = (1/n^2)(f_0 N^2 a^2/3\pi^2 k T) \qquad (6.13a)$$

and

$$1/E_n = (1/n^2)(8/3\pi^2 \nu k T) \qquad (6.13b)$$

which in turn means that η_n is given by

$$\eta_n = \nu f_0 N^2 a^2/8 \qquad (6.13c)$$

These relations show that each Kelvin element has the same value for η, but the various spring constants increase as n^2. In addition, it is interesting to notice that Eq. (6.13c) for the viscous element in the Kelvin model is equal, except for a factor of ⅔, to the viscosity of a polymer without entanglements given in Eq. (3.16). Even though the series of Kelvin elements shown in Figure 37 duplicates the behavior of an actual freely orienting chain, it is clear that the individual elements have little relation to the physical elements composing the chain. They do, however, represent the contribution of the various individual modes of motion of the chain to its over-all elongation.

5. Effect of Network-junction Motion (75)

The elongation under constant load of a rubber network as predicted by Eq. (6.11), or its equivalent from Eq. (6.12), is shown in Figure 33 by the broken curve. Although Eq. (6.11) is a better representation of the experimental data than was the equation describing a single Voigt-Kelvin model, the agreement is still far from satisfactory. In particular, the elongation predicted for long times is far from correct. Apparently the network keeps elongating for a much longer time than Eq. (6.11) predicts would be required to elongate a single chain. One is forced to conclude that Eq. (6.11) is in error at long times, and two sources for this error present themselves.

First, the model chain used for the computation is rather crude. It does not take into account the actual structure of the freely orienting segments. However, short-range structure along the chain will only be of significance for the high modes of chain vibration where the distance between nodes becomes comparable to segment size. These modes of motion are only influential at very short times. For this reason, one would not expect this source of error to be responsible for the deficiency of Eq. (6.11) at long times.

Second, it was assumed in deriving Eq. (6.11) that the sample as a whole elongated in the same way as the individual chains elongated. This assumption is inherent in the whole idea of the affine deformation of the network. Although it is probably not too inaccurate an approximation to say that the distance between network junctions will change in the same way as the whole rubber deforms, small motions of the junctions must occur. It is apparently this very slow movement of the network junctions which gives rise to the inaccuracy of Eq. (6.11) at long times. This limitation will be explained in the discussion that follows.

Let us consider a very lightly crosslinked rubber. If the degree of crosslinking is such that the rubber is near its gel point, each chain will on the average have one other chain crosslinked to it. This situation is represented in the upper part of Figure 38, where the series of linked molecules should be extended to a number much larger than shown. Under these conditions the whole network is not too different from a giant linear molecule. According to Eq. (6.8), the longest relaxation time for such a giant molecule will be nearly infinite, and the fact that the individual network chains are much shorter than the combined chain cannot alter this condition. Obviously, this extremely loose network will not be adequately described by Eq. (6.11), for the network will elongate over a much longer time period than Eq. (6.11) predicts.

The case of a perfect (i.e., no loose chain ends) tetrahedral network is shown schematically in the right-hand portion of Figure 38. Once again only a very small portion of the network is

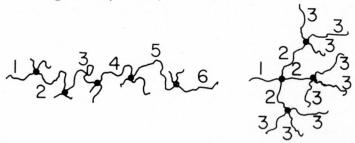

Figure 38.   Schematic diagrams showing chains vulcanized to various extents.

shown. If one pulls toward the left on chain 1, then chains 2 will also move toward the left. These in turn will pull chains 3 toward the left, and so on. The response of chain 1 will be quicker than the response of chains 2, and they in turn will respond more quickly than chains 3. Hence it is clear that network movements toward an equilibrium configuration under an applied force will require a time much longer than the response time of an individual network chain.

An abbreviated outline of the computation needed to describe the effects of the network-junction motions is given in Appendix 10. It becomes evident (75) that the compliance can be expressed approximately as follows:

$$D(t) = D_0(t) + (1/3\nu kT) \Sigma \beta^{-n} [1 - \exp(-t/\tau_1\beta^{2n})]$$
$$n = 1, 2, \cdots, \infty \qquad (6.14)$$

where $D_0(t)$ is the value of $D(t)$ given by Eq. (6.11). The quantity β used in this expression is defined as the average number of number 2 chains in Figure 38 that are crosslinked to one other chain in addition to the number 1 chain. For example, β equals 1 for the left-hand diagram in Figure 38 and 3 for the right-hand diagram.

The compliance curves predicted by Eq. (6.14) for various

values of β are shown in Figure 39. The cases of $\beta = 10$ and $\beta \to \infty$ are unrealistic, since a tetrahedral crosslink can at most have $\beta = 3$. However, the $\beta \to \infty$ case is included, since this is equivalent to the result given in Eq. (6.11). If β is infinitely large, no motion of the crosslink will occur, since chain 1 in Figure 38 would have to pull an infinite number of chains along with it if the junction were to move.

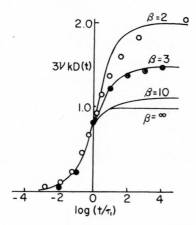

Figure 39.   The lines represent compliance curves predicted by Eq. (6.14), using the values of β indicated. Data for the natural rubber of Figures 30 and 33 are shown ($\circ$) together with data for crosslinked polyethyl methacrylate ($\bullet$) (75).

To see how the result of Eq. (6.14) agrees with experiment, it is profitable to compare the data for natural rubber in Figure 33 with the curves of Figure 39. Two parameters are available for adjustment when making this comparison, the experimental value of νkT and the experimental value of τ_1. These values have been chosen to fit the experimental data to the curve for $\beta = 2$ at two points, the midpoint and the long-time end. The experimental data for natural rubber are shown as the open circles in Figure 39. It is apparent that the agreement could be made better by using a slightly smaller value for β; nevertheless, the agreement is already quite good without making such an adjustment.

Also shown in Figure 39 are some experimental data for a crosslinked polyethyl methacrylate above its glass temperature (75). In this case, the data fit the curve for $\beta = 3$ with reasonable precision. This polymer may be expected to show a β value near 3, the value for the perfect tetrahedral network, since the value of M_c was much smaller than the estimated M_n value. This would mean that the number of chain-end defects would be small. Since the natural rubber used to fit the curve for $\beta = 2$ had been milled before vulcanization, appreciable breakdown had undoubtedly occurred; hence, the effect of chain-end defects would be large, thereby giving rise to a smaller value for β. In any event, the agreement between the theoretical relation in Eq. (6.14), and the experimental results is good enough to justify confidence in the molecular picture postulated.

6. Modified Voigt-Kelvin Model

The modification of a simple Kelvin spring-dashpot model to obtain the model shown in Figure 37 was made necessary in order that the model elongate according to Eq. (6.11). Since the elongation represented by Eq. (6.11) is represented by the term $D_0(t)$ in Eq. (6.14), the multiple Kelvin model shown in Figure 37 will give rise to that portion of the elongation represented by $D_0(t)$. The remaining terms in Eq. (6.14) will require an infinite number of Kelvin elements for their representation.

Each term of the sum in Eq. (6.14) can be represented by a Kelvin element with η_n/E_n equal to $\tau_1 \beta^{2n}$ and with E_n equal to $3\nu k T \beta^n$. An infinite number of these elements, hooked in series with the system shown in Figure 37, will be required. The values of n will, of course, be the integers running from 1 to infinity. Although no use will be made of the fact until later, it is worth while to point out that Eq. (6.14) is equivalent to the response of an infinite number of Voigt-Kelvin elements hooked in series. The retardation times of these elements are distributed according to the values mentioned above, namely, $\tau_1 \beta^{2n}$.

7. Temperature-Time Superposition Principle

Equation (6.14) describes the time dependence for the elongation of a rubber network under constant stress. It is interesting and informative to notice that this equation can be written in the following functional form:

$$3 \nu k T D(t) = \psi(t/\tau_1) \qquad (6.15)$$

The function on the right-hand side of Eq. (6.15) involves no quantities other than β and t/τ_1. Since β is a constant of the network system, it is apparent that $TD(t)$ is a function of only one variable, t/τ_1.

The quantity τ_1 is given in Eq. (6.8) and is equal to network constants multiplied by f_0/T. Hence, τ_1 is essentially a measure of the segmental friction constant. If the temperature of the rubber is increased, f_0/T will invariably decrease, and therefore so will τ_1. But since $TD(t)$ is a function of the ratio t/τ_1 alone, it is apparent that the shape of the response function $TD(t)$ will not change but will merely be shifted to shorter times. Consequently, one is led to the conclusion that time and temperature are intimately related. An increase in T does not change the function $TD(t)$ but merely causes the time scale to be changed by some common factor.

As a concrete example, suppose that the temperature of a rubber is increased from T to T'. Then $\tau_1' = a_T \tau_1$, where a_T will in this case be less than unity since the response time τ_1' at the higher temperature will be shorter than τ_1 at the lower temperature. The quantity a_T is called the "shift factor," for reasons that will become apparent later.

Since the response at T' takes only a fraction (a_T) of the time it would take at T, it is at once apparent that at temperature T'

$$3 \nu k T' D(t) = \psi(t/a_T \tau_1) \qquad (6.16)$$

In other words, the time scale at T' has been shifted by a factor a_T from what it was at T. This means that a graph of $T'D(t)$

vs. log t for temperature T' will look exactly the same as a graph of $TD(t)$ vs. log t for temperature T. Only one difference will occur. The two curves will be displaced along the log t axis relative to each other by an amount log a_T. This fact has already been shown in Figure 30, where the response curve for natural rubber at two temperatures is plotted.

This so-called "temperature-time superposition principle" was first discovered by Leaderman (76), and independently by Ferry (77) and Tobolsky and Andrews (78). It has great practical significance, and its utility may be seen by reference to Figure 30.

To obtain the 10°C-curve data shown in Figure 30 would be a difficult experimental problem if a temperature-time superposition could not be resorted to. It would necessitate the measurement of sample response at times less than 10^{-7} sec, as well as for times of several hours. Although such measurements are not wholly inconceivable, they would require very complex instrumentation. On the other hand, the $-30°C$ curve would be

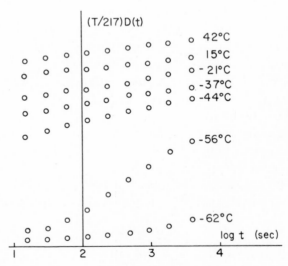

Figure 40.   Compliance curves obtained for a vulcanized rubber at several temperatures.

somewhat easier to measure in the short-time range, since measurement times of about 10^{-3} sec would suffice. However, to obtain the long-time portion of this curve the measurements would have to be continued for centuries. Although theoretically this is not impossible, it would inordinately delay the acquisition of data. Presumably, the early part of the response curve would be simple to obtain at $-50°C$, since measurement times of less than about a second would not be required; however, the long-time portion of the curve would be unobtainable at this temperature because of the great lengths of time involved.

In practice these difficulties are avoided by measuring convenient portions of the response curve at each of several temperatures. Typical data obtained in this way for natural rubber are shown in Figure 40 (72). The temperature-time superposition principle now allows these data at different temperatures to be reduced to a single temperature. For example, if one wished to take $-56°C$ as the response temperature, one would merely shift the curves obtained at other temperatures parallel to the log t axis until they joined smoothly with the curve for

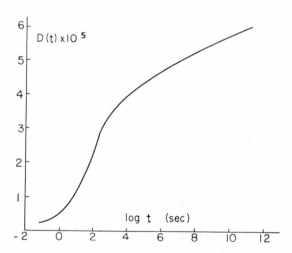

Figure 41. The composite compliance curve at 217°K for the rubber shown in Figure 40. The units of $D(t)$ are cm²/gm.

$-56°C$. The amount by which a given curve needs to be shifted is equal to log a_T, since a_T is the factor by which the time scale is changed as one goes from one temperature to the other. The composite curve obtained by this shifting procedure is shown in Figure 41, where it is understood that the temperature of measurement is $-56°C$.

8. The WLF Equation and a_T

From the last section, a_T is by definition the ratio of the response time τ_1' at temperature T' to the response time τ_1 at temperature T. If T is arbitrarily selected as the glass temperature T_g,

$$a_T = \tau_1'/\tau_{1g} \tag{6.17}$$

But from the definition of τ_1,

$$a_T = f_0' T_g / f_{0g} T' \tag{6.18}$$

In addition, making use of the relation between jump frequency ϕ and f_0 given by Eq. (3.8), one finds

$$a_T = \phi_g/\phi' \tag{6.19}$$
$$= \exp\{\beta^* v^*[(1/v_f') - (1/v_{fg})]\}$$

To obtain the latter form of Eq. (6.19), use has been made of Eq. (4.19) for ϕ.

Comparison of Eqs. (4.25), (4.30), and (6.19) leads finally to the result (49) that

$$\ln a_T = -40(T - T_g)/[52 + (T - T_g)] \tag{6.20}$$

This expression is an alternate form of the WLF equation. It expresses the shift factor in terms of a readily measured quantity T_g. Of course, the same restrictions apply to the use of Eq. (6.20) as held for Eq. (4.30). In general, it is reasonably accurate in the range $T_g < T < T_g + 120°C$.

9. Conclusions and Critique

It should first be pointed out that the discussions in this chapter, although carried out in terms of the tensile compliance $D(t)$, may also be extended to the shear compliance $J(t)$. This may be done by replacing the term $3\nu k T$ in all the equations for $D(t)$ with $\nu k T$; in other words, the shear compliance $J(t)$ is three times larger than the tensile compliance.

The discussion in this chapter has been restricted to low deformations. This restriction is inherent in the assumption made throughout that the stress was directly proportional to strain. In this regard, the shear compliance should probably obey the current equations to higher elongations than the tensile compliance, since the equilibrium shear compliance follows Hooke's law to higher extensions than does tensile compliance (see Chapter 2). Both types of compliance fail at high elongations, where the gaussian model for a chain will no longer be applicable.

A much more sophisticated theory for the description of network creep than the one given here can be presented. Although the model used in this chapter is qualitatively reasonable, it is open to several objections. Among these can be listed the effects of varying chain lengths between network junctions. The present treatment assumes all chains to be identical in molecular weight; however, it can be shown that this neglect of differences does not influence the results given in this chapter to any serious extent. The dispersion region would be only slightly widened if this effect were included.

A second objection to the theory given in this chapter is involved with the failure of the gaussian segment model to describe very short time phenomena. As was seen in Figure 33, the short-time response is dependent upon the very highest modes of vibration. Modes that split the chain into segments of the same length as a few monomer units will not be reliably described by the present model. Fortunately these modes are only of importance for the near glasslike response of the polymer (i.e., the first per cent or two of its equilibrium elongation under the applied stress) and are not important for rubberlike behavior. No acceptable method has yet been found to extend the model into this region of extremely short-time response.

A third and more abstruse objection has to do with the neglect of Brownian motion. Although the spring constant for each segment or submolecule accounts reasonably well for the Brownian motion within a submolecule, the submolecules as a whole will undergo thermal diffusive motion as well. Properly, an internal diffusion term should be included in the equation of motion for the chain. This has actually been done in a more accurate mathematical treatment of the model used here. A successful computation of the submolecule model's motion that took into account Brownian motion was carried out by Rouse (79). His computation was restricted to the behavior of a single chain immersed in a low-molecular-weight fluid that was being subjected to shear. Later, the Rouse computation was extended by Nakada (80), and an especially detailed treatment of the Rouse model has been given by Zimm (81). His effort was undertaken primarily to include in Rouse's computation the effect of solvent immobilization by the polymer molecule. This effect is of primary importance in dilute solutions but is assumed to be inconsequential at the higher polymer concentrations treated in this book.

Several attempts have been made to compare the results of the model used in this chapter with the Rouse model, which includes Brownian motion. In particular, Ferry and coworkers (82) have extended the results of Rouse and Zimm to the case of undiluted polymers and have obtained fair agreement with the model used here. More fundamentally, Miyake (83) has shown that in all practical cases the average effect of Brownian motion will not seriously influence the result. Hence one concludes that the two methods for treating the submolecule model will give essentially the same result. This has also been demonstrated by Gross and Fuoss (84).

APPENDIX 9
Chain Dynamics (73)

Equation (6.5) of the text gives the x component of the force on the i'th bead in Figure 35. To find the response of such a bead in the absence of friction forces, the force in Eq. (6.5) is simply equated to the mass times the x component of the acceleration:

$$m\ddot{x}_i = e(x_{i+1} - 2x_i + x_{i-1}) \qquad \text{(A9.1)}$$

There are N equations similar to Eq. (A9.1) for the total N beads of the chain. The beads on the two chain ends have slightly different equations of motion, since they are not constrained on one side:

$$m\ddot{x}_0 = e(x_1 - x_0)$$

and

$$m\ddot{x}_N = e(x_N - x_{N-1}) \qquad \text{(A9.2)}$$

The solutions of these equations are of form

$$x_{in} = \exp(j\omega_n t) \cos(ik_n) \qquad \text{(A9.3)}$$

with

$$e = 3kT/a^2$$

and

$$\omega_n^2 = 2e(1 - \cos k_n)/m \qquad k_n = n\pi/N$$

The quantity j is $\sqrt{-1}$, and n takes on all the integer values from zero to N.

Even if friction forces act upon the beads, the above equations can be handled in a straightforward way to obtain the motion of the system. This is most easily done by the method of normal coordinates. Mathematically the present problem is nearly identical to the problem of the vibration of N equal masses suspended at equal distances on a string in a viscous medium. Although the solution to this problem is well known, it is a rather lengthy and involved computation. For this reason, only the result will be given here.

In terms of the normal coordinates q_n, the displacement of the i'th particle is given by

$$x_i = \sum_{n=1}^{N} [2q_n/(2mN)^{1/2}] \cos(ik_n) \qquad \text{(A9.4)}$$

The normal coordinates are to be determined from the differential equation

$$\ddot{q}_n + (f_0/m)\dot{q}_n + \omega_n^2 q_n = F_n \qquad \text{(A9.5)}$$

where $-f_0 \dot{x}_i$ is the viscous force on the i'th segment because of its motion through the polymer matrix, and F_n is a function of the external forces $\Phi(i,t)$ applied to the segments, as defined by the relation

$$F_n = \sum_{i=0}^{N} [2\Phi(i,t)/(2mN)^{1/2}] \cos (ik_n) \qquad (A9.6)$$

As a simple example of the use of these equations, consider the response of the chain to a force F applied at each end of the chain so as to stretch it:

$$\Phi(0,t) = -F$$
$$\Phi(N,t) = +F$$

All the other values of Φ are zero. Substitution of these values into Eq. (A9.6) yields

$$F_n = 0 \qquad \qquad \text{for } n \text{ even}$$
$$F_n = -2F/(mN/2)^{1/2} \qquad \text{for } n \text{ odd}$$

Since the viscous forces will be assumed large enough so that all inertia effects will be negligible, the solution of Eq. (A9.5) is simply

$$q_n = (F_n/\omega_n^2)[1 - \exp(-t/\tau_n)] \qquad (A9.7)$$

with

$$\tau_n = f_0/\omega_n^2 m$$

Substitution of Eq. (A9.7) in Eq. (A9.4) yields the following expression for x_0 and x_N:

$$x_0 = \sum_{n=1}^{N} [2/(2mN)^{1/2}](F_n/\omega_n^2)[1 - \exp(-t/\tau_n)]$$

and $\qquad\qquad\qquad\qquad\qquad\qquad\qquad\qquad\qquad\qquad$ (A9.8)

$$x_N = -\sum_{n=1}^{N} [2/(2mN)^{1/2}](F_n/\omega_n^2)[1 - \exp(-t/\tau_n)]$$

If F_n is now replaced by the values found above and if the constants are removed from under the summation signs, the value of $x_N - x_0$ can be written down at once. The result has been given as Eq. (6.8) in the text.

APPENDIX 10
Motion of Network Junctions (75)

Consider the portion of a network shown in Figure 38. It is possible, following Gross and Fuoss (84), to assign to chain 1 a modulus of elasticity per unit length (e) and a friction constant per unit length (λ). There will be β number 2 chains attached to chain 1 if only those chains which continue on to number 3 chains are counted. Each of these chains has an elasticity modulus e and friction constant λ.

The β number 2 chains may be replaced by a single equivalent chain with modulus e and friction constant $\beta\lambda$. Similarly, the number 3 chains are equivalent to a chain with modulus e and friction constant $\beta^2\lambda$. In general, the n'th chains are equivalent to a chain with modulus e and friction constant $\beta^{n-1}\lambda$.

Gross and Fuoss (84) have shown that the motion of a chain with elasticity modulus e and friction constant λ can be accurately treated as an equivalent uniform elastic rod in a viscous medium. In the present instance, instead of a single uniform rod there is a sectioned rod, each section having elasticity modulus e but with different friction coefficients. The end section has friction coefficient λ, the friction constant of the next section is $\beta\lambda$, that of the third is $\beta^2\lambda$, and so on.

It is possible to work out the response of such a sectioned bar when a force is applied to its end. The method of solution is quite involved and is not readily carried through exactly. The computation is simplified by assuming that the overtone vibration modes of the individual chains are not needed. This is equivalent to dropping all but the $(n = 1)$ term in Eq. (6.11). With this approximation,

$$3vkTD(t) = [1 - \exp(-t/\tau_1)] + \sum_{n=1}^{\infty} \beta^{-n}[1 - \exp(-t/\tau_1\beta^{2n})]$$

$$(A10.1)$$

The first term in Eq. (A10.1) is the first term in Eq. (6.11).

If the higher-overtone vibrations had been carried through the calculation, this term would have appeared as the sum in Eq. (6.11). It is not completely clear whether the overtone vibrations would alter the last term in Eq. (A10.1). However, because this term is only important when t is large, the overtone omission should not be expected to change it seriously, since the overtones are usually associated with short-time phenomena. After correcting the first term in Eq. (A10.1), one obtains Eq. (6.14) of the text.

PROBLEMS

1. Suppose one has two Kelvin elements in series. The parameters of the elements are $E_1 = E_2 = 6\nu kT$ and $\eta_1 = \eta_2/10 = \tau/E_1$. Derive the creep response of this system to a constant stress σ. Plot your result in the form y/σ vs. $\log (t/\tau)$. On the same graph, plot the response of a single Kelvin element having $E_3 = 3\nu kT$ and $\eta = \tau/E_1$.

2. The various terms in the sum of Eq. (6.11) give the contributions of the various modes of motion to the total sample elongation. Using the same scale, plot on the same axes each of the first four terms of the sum of Eq. (6.11) vs. $\log (t/\tau_1)$.

3. How much faster will be the creep response of polystyrene at 150°C than at 120°C? Than at 105°C?

4. In Chapter 2, the kinetic theory led to the equation $D(\infty) = \frac{1}{3}\nu kT$ when one uses the notation of Chapter 6 and assumes small elongations. This is also the result given by Eq. (6.11) at long times. The more correct value including network junction motion, is given in Eq. (6.14). Find $D(\infty)$ from that equation and compare it with the simple kinetic theory result in the special case of a perfect tetrahedral network.

[Notice that $\sum\limits_{1}^{\infty} (x)^n = x/(1 - x)$.]

Chapter 7

RETARDATION- AND RELAXATION-TIME SPECTRA

1. The Value of Models

The response of a network polymer to constant load has been treated in the last chapter. By using a rather simple molecular model, it was possible to show that the mechanical response of this molecular model conformed reasonably well to the observed creep response of real networks. In addition, it was shown that the molecular model was equivalent to an infinite series of Voigt spring-dashpot elements. The constants of the springs and dashpots were determined from the molecular model and were therefore known.

Next, one would like to compute the way in which the molecular network behaves under various other experimental conditions. For example, it would be of value to know how such a network responds to a sinusoidal driving force. This particular type of experimental response is of great interest, since any time-dependent force can be considered to be the appropriate combination of various sinusoidal forces. That is to say, any practical applied force can be represented as a Fourier series of sine and cosine forces. Hence, if it is assumed that a superposition principle applies, so that the total response of the network is the sum of the individual responses the network would give to each of the sinusoidal forces, the general response problem can be much simplified. One need only know what the network response

153

to the general sinusoidal force would be, and the response to any arbitrary type of force could then be calculated.

Another type of experiment for which it is important to know the response of a polymer network is the stress-relaxation experiment. This experiment consists of stretching the network to some constant elongation value and observing how the stress needed to preserve this elongation decreases with time. It differs in a very fundamental way from the experiments involving creep and sinusoidal applied force. In the stress-relaxation experiment the force is unknown, while the elongation is known. For the other two experiments the force is known, but not the elongation.

One is now faced with the problem of describing the response of the molecular network to sinusoidal-force and stress-relaxation experiments. It would be possible to return to the molecular models and recompute them for these new conditions. Notice that two separate computations are needed, a computation of the response of the individual chains and a computation of the response of the network junctions. Since a general method of solution has been worked out for the individual chains, this portion of the computation is easy and has been carried out for the sinusoidal-force case. No general solution for the network-junction motion has yet been given, and it will undoubtedly be quite formidable when obtained. The stress-relaxation case, since the forces are not known at the outset, presents more serious computational difficulties for the general solution of the individual-chain problem. Of course, in principle at least, these solutions can always be carried out.

It would be of value, however, to have available a more direct method for solving the problem of network response after one type of response has been found. It is inconvenient to go back to the molecular model in each case and recompute the whole problem. Instead, there is a need for a method of transposing the results of one experimental situation in order to describe a different experiment on the same material. Such a method does exist in principle at least. It proceeds from the fact that the real molecular system can be represented by a properly chosen set of springs and dashpots. The response of this model system is then discussed in terms of its molecularly specified parameters. In particular, the response of the molecular system is completely derivable from a knowledge of its retardation, or response, time distribution. This procedure will be discussed in detail in the remainder of this chapter.

2. Sinusoidal Vibration: Single Voigt Element

The Voigt-Kelvin model discussed in the last chapter is of particular value in computations where the applied force is specified. Consider the response of a single Voigt element consisting of a spring with modulus E in parallel with a dashpot with viscosity η, such as is shown in Figure 32. At any instant the applied stress must equal the sum of the two forces given by the tension in the spring and the resistance of the dashpot. Therefore,

$$\sigma = Ey + \eta \dot{y} \qquad (7.1)$$

where $\dot{y}$ is written in place of (dy/dt).

If σ is a sinusoidal stress given by the relation

$$\sigma = \sigma_0 \exp(j\omega t) \qquad (7.2)$$

where $j = \sqrt{-1}$ and ω is the frequency of vibration, the solution of Eq. (7.1) is quite straightforward. (See Appendix 11 for a more elementary treatment of the problem.) It is, as may be verified by substitution,

$$(y/\sigma_0) = (1/E)(1 + j\omega\tau)^{-1} \exp(j\omega t) \qquad (7.3)$$

where

$$\tau = \eta/E$$

The tensile compliance given by Eq. (7.3) is a complex number (i.e., part real and part imaginary) and is therefore referred to as the "complex compliance." By this expression, the complex compliance is meant to be

$$D^*(\omega) = (1/E)(1 + j\omega\tau)^{-1} \qquad (7.4)$$

A similar form would be given for the complex shear compliance $J^*(\omega)$.

The complex compliance may be separated into real and imaginary terms by multiplying the numerator and the denominator in Eq. (7.4) by $(1 - j\omega\tau)$:

$$D^*(\omega) = [(1/E)(1 + \omega^2\tau^2)^{-1}] - [(j\omega\tau/E)(1 + \omega^2\tau^2)^{-1}] \quad (7.5)$$

The first term in Eq. (7.5) is the real compliance, which gives the portion of the displacement in phase with the force and which is given as

$$D'(\omega) = 1/[E(1 + \omega^2\tau^2)] \quad (7.6)$$

This quantity is often called the "storage compliance," since it gives rise to the recoverable energy stored in the spring element.

The imaginary quantity in Eq. (7.5) is designated the "loss compliance," and its value is

$$D''(\omega) = \omega\tau/[E(1 + \omega^2\tau^2)] \quad (7.7)$$

The adoption of the term "loss compliance" derives from the fact that this portion of the deformation gives rise to nonrecoverable work being done by the applied force. This will be shown in the discussion that follows.

Since work is the integral of force times incremental distance, the work done by the driving stress σ during one complete vibration or cycle is given by

$$\text{Work/cycle} = \oint \sigma \, dy$$

$$= \oint \sigma(dy/dt) \, dt \quad (7.8)$$

If σ is assumed to vary as $\sigma_0 \cos(\omega t)$, then

$$y/\sigma_0 = [D'(\omega) - jD''(\omega)] \exp(j\omega t)$$

which is more conveniently expressed as

$$y/\sigma_0 = D'(\omega) \cos(\omega t) + D''(\omega) \sin(\omega t) \quad (7.9)$$

Taking the derivative of Eq. (7.9) with respect to t and substituting into Eq. (7.8) gives

$$\text{Work/cycle} =$$
$$\oint \sigma_0^2 \omega[-D'(\omega) \sin(\omega t) + D''(\omega) \cos(\omega t)] \cos(\omega t) \, dt \quad (7.10)$$

The first term of the integral is an odd function of ωt and therefore integrates to zero over one cycle. The second term of the integral is always positive and therefore cannot be zero.

$$\text{Work/cycle} = 0 + \pi\sigma_0{}^2 D''(\omega) \qquad (7.11)$$

Hence, the storage compliance does not give rise to an energy loss, whereas the loss compliance does. Although the $D'(\omega)$ term of y does give rise to work on the part of the applied force, this energy is stored in the spring during the compression part of the cycle. The energy is then released in the next part of the cycle and actually aids the applied force; therefore the storage compliance results in neither a net gain nor a loss of energy by the applied force. The total energy loss occurs because of the loss-compliance term.

It is interesting to see how the energy loss per cycle varies with applied frequency. This may be done by examining the last term in Eq. (7.11), which shows this energy loss to be $\pi\sigma_0{}^2 D''(\omega)$. From the definition of $D''(\omega)$,

$$\text{Loss per cycle} = \pi\sigma_0{}^2 \omega\tau / [E(1 + \omega^2\tau^2)] \qquad (7.12)$$

Since one is usually interested in the energy loss per second W,

$$E\tau W / 2\sigma_0{}^2 = \omega^2\tau^2 / (1 + \omega^2\tau^2) \qquad (7.13)$$

This quantity is plotted in Figure 42 as a function of $\log(\omega\tau)$.

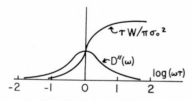

Figure 42.   The loss compliance $D''(\omega)$ and the energy loss per second W for a single Voigt element plotted as a function of applied frequency.

The loss function given in Eq. (7.13) increases as ω^2 at low frequencies; at high frequencies it reaches a constant value. Of course, the loss per cycle is proportional to $D''(\omega)$, which is also shown in Figure 42. It should be noticed that the curve for energy loss per second, or power loss, is far different from the curve for energy loss per cycle. Although the energy loss per cycle decreases rapidly at high frequencies, the power loss, being the product of an increasing and a decreasing function, becomes a constant at high frequencies.

It is of value to write Eq. (7.9) in a somewhat different way. From a well-known trigonometric identity,

$$p \cos A + q \sin A = r \cos (A - \delta)$$

where

$$r = (p^2 + q^2)^{1/2} \qquad \text{and} \qquad \tan \delta = q/p$$

Applying this to Eq. (7.9) gives

$$y/\sigma_0 = (D'^2 + D''^2)^{1/2} \cos (\omega t - \delta) \qquad (7.14)$$

with

$$\tan \delta = D''/D'$$

The quantity $\tan \delta$ is called the "loss tangent" or "damping." It is a measure of the energy loss per cycle.

Equation (7.14) shows clearly that the response of the Voigt model is sinusoidal, even though the displacement has a phase difference δ in comparison with the applied force. In addition, it shows clearly how the amplitude of the response varies with frequency.

$$Ey/\sigma_0 = (1 + \omega^2 \tau^2)^{-1} \cos (\omega t - \delta) \qquad (7.15)$$

Hence at low frequencies the amplitude of vibration is constant and is given by

$$\text{Amplitude} \cong \sigma_0/E \qquad \omega \ll 1 \qquad (7.16)$$

Similarly, for high frequencies,

$$\text{Amplitude} \cong (\sigma_0/E)(1/\omega^2 \tau^2) \qquad \omega \tau \gg 1 \qquad (7.17)$$

The actual variation of amplitude over the whole range is shown in Figure 43, together with $D''(\omega)$ and $D'(\omega)$.

These results can be explained qualitatively as follows. At very low frequencies the movement is very slow, and the viscous drag of the dashpot will be very small; hence, the energy loss and loss compliance will be small at these frequencies. The maximum displacement will occur when the tension in the spring equals the applied stress; consequently, the maximum displacement will be large and essentially constant.

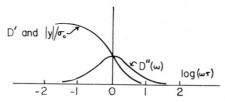

D' and $|y|/\sigma_o$ D''(ω)   log ($\omega\tau$)

-2   -1   0   1   2

Figure 43.   Loss compliance $D''(\omega)$, storage compliance $D'(\omega)$, and amplitude of vibration y for a single Voigt element as a function of applied frequency.

At higher frequencies the dashpot must move more swiftly, and the viscous force will therefore increase. As a result, the applied stress must both stretch the spring and counterbalance a rather large viscous force. The spring elongation, and $D'(\omega)$, will therefore decrease while the loss compliance increases.

At very high frequencies the dashpot will offer great viscous resistance and will not allow the spring to elongate. It is for this reason that $D'(\omega)$ approaches zero at high frequencies. At the same time, however, the displacement of the dashpot becomes so small that the energy loss per cycle, and $D''(\omega)$, also approaches zero. Large amplitudes of vibration at low frequencies are therefore observed changing to low amplitudes at high frequencies.

The loss tangent, tan δ, is the ratio of $D''(\omega)/D'(\omega)$. It is zero for low frequencies and becomes very large at high frequencies; hence, the loss angle δ varies from zero at low frequencies to $\pi/2$ at high frequencies.

Certain general statements can also be made concerning the temperature variation of the vibration amplitude, $D'(\omega)$ and $D''(\omega)$ for the Voigt model. Since a molecular system based on this model would show a decreasing viscosity with increasing temperature, the quantity $\tau = \eta/E$ would decrease with increasing temperature also. However, since the behavior of the model depends only on the product $\tau\omega$, a decrease in τ is equivalent to a decrease in ω. Therefore, the behavior at low temperatures will be similar to the behavior at high frequencies. This means the quantity $D'(\omega)$ and the vibration amplitude will be large at high temperatures but will approach zero at low temperatures. The loss and $D''(\omega)$ will evidence a maximum at intermediate temperatures.

It is apparent that, since the behavior of the model depends only upon the product $\tau\omega$, a temperature-time superposition principle applies (76,77,78). Hence, the properties of this model when plotted as a function of log (ω) will give rise to identical curves for various η values. These curves will be shifted along the log (ω) axis by an amount proportional to the logarithm of the viscosity.

3. Sinusoidal Vibration: Voigt Elements in Series

In the last chapter it was shown that a single Voigt-Kelvin element was not capable of representing the true response of a rubber network polymer. The appropriate response behavior can only be obtained from a combination of several springs and dashpots. One possible proper spring-dashpot combination was found in Chapter 6 from an analysis of the molecular dynamics. This representation consisted of a large number (essentially an infinitely large number) of Voigt elements in series. The proper values to be assigned to the various springs and dashpots were also found.

Since the molecular behavior can be adequately described by many Voigt elements in series, as illustrated in Figure 37, it is of interest to examine the response of such a system to a sinusoidal driving force $\sigma_0 \cos \omega t$. This force acts on each Voigt element simultaneously. The response of the system is the sum of the responses of its various elements. From Eq. (7.3),

$$y/\sigma_0 = \Sigma \, (D'_n - jD''_n) \exp \, (j\omega t) \qquad (7.18)$$

where the sum extends over all the Voigt elements in Figure 37. As before,

$$D'_n = 1/[E_n(1 + \omega^2 \tau_n{}^2)]$$

and   (7.19)

$$D''_n = \omega \tau_n/[E_n(1 + \omega^2 \tau_n{}^2)]$$

where

$$\tau_n = \eta_n/E_n$$

Although the proper values for η_n and E_n were found in the last chapter, the present discussion will not be limited to those values only. It will be assumed for the present that the spring-dashpot model consists of a large number of Voigt elements in series, with no restriction being placed upon the various η_n and E_n values.

The total compliance of the system is defined as the sum of the individual compliances. Hence,

$$D'(\omega) = \Sigma \ (1/E_n)[1/(1 + \omega^2 \tau_n{}^2)]$$

and   (7.20)

$$D''(\omega) = \Sigma \ (1/E_n)[\omega \tau_n/(1 + \omega^2 \tau_n{}^2)]$$

The variation of $D'(\omega)$ and $D''(\omega)$ with frequency is actually obtained by the superposition of many individual curves such as those shown in Figure 42. Each of these curves will be displaced along the log $\omega \tau_n$ axis with respect to the other curves; in addition, the height of each curve will be in proportion to $1/E_n$. Hence, the curves for $D'(\omega)$ and $D''(\omega)$ given by Eq. (7.20) will be much broader in general than the curves shown in Figure 42. It will be seen in a later chapter that the experimental curves for a network rubber are quite broad, as would be expected.

4. Retardation-time Spectra

The response of a Voigt element to constant load was shown in the last chapter to be given by

$$y/\sigma_0 = (1/E)[1 - \exp{(-t/\tau)}] \qquad (7.21)$$

For a large number of Voigt elements in series the response would be

$$D(t) = y/\sigma_0 = \Sigma \ (1/E_n)[1 - \exp{(-t/\tau_n)}] \qquad (7.22)$$

Notice that the contribution of each Voigt element to the equilibrium compliance is merely $1/E_n$; in other words, each retardation time τ_n is associated with a compliance $1/E_n$. One is therefore led to adopt a terminology in which one speaks of a spectrum of retardation times, each of strength $1/E_n$.

It frequently happens that the retardation times become so closely spaced and so numerous that the sum of Eq. (7.22) can be replaced by an integral. Then,

$$D(t) = \int (1/E)[1 - \exp(-t/\tau)]\, d\tau \qquad (7.23)$$

Usually data are plotted as a function of $\log(t/\tau)$, and it is therefore more convenient to express the integral in terms of $\ln \tau$. Since

$$d(\ln \tau) = \tau^{-1}\, d\tau$$

then

$$D(t) = \int (\tau/E)[1 - \exp(-t/\tau)]\, d(\ln \tau) \qquad (7.24)$$

where it is understood that all values of τ are to be covered by the integral.

The quantity τ/E in Eq. (7.24) is the contribution of retardation times in the range $d(\ln \tau)$ to the creep compliance. It is often referred to as the "retardation spectrum" and is represented by the symbolism $L(\tau)$. If this terminology is used,

$$D(t) = \int L(\tau)[1 - \exp(-t/\tau)]\, d(\ln \tau) \qquad (7.25)$$

It is also common to define $L(\tau)$ by an equation similar to Eq. (7.25), but with $D(t)$ replaced by the shear compliance $J(t)$. Since $J(t) = 3D(t)$ for rubbers, the two definitions differ by a factor of 3. The definition used will usually be clear from the context.

In similar fashion, for Eq. (7.20) the following representation is employed:

$$D'(\omega) = \int L(\tau)(1 + \omega^2\tau^2)^{-1}\, d(\ln \tau)$$

$$D''(\omega) = \int L(\tau)(\omega\tau)(1 + \omega^2\tau^2)^{-1}\, d(\ln \tau)$$

$$(7.26)$$

These relations as well as Eq. (7.25) contain the retardation-time distribution function $L(\tau)$. It is a measure of the contribution of retardation times within the range $d(\ln \tau)$ to the total compliance. When its value is known for all retardation times, $L(\tau)$ may be substituted in Eqs. (7.25) and (7.26), and the compliance can be computed.

5. Stress Relaxation: Maxwell Model

In a stress-relaxation experiment the sample is rapidly stretched to a fixed elongation, and then the force needed to hold the sample at that elongation is measured as a function of time. The probable behavior can be qualitatively surmised from the following considerations.

At very short times, the elongation of a material will be the result of the response of elements having very short retardation times. Ordinarily these elements will contribute only a small portion of the equilibrium compliance; however, the elongation at short times can be made appreciable if the applied stress is large, for then the elongation of these short-retardation-time elements will be large. As time goes on and the elements having longer retardation times begin to elongate, the stress needed to hold the sample at constant extension will decrease. Upon a decrease of the stress, the elements with very short retardation times will retract and compensate for the continuing elongations of the slowly responding elements.

Apparently, then, the initial elongation is mostly supplied by the elements with very short response times. As the slower elements elongate under the stress, the stress can be decreased. The fast elements therefore retract and exactly balance out the extra elongation caused by the slower-responding elements. For a molecular network represented by a series of Voigt elements, the stress will decay to some equilibrium value which is the same as the stress for that equilibrium elongation in a creep experiment.

There is some difficulty, however, in carrying out such a

computation for a series of Voigt elements. It should be noticed that a single Voigt element is inadequate for describing a stress-relaxation experiment. This is a result of the fact that the dash-pot and spring are always equally elongated in such a model; hence, a force decrease automatically means that the elongation will decrease. Stress relaxation at constant elongation is there-fore impossible with such a model.

Two Voigt elements having different retardation times can give rise to stress relaxation at constant elongation. In the case of two or more Voigt elements in series, however, the differential equations of motion become quite complicated if one wishes to treat the case of changing force and constant elongation. Al-though these equations can always be solved in principle at least, the general problem of a large number of elements in series becomes prohibitively complicated (85,86). As shown in the last chapter, this extended model containing a large number of Voigt elements is the one needed to describe a network polymer.

Fortunately, another mechanical model system can be set up to describe the physical situation. In its simplest form it consists of a spring and dashpot in series as shown in Figure 44a. This

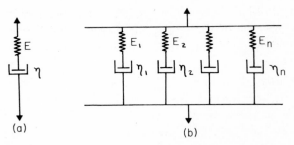

Figure 44. Single and multiple Maxwell element systems.

is called the "Maxwell element." The advantage of this element in treating stress-relaxation experiments arises from the fact that a single element can show stress relaxation. If a force is suddenly applied, the spring E will stretch to some elongation value. As time goes on, the dashpot element will flow. Since a constant total elongation value is maintained for the element, the flow of the dashpot will relax the spring. Hence, the applied force needed to maintain the constant elongation will decrease.

The problem can be handled mathematically by noting that the tension in the spring must equal the force applied to the dashpot, which in turn is equal to the applied force. Since the total change in length of the element must be zero at all times after the stress-relaxation experiment starts, the dashpot flow must equal the decrease in spring elongation. Hence,

$$\sigma/\eta = -(1/E)\dot{\sigma} \tag{7.27}$$

where $\dot{\sigma}$ is written for $d\sigma/dt$

Equation (7.27) must be solved subject to the boundary condition that $\sigma = \sigma_0$ at time zero. The solution is

$$\sigma = \sigma_0 \exp\left(-t/\tau\right) \tag{7.28}$$

Equation (7.28) shows that the stress decays in a Maxwell element in a simple exponential fashion. The *relaxation time* of such an element is τ and is equal to η/E. A similar value was found for the *retardation time* of a Voigt element, but it should be noted that the two elements are far from equivalent in other ways.

A convenient combination of Maxwell elements for discussing real materials is the generalized Maxwell system shown in Figure 44b. It is assumed that all elements of this system have the same over-all elongation. In order for this system to represent the response of a rubber network, one of the dashpots must be assumed to have infinite viscosity. If this were not the case, the stress in the model would decrease to zero at long times. If chemical breakdown of the network were ignored, such behavior would not actually be found for a real material.

The stress relaxation of the system shown in Figure 44b is easily found. Each Maxwell element will relax in accord with Eq. (7.28); hence, the total stress at time t after the stress is applied is

$$\sigma = y \, \Sigma \, E_n \exp\left(-t/\tau_n\right) \tag{7.29}$$

where y is the constant elongation and $\tau_n = \eta_n/E_n$. The sum is to be taken over all the Maxwell elements, of course.

Since σ/y has the units of a modulus, a quantity called the "relaxation modulus" $E(t)$ can be defined by the relation

$$E(t) = \Sigma\, E_n \exp\left(-t/\tau_n\right) \tag{7.30}$$

A corresponding quantity exists to represent stress relaxation in shear and is written as $G(t)$. If the material is assumed to have a Poisson ratio of $1/2$, it may be shown (85,86) that $E(t) = 3G(t)$.

It is at once apparent that the relaxation curve given by Eq. (7.29) is much broader in time scale than the simple exponential decay found for a single Maxwell element. In view of the discussion concerning the creep behavior of real materials, it is reasonable to expect that more than one Maxwell element will be needed to describe stress relaxation. Before the problem of the proper values of E_n and η_n needed to represent true network behavior is treated, the response of the Maxwell element to a sinusoidal force will be discussed.

6. Sinusoidal Response of Maxwell Elements

Consider a Maxwell element such as the one pictured in Figure 44a when subjected to a sinusoidal strain $y = y_0 \sin \omega t$. The rate of elongation at any instant is the sum of the velocity of the dashpot (σ/η) and the change in length of the spring in time dt, namely, $\dot\sigma/E$; hence,

$$\sigma/\eta + \dot\sigma/E = y_0\omega \cos \omega t \tag{7.31}$$

The solution of Eq. (7.31) is of the form

$$\sigma/y_0 = E'(\omega) \sin \omega t + E''(\omega) \cos \omega t \tag{7.32}$$

with

$$E'(\omega) = E\omega^2\tau^2/(1 + \omega^2\tau^2) \text{ and } E''(\omega) = E\omega\tau/(1 + \omega^2\tau^2) \tag{7.33}$$

where

$$\tau = \eta/E$$

It is customary to refer to the component of the modulus in

phase with the displacement, designated $E'(\omega)$, as the "storage modulus." The other component $E''(\omega)$ is termed the "loss modulus." Similar quantities exist for shear deformation and are denoted as $G'(\omega)$ and $G''(\omega)$. The quantity $E''(\omega)/\omega$ has the dimensions of viscosity and is sometimes referred to as the "dynamic viscosity."

It is worth while to note at this point that a simple relation exists between the complex dynamic modulus, $E^*(\omega) = E'(\omega) + jE''(\omega)$, and the complex dynamic compliance, $D^*(\omega) = D'(\omega) + jD''(\omega)$. The relation comes about from the fact that, from the definition of the modulus and compliance, the following expression can be written in analogy to Eq. (7.14):

$$y/\sigma_0 = (E'^2 + E''^2)^{-1/2} \cos{(\omega t - \delta)} \qquad (7.34)$$

with

$$\tan \delta = E''/E'$$

Hence,

$$|D^*(\omega)| = |1/E^*(\omega)| \qquad (7.35)$$

Also,

$$D' = E'/(E'^2 + E''^2)$$
$$D'' = E''/(E'^2 + E''^2)$$

These are, of course, general relations which hold no matter what the spring-dashpot system may be.

The variation of $E'(\omega)$ and $E''(\omega)$ with log frequency, log ω, is shown in Figure 45. The same figure includes the simple relaxation modulus $E(t)$. These curves can be explained qualitatively as follows.

At very low frequencies of oscillation, because the dashpot moves extremely slowly, the energy loss in it is very small. Since $E''(\omega)$ is proportional to the component of the force out of phase with the displacement, it is proportional to the energy loss; hence $E''(\omega)$ will be small at low frequencies. Also, since the dashpot need flow only at very small velocity in order to provide the requisite elongation at low frequencies, only very slight elongation of the spring results. As a result, the tension in the spring is very small at low frequencies; and the value of $E'(\omega)$, the component of the modulus in phase with the displacement, is also small.

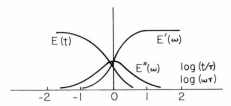

Figure 45. Variation of the storage and loss moduli with frequency for a single Maxwell element. The relaxation modulus $E(t)$ is also shown as a function of time.

At frequencies near the relaxation time of the system, the dashpot flows relatively fast and still responds through a rather large distance. Hence the viscous losses increase greatly, and therefore $E''(\omega)$ increases as well. Since larger forces must be applied to the dashpot in this frequency range, the spring will need to be stretched further. As a result, $E'(\omega)$ begins to rise as $\omega\tau$ approaches unity.

When the frequency becomes very large, the dashpot is required to move very swiftly if it moves at all. However, under these conditions the viscous force becomes very large, and the spring will stretch quite far. Consequently the elongation is almost entirely a result of the stretching of the spring, while the dashpot scarcely moves at all. Since the dashpot is essentially immobile at these frequencies, the viscous loss in it becomes small, as does $E''(\omega)$ as well. At the same time, because the spring must furnish essentially all the elongation, $E'(\omega)$ becomes large and approximately equal to σ_0/y_0, which in turn is equal to E.

The result given in Eqs. (7.32) and (7.33) can be generalized to the extended Maxwell model shown in Figure 44b. Each Maxwell element will contribute a stress that is given by an expression such as Eq. (7.32). Therefore, for the generalized Maxwell model,

$$E'(\omega) = \Sigma \; \omega^2\tau_n{}^2E_n/(1 + \omega^2\tau_n{}^2)$$

and   (7.36)

$$E''(\omega) = \Sigma \; \omega\tau_nE_n/(1 + \omega^2\tau_n{}^2)$$

In this case, too, it is evident that the characteristic curves for
the generalized Maxwell model are much broader on a log ω
scale than are the curves for a single Maxwell element. It remains yet to specify the various E_n and τ_n in such a way that
the model fits the actual molecular situation. If the relaxation
times are very closely spaced, the sums of Eq. (7.36) can be
replaced by integrals. Following the procedure used in obtaining
Eq. (7.25), one finds, in place of Eq. (7.36),

$$E'(\omega) = \int [H(\tau)\omega^2\tau^2/(1 + \omega^2\tau^2)] \; d(\ln \tau)$$
(7.37)
$$E''(\omega) = \int [H(\tau)\omega\tau/(1 + \omega^2\tau^2)] \; d(\ln \tau)$$

and in place of Eq. (7.30),

$$E(t) = \int H(\tau) \exp (-t/\tau) \; d(\ln \tau)$$ (7.38)

where $H(\tau) = \tau E(\tau)$. The quantity $H(\tau)$ is called the "relaxation-time distribution function," or the "relaxation spectrum."
It is understood that the integrals are to extend over all possible
values of τ. Frequently $H(\tau)$ is defined in terms of G, the shear
modulus, rather than the tensile modulus E. The two definitions
differ by a factor of 3 in the case of rubbers.

7. Experimental Determination of $H(\tau)$ and $L(\tau)$

Two possible approaches may be taken to provide numerical,
molecularly valid values for the various E_n and τ_n postulated in
the Voigt and Maxwell systems. In the last chapter the various
E_n and τ_n for a Voigt system were found from a molecular
treatment of the creep response of a molecular network. The
theoretical predictions were then shown to correspond to experimental fact. Equally valid would have been an approach that
started from the observed experimental data and found a set

of E_n and τ_n capable of representing the data. It is this latter approach which will now be investigated (85,86).

As the typical creep curve in Figure 33 shows, the response of a single Voigt element occurs in a relatively short time range compared with the time range of response of the whole network. This is also true for the stress relaxation of a single Maxwell element when compared with the relaxation time of an actual rubber network such as that shown in Figure 46. One is therefore led to make the following approximation to Eq. (7.38).

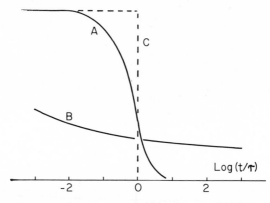

Figure 46. Curve A is the stress-relaxation behavior predicted for a single Maxwell model. The actual stress relaxation of synthetic SBR rubber is shown (in part) as curve B. Curve C is the step function discussed in the text.

For a first approximation, replace the exponential $(-t/\tau)$ by a step function that is unity for $t < \tau$ and zero for $t > \tau$. This function is also shown in Figure 46. What this amounts to is an assumption that the actual stress-relaxation curve will not change very rapidly in a range of a decade of time on each side of τ, so that a loss in detailed structure in this range will be inconsequential. With the step function in place of the exponential,

$$E(t) = \int_t^\infty H(\tau)\, d(\ln \tau) \tag{7.39}$$

After taking the derivative of Eq. (7.39) with respect to $\ln t$,

$$H(t) = -dE(t)/d(\ln t) \qquad \text{(1st approximation)} \qquad (7.40)$$

Since $dE(t)/d(\ln t)$ is merely the slope of the logarithmic stress-relaxation curve, a first approximation to $H(t)$ is easily found.

Similarly, if the same type of operation is applied to Eq. (7.25) for the creep compliance of a system of Voigt elements,

$$L(t) = dD(t)/d(\ln t) \qquad \text{(1st approximation)} \qquad (7.41)$$

Here, too, the retardation spectrum can be found to a first approximation from the slope of the logarithmic creep curve.

Although Eqs. (7.40) and (7.41) provide reasonable approximation values for $L(t)$ and $H(t)$, the results cannot be expected to show fine detail in the relaxation and retardation spectra. Higher-order approximations have been found by various investigators. These are reviewed by Leaderman (85), Ferry (86), and Staverman and Schwarzl (87). In general, these approximations involve higher derivatives of the creep and stress-relaxation curves. Typical forms are the following:

$$H(t/2) \cong -[d/(\ln t) - d^2/d(\ln t)^2]E(t) \qquad (7.42)$$

and

$$L(t/2) \cong +[d/d(\ln t) - d^2/d(\ln t)^2]D(t) \qquad (7.43)$$

It is also possible to obtain the relaxation and retardation spectra from the results of sinusoidal-vibration experiments. Only the first-approximation results will be given here:

$$H(1/\omega) \cong dE'(\omega)/d(\ln \omega) \qquad (7.44)$$

and

$$L(1/\omega) \cong -dD'(\omega)/d(\ln \omega) \qquad (7.45)$$

Higher-order approximations are also available (85,86,87).

Since the retardation and relaxation spectra can be determined from the respective creep and stress-relaxation experiments or the various vibration experiments, it is a rather simple matter to obtain $H(\tau)$ or $L(\tau)$. The great advantage of knowing either one or the other of these spectra is that $H(\tau)$ can be obtained from a knowledge of $L(\tau)$, and vice versa. After considerable complicated calculation, which will not be given here, it is found that these two quantities are related as follows (86,88):

$$L(\tau) = H(\tau)/\left\{\left[\int_{-\infty}^{\infty} H(\xi)\, d(\ln \xi)/(1 - \xi\tau^{-1})\right]^2 + \pi^2 H^2(\tau)\right\}$$

and   (7.46)

$$H(\tau) = L(\tau)/\left\{\left[\int_{-\infty}^{\infty} L(\xi)\, d(\ln \xi)/(1 - \xi\tau^{-1})\right]^2 + \pi^2 L^2(\tau)\right\}$$

An approximate method for carrying out this transformation has been given by Hopkins and Hamming (89).

Because of the existence of the relations given in Eq. (7.46), experimental behavior can be predicted for a creep experiment, a stress-relaxation experiment, and a sinusoidal-vibration experiment provided that the results of one of these experiments is known. For example, if creep measurements have been made, $L(\tau)$ may be computed from Eq. (7.43). The value of $H(\tau)$ is then obtainable through Eqs. (7.46). When these quantities are known, Eqs. (7.37) and (7.38) or (7.25) and (7.26) can be used to obtain the behavior in other experiments.

Another interesting consequence of the existence of Eqs. (7.46) is that they imply there is a Maxwell model system equivalent to a given Voigt model system. The reverse is also true. Unfortunately, Eqs. (7.46) apply only to a system with very closely spaced relaxation or retardation times. They do not apply very well to the very longest retardation times found in Chapter 6 for a network polymer, since these times are quite widely separated.

There are general methods available for changing a noncontinuous spectrum of retardation times to an equivalent relaxation spectrum (86); however, they are quite complex and are therefore not convenient to use. It is usually more satisfactory to replace the line spectrum of retardation times by an equivalent continuous distribution at the outset and then compute the relaxation spectrum by use of Eqs. (7.46) or by known approximation methods (86).

8. Boltzmann Superposition Principle

It is an inherent property of Hooke springs that the application of an incremental load to such a spring will change the elongation by the same amount, no matter what load the spring is already holding. Therefore, the response of a spring to an increase or decrease of the stress applied to it is not dependent upon the past history of the spring. Furthermore, a Newtonian dashpot (i.e., one that obeys the relation force $= \eta v$, with η being a constant for all forces and velocities) will show the same increase (or decrease) in its flow velocity under a given load increment (or decrement) independent of the load it already holds. Hence, springs and dashpots of the type considered in this chapter respond to an applied stress in a fixed fashion that is independent of their previous history. This fact is of great practical importance for understanding the behavior of the molecular system they represent.

As a simple example of the application of this idea, consider the creep response of a system having a single retardation time. Suppose that a load σ_1 is applied at time $t = t_1$. According to Eq. (7.21), the system will respond as follows:

$$y_1 E = \sigma_1 \{1 - \exp[-(t - t_1)/\tau]\} \qquad (7.47)$$

If at some later time t_2 an additional load σ_2 is applied to the system, the elongation under this load will be given by

$$y_2 E = \sigma_2 \{1 - \exp[-(t - t_2)/\tau]\} \qquad (7.48)$$

The total elongation under these two loads will be

$$yE = \sum_{n=1,2} \sigma_n \{1 - \exp[-(t - t_n)/\tau]\} \qquad (7.49)$$

In general, the elongation under a large number of such load applications would be

$$yE = \sum \sigma_n \{1 - \exp[-(t - t_n)/\tau]\} \qquad (7.50)$$

where the sum extends over all the load increments (or decrements). If the applied stress changes continually, then σ_n can be replaced by a continuous variable $d\sigma(\xi)/d\xi$, where ξ is the time at which the load $\sigma(\xi)$ existed. Then,

$$y = E^{-1} \int_{\xi=-\infty}^{t} [d\sigma(\xi)/d\xi]\{1 - \exp[-(t-\xi)/\tau]\}\, d\xi \quad (7.51)$$

The general equation for the response of a Voigt system with a retardation time spectrum $L(\tau)$ would be obtained by multiplying the right-hand side of Eq. (7.51) by $L(\tau)$ and integrating over all values of τ. Notice that the resulting equation will completely describe the creep response of the system for any type of applied stress. A similar equation can be written for the stress relaxation of a system under variable strain. This expression will completely describe the stress-relaxation behavior of the system under any type of strain.

The validity of this superposition principle has been proved for many rubberlike polymers. There appears to be no evidence that it will fail seriously for any amorphous, rubbery polymer at low elongations. Tensile creep phenomena will fail to obey the principle at moderate elongations. This failure is the result of the non-Hookean response of a rubber network under tensile stress, as predicted by the factor $(\alpha - \alpha^{-2})$ in the result for the elasticity of such a network. However, creep under a shearing stress is not subject to this restriction, as was shown in Chapter 2.

Many cases exist where the superposition principle is known to fail. These cases involve complicating factors such as crystallization under stress, alignment of crystallites, destruction of chains and crosslinks at high stress, breakup of filler aggregates, etc. However, these obvious failures of the superposition principle cannot obscure the fact that it provides an effective tool for handling certain problems in the dynamic behavior of polymers.

APPENDIX 11

Sinusoidal Response of Voigt-Kelvin Model

The equation of motion for the spring-dashpot system was given as Eq. (7.1) in the text:

$$\sigma = Ey + \eta \dot{y}$$

If the applied stress σ is of form $\sigma_0 \cos (\omega t)$, Eq. (7.1) can be written as

$$\sigma_0 \cos (\omega t) = Ey + \eta \dot{y} \qquad \text{(A11.1)}$$

The general solution of Eq. (A11.1) is of form

$$y = A \sin (\omega t) + B \cos (\omega t) \qquad \text{(A11.2)}$$

and the constants A and B may be found by substitution in Eq. (A11.1), resulting in

$$\sigma_0 \cos (\omega t) = EA \sin (\omega t) + EB \cos (\omega t)$$
$$+ \eta A\omega \cos (\omega t) - \eta B\omega \sin (\omega t) \qquad \text{(A11.3)}$$

Equation (A11.3) can be true only if the coefficients of $\sin (\omega t)$ add up to zero, and the same requirement holds true for the coefficients of $\cos (\omega t)$. Hence,

$$-EA + \eta B\omega = 0$$
$$-\sigma_0 + EB + \eta A\omega = 0 \qquad \text{(A11.4)}$$

Solving Eqs. (A11.4) simultaneously for A and B gives

$$A = (\sigma_0/E)(\omega\tau)/(1 + \omega^2\tau^2)$$

and

$$B = (\sigma_0/E)/(1 + \omega^2\tau^2) \qquad \text{(A11.5)}$$

with

$$\tau = \eta/E$$

Therefore, upon substitution into Eq. (11.2),

$$y/\sigma_0 = D'(\omega) \cos (\omega t) + D''(\omega) \sin (\omega t) \qquad \text{(A11.6)}$$

In this equation $D'(\omega)$ and $D''(\omega)$ are the storage and loss compliance, respectively. They are discussed in detail in the text, where Eq. (7.9) is equivalent to the above equation.

PROBLEMS

1. The tensile creep data obtained for a particular rubber sample are given in the accompanying table. Data were taken at several temperatures as indicated and the elongations were kept small enough so that the stress was essentially constant. Although the original data obtained were Δx, the elongation, as a function of time, these data have been changed to $D(t) = (\Delta x/L_0) \div (F/A)$, where L_0 and A are the original length and cross-sectional area of the sample, and F is the applied load. Actually, the listed values of $D(t)$ have been multiplied by the ratio $T/217$. Why? Using these data and the superposition principle, plot the complete $D(t)$ vs. log t curve for this material at $-56°C$. Plot a similar curve for this material at $42°C$.

Creep Compliance†

	$(T/217) \times$ compliance $\times 10^5$, cm²/gm						
Time, sec	$-62°C$	$-56°C$	$-44°C$	$-37°C$	$-21°C$	$15°C$	$42°C$
15	0.20	0.48	3.18	3.97	4.40	5.07	5.50
30	0.22	0.51	3.42	4.02	4.45	5.17	5.59
60	0.24	0.79	3.58	4.13	4.58	5.22	5.66
120	0.31	1.09	3.73	4.23	4.63	5.25	5.73
240	0.33	1.51	3.86	4.33	4.71	5.29	5.79
480	0.39	1.96	3.99	4.45	4.78	5.37	5.87
960	0.48	2.35	4.10	4.51	4.95	5.41	5.95
1920	0.59	2.79	4.22	4.60	5.06	5.49	6.01
3840	0.78	3.09	4.35	4.70	5.15	5.56	6.10

† These data were taken on natural rubber containing 30 parts HAF black and vulcanized 60 min at 280°F with sulfur.

2. Plot the storage and loss compliance as a function of log ω for a Kelvin element having $E = 5 \times 10^6$ dynes/cm² and $\tau = 10^{-3}$ sec. On a second graph plot the loss per cycle and the loss per second for this same element.

3. For the Kelvin element of problem 2, plot both $D(t)$ vs. log t and $D'(\omega)$ vs. log $(1/\omega)$ to the same scale on the same graph. Comment on the important correspondences between these curves.

4. Using the Kelvin element of problem 2 plot the slope of the $D(t)$ vs. log t curve against log t. On the same axes, plot the $D''(\omega)$ vs. log $(1/\omega)$ curve. Comment on the important correspondences between these curves.

5. Suppose the system described by the Kelvin element of problem 2 obeys

the WLF equation and the values listed therein apply at a temperature of 300°K. If the glass temperature for this system is 200°K, what would be the frequency of the maximum in $D''(\omega)$ at a temperature of 240°K?

6. Determine the response of the two series Kelvin elements used in problem 1, Chapter 6 to a force $\sigma = \sigma_0 \cos(\omega t)$. Plot both the in-phase and out-of-phase parts of y/σ vs. log $(\omega\tau)$. Compare these curves with the similar curves obtained for the single element of problem 1, Chapter 6.

7. Using the method of Eq. (7.41), determine $L(t)$ from a plot of $D(t)$ vs. log t for the system of problem 2.

8. Using the method of Eq. (7.45), determine $L(t)$ from a plot of $D'(\omega)$ vs. log ω for the system of problem 2. Compare the results of problems 7 and 8.

9. Compare a plot of $L(t)$ vs. log ω as obtained in problem 8 with a plot of $D''(\omega)$ vs. log ω for the same system. What conclusion can you draw from this comparison?

10. Plot the storage and loss modulus as a function of log ω for a Maxwell element having $E = 5 \times 10^6$ dynes/cm^2 and $\eta = 10^3$ poise.

11. On the same axes, plot a graph of E'' vs. log $(1/\omega)$ and a graph of [the slope of the $E(t)$ vs. log t curve] vs. log t for the Maxwell element of problem 10.

12. On the same axes, plot a graph of E' vs. log $(1/\omega)$ and a graph of $E(t)$ vs. log t for the Maxwell element of problem 10.

13. For the model of problem 10, determine H by both Eq. (7.40) and Eq. (7.44). Compare the results.

14. Plot the $E(t)$ vs. log t curve for two Maxwell elements in parallel whose parameters are $E_1 = 10^{10}$ dynes/cm^2, $E_2 = 10^6$ dynes/cm^2, $\eta_1 = 10^2$ poise, and $\eta_2 = 10^5$ poise. (This model is a first approximation to the behavior of an unvulcanized high-molecular-weight polymer; see Chapter 9.)

Chapter 8

DYNAMIC MEASUREMENTS: APPLICATION TO VULCANIZED RUBBERS

1. Methods of Measurement

In the previous chapter it was shown that the dynamic properties of a network system could be completely specified by a knowledge of its retardation-time spectrum $L(\tau)$. Fully equivalent to this method would be a knowledge of the relaxation-time spectrum $H(\tau)$. This all assumes, however, that one is dealing with a linear system for which the superposition principle may be assumed to hold true. Complications involving nonlinearity will not be considered in this chapter.

The retardation-time spectrum can often be obtained conveniently from a simple creep experiment. $L(\tau)$ may be determined from the slope of the logarithmic creep curve, as was pointed out in the last chapter. This is an extremely useful tool, as will be shown in the next chapter.

The relaxation-time spectrum $H(\tau)$ can usually be obtained from the results of a stress-relaxation experiment. This method is similar to the creep experiment in ease of execution and simplicity of interpretation. When the stress-relaxation curve for a material is known over a wide time range, the dynamic properties of the material are completely known within the limitations of a linear system. An amplified discussion of this method will be given later in this chapter.

The third and most involved method for determining either the relaxation- or retardation-time spectrum involves the measurement of the vibration characteristics of the material. There are many modifications of this general type of measurement. The best of these measurement methods affords precise knowledge of $H(\tau)$ and $L(\tau)$ simultaneously. Some of the less refined versions of these vibration techniques allow determination of the sample response over a very limited portion of the time scale. The vibration methods are also discussed in this chapter.

2. Creep Measurements

A typical apparatus for measuring the dynamic behavior of a material in a creep experiment is shown in Figure 47. The

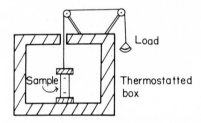

Figure 47.   A typical tensile creep apparatus. The elongation of the sample is measured by monitoring bench marks on the sample with a cathetometer.

sample is maintained at constant temperature within a suitable cabinet or bath. After the material has been allowed to reach equilibrium (or some predictable state of flow) under the action of the load hanger and clamps, an extra load is added. The elongation of the sample is usually monitored with the aid of a cathetometer. A common technique is to measure the separation of two fiducial marks placed directly on the sample. Elongations should never exceed a few per cent, since the stress can no longer be considered constant if the sample cross section changes appreciably.

Usually the elongation is measured over a time period from about 10 sec to several hours. This measurement provides a time scale of a little more than three decades. As will be seen later in this chapter, such a time range is neither exceptionally long nor exceptionally short. The creep technique is, however, restricted to the region of fairly long times. By using much more complicated systems than the one illustrated, the measurements can be extended to somewhat shorter times.

Since the behavior of a rubber network in tension departs from Hooke's law at relatively small elongations (see Chapter 2), it is sometimes preferable to measure creep under shear rather than under tension. An apparatus for this purpose is illustrated in Figure 48; of course, this apparatus must be maintained at

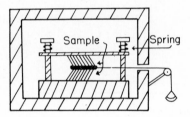

Figure 48.   A typical apparatus for measuring creep in shear. The movement of the flat plate separating the two halves of the sample is monitored using a cathetometer.

constant temperature. The creep of the sample is conveniently monitored with a cathetometer.

Data obtained (90) for the creep of a crosslinked sample of styrene-butadiene rubber (SBR) is shown in Figure 49. The temperatures at which the various curves were obtained are indicated on the curves. These data have been reduced to a standard temperature T_0 by multiplying $D(t)$ by the ratio T/T_0, where T is the temperature of the actual measurements. After the curves have been so adjusted, they may be shifted along the log t axis until they join into a single master curve. This is, of course, merely an application of the Leaderman-Ferry-Tobolsky temperature-time superposition procedure discussed in Chapter 6. The composite master curve so obtained is shown in Figure 50.

The retardation-time spectrum may be obtained from the

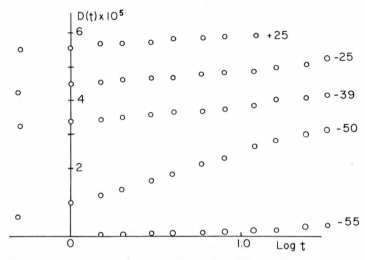

Figure 49. Typical creep measurements for a crosslinked SBR rubber at the temperatures indicated on the curves. These data have been reduced to 25°C. $D(t)$ is measured in cm²/gm and t is in minutes.

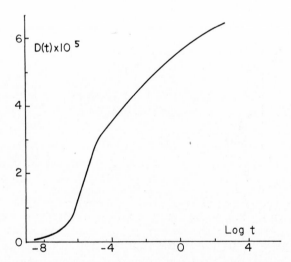

Figure 50. The composite creep curve at 25°C obtained from the data of Figure 49 plus data at still other temperatures. $D(t)$ is measured in cm²/gm and t is in minutes.

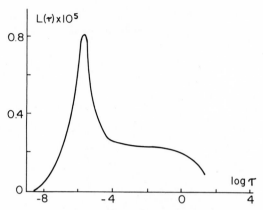

Figure 51.   The retardation-time spectrum obtained from the data of Figure 50. Units are cm²/gm.

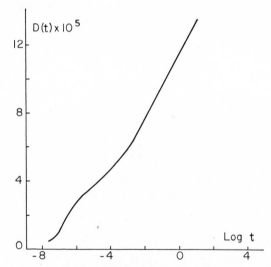

Figure 52.   The composite creep curve for a rubber similar to the one used for Figure 50 but not crosslinked as highly as the material used there. $D(t)$ is in cm²/gm and t is in minutes. All data have been reduced to 25°C.

data of Figure 50 by use of the approximation methods outlined in Chapter 7. The retardation spectrum $L(\tau)$ obtained from these data is shown in Figure 51. It was shown in Chapter 6 that the short-time portion of this spectrum was the result of the short-range motion of the chains. The long retardation times are the result of the motion of the network junctions. For a less tightly crosslinked network, the value of $L(\tau)$ at long times would be much larger than shown in Figure 51, since the network junctions will move more easily in that case. This condition is illustrated in Figures 52 and 53, where the creep curves

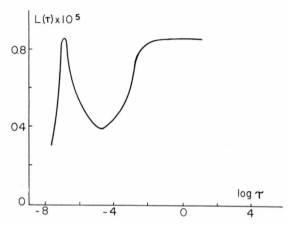

Figure 53.   The retardation-time spectrum obtained from the data of Figure 52. Units are cm²/gm.

and retardation-time spectrum for a less tightly vulcanized SBR are shown.

3. Stress Relaxation

In a stress-relaxation experiment the sample is quickly stretched to a certain elongation, often as large as $\alpha = 1.5$. The force needed to maintain this elongation is then measured as a function of time. A rather simple device for accomplishing this measurement is shown in Figure 54, where a strain gauge is used in conjunction with a recorder to monitor the stress required to hold the elongation constant. The arm holding the strain gauge can be placed at various fixed heights by means of pins as shown.

 A typical set of data (90) for an SBR rubber is shown in

Figure 55. This is the same rubber as was used in obtaining Figures 50 and 51. By multiplying the observed stresses by the ratio T_0/T, the various data can be reduced to a common temperature T_0. By using the temperature-time superposition procedure, the curves of Figure 55 can be combined into a single master curve for the temperature $T_0 = 25°C$. This curve is shown in Figure 56.

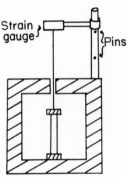

Figure 54.   A typical stress-relaxation device. The electrical response of the strain gauge is fed directly into a recorder.

The master curve of Figure 56 can be used to obtain the distribution of relaxation times. If the approximate procedures outlined in Chapter 7 are used, the values of $H(\tau)$ shown in Figure 57 are obtained. Here, as in the case of the creep retardation-time spectrum, the very short relaxation times result from short-range chain motions. The long-range motions due to movement of the network junctions give rise to the very long relaxation times.

It is of interest to compare the retardation-time spectrum $L(\tau)$ with the relaxation-time spectrum $H(\tau)$. This comparison is made in Figure 57. Although the two spectra are far from identical, they do show a great deal of similarity. This similarity is a natural result of the fact that both the stress-relaxation and creep curves of Figures 55 and 50 are alike in many ways. Both the creep and stress-relaxation curves are reasonably flat at very short and very long times. This indicates at once that the

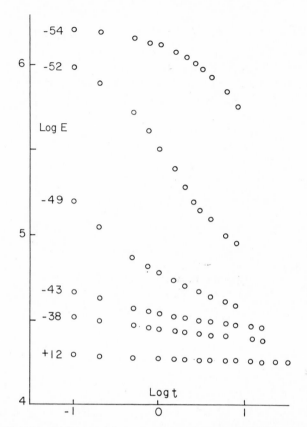

Figure 55. Typical stress-relaxation measurements for the rubber used in Figures 49, 50, and 51. The data were taken at the temperatures indicated and have been reduced to 25°C. The units of E are gm/cm² and t is measured in minutes.

relaxation- and retardation-time spectra are nearly zero in these time ranges. The rapid variation in creep and stress relaxation with time at intermediate times is a reflection of the large values of $L(\tau)$ and $H(\tau)$ in this time range. It should also be noticed that the stress-relaxation curve of Figure 56 is nearly the inverse of the creep curve of Figure 50.

Both the creep and stress-relaxation experiments yield equivalent amounts and types of data. Although one method gives the

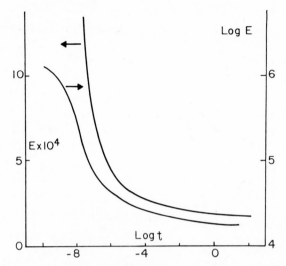

Figure 56.   The composite stress-relaxation curve for the rubber of Figure 55. These data have been reduced to 25°C, and both E and log E are shown. E is measured in gm/cm² and t is in minutes.

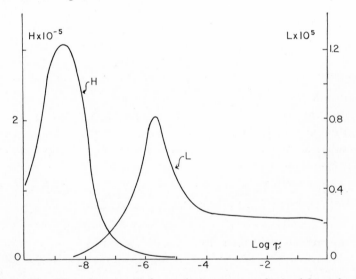

Figure 57.   The relaxation and retardation spectra obtained from the data of Figures 56 and 50 for the same vulcanized SBR rubber are reduced to 25°C. The units are gm/cm² and cm²/gm for H and L, respectively.

results in terms of relaxation times and the other in terms of retardation times, these two representations are equivalent and
can be interconverted. Each method covers about the same
time-scale range.

Two factors lead to a preference for the stress-relaxation
method over the creep method. The first of these involves
experimental convenience. It appears that stress-relaxation
measurements can be easily mechanized with the use of re-
corders and strain gauges; but such does not appear to be the
case for creep experiments. Second, and perhaps more important, stress relaxation has usually proved to be more linear with
regard to stress and strain changes than creep has (91). That is
to say, the superposition principle appears more nearly satisfied
in stress relaxation than in creep at relatively large elongations.
This fact, however, in some ways furnishes an argument in favor
of the creep technique, since more insight into the molecular
mechanisms can be obtained through the existence of this nonlinear behavior.

Certain investigators have preferred to use creep experiments
rather than stress relaxation in spite of the above factors. They
contend that response during a creep experiment is conceptually
less difficult to understand than response in stress relaxation.
This is, of course, purely a subjective judgment. However, if it
is true that molecular response under constant load is easier to
picture than molecular response at fixed sample elongation, the
creep experiment has a great advantage over stress relaxation.
Nevertheless, stress relaxation data can always be transposed to
creep behavior by the methods outlined in the last chapter.
This transformation is seldom made, however, since the effort
involved is not insignificant.

4. Free-vibration Methods

There are many variations of the free-vibration method of measurement. In essence, all involve a test sample solidly clamped
at one end and free to move together with a large mass at the

other end. One possible arrangement is shown schematically in Figure 58. The sample acts essentially as a spring with a mass m at its end. Motion of the mass m can conveniently be monitored by using a magnetic pickup coil system. In such a system, a wire coil attached to m oscillates in a magnetic field provided by an external magnet. Oscillation of the coil in the field sets up an induced voltage in the coil that can be recorded after amplification. The motion of the mass m can therefore be recorded.

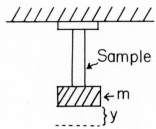

Figure 58.   A schematic diagram to illustrate the free-vibration method of dynamic measurement.

If the rather large mass m is assumed to be displaced vertically through a distance y_0, the restoring force furnished by the stretched sample will be $K'y_0$, where K' is a spring constant. In this case it will be equal to some geometrical constant relating to the length and size of the sample (K) times the tensile modulus of the material (E^*). For the present purposes, it will be assumed that the viscous loss in the rubber sample is relatively small, so that the complex modulus E^* may be assumed equal to the storage modulus E'. It is necessary to consider the dynamic moduli in this instance because the sample will be vibrating during the interval when the present calculations are expected to apply. If $E^* \cong E'$, then the restoring force can be considered in phase with the displacement.

At any instant, Newton's law stipulates that the mass times its acceleration, or $m\ddot{y}$, must equal the spring force $-KE'y$ plus the frictional forces $-f\dot{y}$. Hence the differential equation of motion is

$$m\ddot{y} + f\dot{y} + KE'y = 0 \qquad (8.1)$$

If the system is assumed to be displaced to $y = y_0$ and then allowed to vibrate freely, the solution to this equation is

$$y = y_0 \cos(2\pi\nu_0 t) \exp(-ft/2m) \qquad KE'm \gg f^2 \qquad (8.2)$$

In this expression, ν_0 is the natural resonant frequency of the system in cycles per second, namely, $(1/2\pi)(KE'/m)^{1/2}$. Note that y oscillates sinusoidally with time, except that the amplitude of oscillation decreases exponentially with time and is $y_0 \exp(-ft/2m)$. This behavior is depicted in Figure 59.

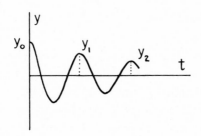

Figure 59.   The damped free vibration of the system shown in Figure 58.

It is more common to write Eq. (8.2) in terms of the "logarithmic decrement" λ, in which case the equation becomes

$$y = y_0 \cos(2\pi\nu_0 t) \exp(-\lambda\nu_0 t) \qquad (8.3)$$

where

$$\lambda = f/2m\nu_0 = \pi f/\sqrt{KE'm}$$

Notice in Figure 59 that $\exp(-\lambda)$ is the ratio of the amplitude y_1 to y_0. It is, as its name implies, the logarithmic decrease in amplitude per cycle.

The logarithmic decrement λ may be related to the storage and loss moduli as well as to the loss tangent. This is easily accomplished by considering the energy loss during a given oscillation cycle; for example, the energy stored in the sample when stretched to length y is simply

$$W = \int_0^y yKE'\, dy = KE'y^2/2 \qquad (8.4)$$

From this, the energy loss during the first cycle is

$$\Delta W = (KE'/2)(y_0{}^2 - y_1{}^2) \qquad (8.5)$$
$$\cong KE'y(y_0 - y_1)$$

where the approximation has been made that $y_0 + y_1 = 2y$, with y being either y_0 or y_1. This is a reasonable approximation if the losses are small. Furthermore, since by definition

$$y_1/y_0 = \exp(-\lambda) \cong 1 - \lambda \qquad (8.6)$$

then

$$\Delta W = KE'y^2\lambda \qquad (8.7)$$

But since the energy stored in the sample is merely $KE'y^2/2$,

$$\lambda \cong \tfrac{1}{2}(\Delta W/W) \qquad (8.8)$$

Hence the logarithmic decrement is equal to approximately one-half the fractional energy loss per cycle. The above relations assume of course that λ is small. If $\lambda < 0.10$, the approximation in Eq. (8.6) gives rise to less than about 5 per cent error in λ in Eq. (8.7). Also for this value of λ, the ratio of y_1/y_0 is about 0.90; therefore it is not accurate to use the above relations for values larger than this.

In the last chapter it was found that the energy loss in a vibrating sample was proportional to E'', the loss modulus. Since the energy loss in Eq. (8.7) is the result of the losses in the vibrating sample, then $E'' \sim \Delta W$. As a matter of fact, an equation analogous to Eq. (7.11) gives the following relation for the energy loss:

$$\Delta W = \pi KE''y^2 \qquad (8.9)$$

Combining this relation with Eqs. (8.4) and (8.8) yields

$$\lambda = \pi E''/E' \qquad (8.10)$$
$$= \pi \tan \delta$$

where $\tan \delta$ is the loss tangent discussed in the last chapter.

Therefore both E'' and E' can be determined from the measurements available in such an experiment. The value of E' can be deduced from the fact that the frequency of free vibration of the sample with mass m is given by the relation defining ν_0, namely,

$$4\pi^2\nu_0^2 = KE'/m \tag{8.11}$$

It will be recalled that K is merely a geometrical constant determined by the sample dimensions. After E' is found from Eq. (8.11), the value of E'' is obtained from Eq. (8.10).

Another term is sometimes used in discussing this type of measurement. It is the "dynamic resilience" R, which is defined as the ratio of the energies stored in two successive cycles. From Eq. (8.4),

$$R = y_1^2/y_0^2 \tag{8.12}$$

which is, from the definition of λ,

$$R = \exp{(-2\lambda)} \tag{8.13}$$

or

$$R = \exp{(-2\pi E''/E')}$$

The last relation was obtained by use of Eq. (8.10). Obviously, the dynamic resilience is a measure of perfect elasticity. If the energy loss is small, R is near unity; for high-loss materials it approaches zero.

The above treatment has been entirely dependent upon the assumption that the sample was vibrating longitudinally, so that the tensile moduli were involved. The same analysis could be carried out for vibration in shear with equivalent results, except that the longitudinal modulus E would have to be replaced by the shear modulus G. In fact, the more common instruments of this type make use of torsional oscillations of the sample. The analysis is identical in any case (86).

Although the free damped oscillation method is valuable for quick, routine testing, it suffers from several serious limitations. Perhaps the chief difficulty with the method is the lack of versatility with regard to frequency of observation. Even though the mass and sample size may be changed to give various resonant frequencies, the frequency range is severely restricted by practical limitations on m and on the sample size.

A second deficiency of the method, which for many purposes is not serious, derives from the fact that the sample should be neither too soft nor too hard for the proper operation of most instruments of this type. The apparatus works very well for the usual vulcanized rubbers in the temperature range where they are rubbery. Obviously, the method will not be easily applied to materials that exhibit viscous flow.

5. Forced-vibration Methods: Resonance Methods

In forced-vibration resonance methods a sinusoidal driving force is applied to the mass shown in Figure 58; or in some cases, the sample is clamped firmly at one end and is free at the other. The sample is then vibrated transversely as a reed. The sinusoidal driving force is in any case adjusted so that its frequency is near the resonant frequency of the system. A plot of vibration amplitude versus applied driving frequency is then made, and a bell-shaped curve such as that in Figure 60 is usually obtained.

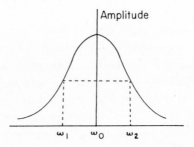

Figure 60. A typical amplitude-frequency curve for a resonant system near the resonance frequency ω_0.

The resonance behavior of this system will not be worked out here. It is sufficient to remark that the resonant frequency itself may be related through the geometry of the sample to the storage modulus (86); hence a measurement of the resonance frequency of the sample yields G' or E'. The value of the loss modulus is related to the angular frequencies ω_1 and ω_2 at half the maximum amplitude by the relation

$$E''/E' = (\omega_2 - \omega_1)/\omega_0\sqrt{3} \qquad (8.14)$$

This method permits the determination of the loss tangent, resilience, and the other quantities mentioned in connection with the free-vibration experiment; and it suffers from many of the same deficiencies mentioned for the free-vibration case as well. In particular, the frequency range is rather restricted. It does, however, furnish a relatively quick method of measurement for routine work.

6. Forced-vibration Methods: Nonresonance Methods

These nonresonance methods are, in principle at least, the most satisfactory means for determination of dynamic properties. All of them are based on the forced sinusoidal oscillation of the sample over a wide frequency range. The applied force and extension are measured simultaneously, usually by electrical methods. Storage and loss compliances or moduli can be determined by the general method outlined below.

Consider a driven system such as the one illustrated in Figure 58. The application of Newton's law, as in Section 8.4 gives the following differential equation of motion:

$$m\ddot{y} + f\dot{y} + KE'y = \sigma_0 \cos(\omega t) \qquad (8.15)$$

The solution of this equation for the displacement y gives a component of the displacement in phase with the force and another out of phase by 90°. If the instrument is designed so that all the energy loss is due to the test sample itself, then the out-of-phase displacement will be proportional to the loss compliance. The in-phase displacement will be proportional to the storage compliance. Hence, both of these quantities may be determined at the frequency of the driving force.

Although there are many possible forms for the solution of

Eq. (8.15), depending upon the mechanical setup involved (86), a particularly simple solution results if $KE' \gg m\omega^2$. Under these conditions the solution of Eq. (8.15) is

$$y/\sigma_0 = (KE')^{-1}\{[1/(1 + \omega^2\tau^2)] \cos \omega t$$
$$+ [\omega\tau/(1 + \omega^2\tau^2)] \sin \omega t\} \qquad (8.16)$$

where $\tau = f/KE'$ is a relaxation time for the system. The coefficients of the cosine and sine terms are proportional to the storage and loss compliances of the sample.

Note that the ratio of the out-of-phase component of y to the in-phase component yields $\omega\tau$. Since ω is known, the value of f/KE' is therefore determined. The value of KE' is obtained directly from the magnitude of the in-phase component of y; therefore E' and f can be valuated, since the value of K is known from the instrument geometry.

It is possible to evaluate the loss modulus E'' in terms of f by following the procedure used to obtain Eq. (8.10). Of course, the logarithmic decrement will not appear as such in this case. As before, the energy loss per cycle is

$$\Delta W = \pi KE'' y_0^2 \qquad (8.17)$$

This quantity may also be computed from Eq. (8.16), from the fact that

$$\Delta W = \oint \dot{y}\sigma_0 \cos \omega t \, dt$$

which yields

$$\Delta W = [\pi\omega\tau/(1 + \omega^2\tau^2)](\sigma_0^2/KE') \qquad (8.18)$$

After assuming low losses so that $y_0 \cong \sigma_0/KE'$, equating the quantities in Eqs. (8.18) and (8.17) gives

$$E'' \cong [\omega\tau/(1 + \omega^2\tau^2)]E' \qquad (8.19)$$

This expression is only approximate, of course, but the exact expression is easily obtained also (86). Alternatively, the values of D' and D'' could have been obtained. From this it is clear that the forced-oscillation technique can yield the values of the storage and loss compliances, as well as the respective moduli.

In Chapter 7 it was shown that both the retardation-time

spectrum $L(\tau)$ and the relaxation-time spectrum $H(\tau)$ can be obtained from oscillation-type measurements. Consequently, the nonresonant forced-oscillation techniques supply the same information as creep and stress-relaxation measurements provide. Furthermore, since $E^* = 1/D^*$, the data can easily be transformed from moduli to compliance. For this reason, it is possible to obtain both $H(\tau)$ and $L(\tau)$ from the same set of data without an excessive amount of labor. In this respect, the method has a decided advantage over creep and stress relaxation.

The vibration technique discussed in this section is applicable over a rather wide frequency range. It is not dependent upon the resonant frequency of the system, and therefore the frequency of measurement can be changed without major apparatus changes. For this reason, the method is probably somewhat preferable to other techniques for most precise scientific investigations.

Although the nonresonant vibration type of measurement has much in its favor, it is not free from disadvantages. Since it is a nonresonance experiment, the vibrations are usually small, and spurious equipment oscillations can become a problem. In addition, the measurement techniques are not simple, since they consist of measuring the magnitude and phase of forces and displacements. It is for these reasons that such techniques have not been as widely applied as creep and stress relaxation. The reader is referred to Ferry's excellent book (86) for a more comprehensive treatment of the instrumentation problem.

7. Energy Loss in Vulcanized Rubber

A practical problem of some importance may be used to demonstrate the utility of the measurements and concepts of the last two chapters. This example is provided by the problem of heat build-up in tires, which is of serious concern since chemical degradation of rubber occurs more rapidly at high temperatures. In addition, it will be shown in Chapter 10 that the tensile strength of rubber decreases rapidly at higher temperatures;

hence it is important to use for tire applications a rubber that shows relatively small hysteresis or heat generation.

In normal applications, a given portion of a tire will be subjected to a rather complex force that is applied with a frequency equal to the tire rotation frequency. This force is certainly not sinusoidal in form, but it can be regarded as being composed of a superposition of many sinusoidal forces. That is, the true force can be represented by a Fourier series. It is reasonable to expect that the most important of these component forces will have frequencies in the general range of the tire rotation frequency. Hence, this expectation leads to the computation of the energy loss in a rubber subjected to a sinusoidal force with angular frequency ω. The value of ω will be within the range of tire rotation frequencies.

In the last chapter it was shown that a rubber subjected to a sinusoidal force $\sigma_0 \cos \omega t$ will respond according to the following equation [cf. Eq. (7.18)]:

$$y/\sigma_0 = \Sigma \ [D_n' \cos \omega t + D_n'' \sin \omega t] \qquad (8.20)$$

The energy loss per cycle is obtained in the same way as Eq. (7.11) and is given as

$$\Delta W = \pi \sigma_0{}^2 \Sigma \ D_n'' \qquad (8.21)$$

where

$$D_n'' = (1/3 \nu_e k T) \omega \tau_n / (1 + \omega^2 \tau_n{}^2)$$

Expressed in words, Eq. (8.21) means that the total energy loss is the sum of the energy losses arising from the individual retardation times of the sample. It will be recalled from Chapter 6 that these retardation times arise from two causes. The shortest ones represent the various modes of motion of the polymer chains between network junctions. Motion of the network junctions gives rise to the very long retardation times. Obviously, D_n'' is largest for $\omega \tau_n = 1$; therefore the retardation times near the time taken for the tire to rotate are most active in causing energy loss or heat production.

As an example, consider the two rubbers whose creep curves

and retardation spectra are shown in Figures 50 to 53. Since a tire rotates on the order of 10 times per sec, the important retardation times will be those near $\tau_n = 0.10$ sec. Of course, since τ_n varies with temperature, the temperature of the tire should be specified. For the present qualitative discussion, the tire will be assumed to be at the temperature specified for Figures 50 to 53, namely, 25°C. If there were no retardation times near 0.10 sec, all the D_n'' values would be small, and the heat loss would be small. Conversely, if there were a relatively large number of retardation times near 0.10 sec, many values of D_n'' would be quite large and, correspondingly, so would the heat build-up. Of course, $L(\tau)$ is a measure of the number of retardation times in the region near τ. From Figures 51 and 53 it is apparent that the tightly crosslinked rubber of Figure 51 has fewer retardation times in the region about $\tau = 0.10$ sec. For this reason, this rubber might reasonably be expected to show less heat generation than the rubber of Figure 53. This fact coincides with experience.

It is interesting to notice how the rubber of Figure 51 could be further improved with regard to heat build-up. As was shown in Chapter 6, the retardation times in the region near $\tau = 0.10$ sec in Figure 53 are the result of the motion of the network junctions. To reduce this motion, the degree of crosslinking can be increased, as was done in going from the material of Figure 53 to the material of Figure 51. Alternatively, the number of chain ends would be reduced by increasing the primary molecular weight of the unvulcanized rubber. It turns out that too high a degree of crosslinking is detrimental to the strength of the rubber; thus the second alternative is the only practical one.

The above factors have been studied rather extensively, and it is generally concluded that the low primary molecular weight of SBR rubber, the polymer used in Figures 51 and 53, is responsible for the rather large heat generation in that material (92). Natural rubber, which has a much higher primary molecular weight than SBR, evidences less heat development than SBR.

In actual tire-tread stocks, carbon black is incorporated into the rubber; however, it appears that this does not alter the conclusions reached in this section (92).

PROBLEMS

1. It is frequently desirable to maintain a constant stress throughout a tensile-creep experiment. If the elongations become large, the stress will increase if the applied force is held constant. (a) Derive an expression for the applied force that should be used in a constant-stress tensile-creep test in terms of the original sample dimensions and the elongation. (b) Devise an automatic means by which the force would change in the appropriate manner.

2. A piece of rubber 10 cm long and having a cross-sectional area of 0.20 cm^2 is clamped at one end, as shown in Figure 58. The mass at the other end is 500 gm. This system has a natural vibration period of 0.60 sec, and the amplitude of vibration decreases by 5 per cent each complete cycle. Compute E', E'', λ, tan δ, and the dynamic resilience for this rubber at this frequency.

3. If $\lambda = 0.020$ for a certain piece of rubber, through how many cycles will the rubber vibrate before its amplitude has dropped to less than half the original value?

4. A certain piece of vulcanized natural rubber has a low-elongation tensile modulus of 200 psi at 23°C. Its logarithmic decrement at low frequencies is 0.050. (a) Compute the following for this material: E', E'', tan δ, and dynamic resilience. (b) What sort of frequency dependence would you predict for these quantities?

5. A rubber sample having the same dimensions as the one used in problem 2 has $\nu_0 = 100$ cycles/sec when allowed to vibrate freely under a load of 50 gm. It is also known that tan $\delta = 0.010$ for this sample. If the mass is now driven sinusoidally by a constant-amplitude force, what will be the frequency width of the resonance curve between the half-maximum points?

6. Referring to the rubber for which data are shown in Figures 50 and 51, if this rubber is subjected to a variable-frequency and constant-amplitude driving force, at what approximate frequency would the loss per cycle be largest?

7. If the rubber shown in Figures 50 and 51 has $T_g = -55°C$, at what temperature would you predict that the rubber will show maximum loss per cycle when vibrated by a constant-amplitude force of 20 cycles/sec?

Chapter 9

VISCOELASTICITY OF LINEAR POLYMERS

1. Creep Experiments

The viscous flow of linear polymers was treated in Chapter 3. Although the polymer exhibits a well-defined viscosity, it shows interesting elastic effects as well. This is true even though no crosslinks are present, and a rubber network as such is non-existent. These facts are conveniently demonstrated by reference to the behavior of a linear polymer in creep.

Typical creep compliance curves for an amorphous linear polymer are shown in Figure 61, where the data shown are for

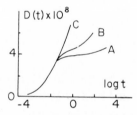

Figure 61.   Creep curve for polymethyl methacrylate at 140°C. The creep compliance is in cm²/dyne and t is in minutes. Curves A, B, and C are for molecular weights of 4×10^6, 6.5×10^5, and 2×10^5, respectively.

polymethyl methacrylate, which is usually considered to be a glass. However, its glass temperature is about 105°C, and it will be soft at temperatures somewhat above this. The data shown in Figure 61 were actually taken at different temperatures and then reduced to 140°C by use of the temperature-time super-position.

199

It is seen from Figure 61 that this polymer extends rather slowly at this temperature. A pseudo equilibrium elongation is reached about a minute after the load is applied in the case of the highest-molecular-weight material; hence, this high-molecular-weight polymer will behave like a "slow" rubber. If the temperature were 10°C higher, the molecules would then move more swiftly, and the plateau elongation would be reached in about 5 sec rather than 1 min (38). The material would appear quite rubbery at this higher temperature.

On the other hand, at 115°C the molecules move much less rapidly than at 140°C. It is found that at 115°C the elongation after 1 min is only about 3 per cent of the plateau elongation. To reach the plateau elongation at this lower temperature requires a time of about a day. Such a material is far too "slow" to classify as a rubber, but it is still not hard enough to be considered a glass. Materials in this range of response are usually referred to as "leathery." In any event, the curves in Figure 61 are not peculiar to this particular polymer. High-molecular-weight linear natural rubber gives rise to very similar creep curves (92), as do many other rubbery materials. The observed differences between these various polymers merely reflect the different rates of molecular motion in them. Far above their glass temperatures, all linear polymers of high molecular weight appear rubbery.

It is apparent that the low-molecular-weight polymer, for which data are shown in Figure 61, is also rather slow to respond at 140°C. A great difference between the polymers is noted at long times, however. The low-molecular-weight polymer does not approach a pseudo equilibrium elongation but continues to elongate. This continued elongation is not as striking as might be inferred from the figure. Since the time scale is logarithmic, the time taken to reach *twice* the plateau height is a factor 100 times longer than the time taken to reach the plateau height. A casual observer might easily infer that the elongation had reached a pseudo equilibrium even in this low-molecular-weight case.

The molecular interpretation of the curves in Figure 61 is quite simple. Since the high-molecular-weight material reaches a pseudo equilibrium elongation under the applied stress, it can be inferred that a network actually exists in the polymer even though it contains no chemical crosslinks. It is not difficult to see that these apparent crosslinks are merely temporary physical crosslinks provided by chain entanglement. A typical entanglement crosslink is shown in Figure 62, where the two chains are

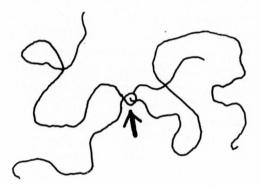

Figure 62. A schematic diagram showing an entanglement at the position indicated by the arrow.

rather firmly held together by the entanglement point indicated by the arrow.

In Chapter 3 it was pointed out that the molecular weight between entanglement points (M_e) could be determined from viscosity data. By that method it is found that M_e for pure polymethyl methacrylate is about 5000; hence the polymers pictured in Figure 61 will have hundreds of entanglements for each chain. Obviously they cannot easily slip free and must therefore behave much like crosslinks, although at long times the network they form will pull apart.

The interpretation of the experimental creep curve from short times up to the plateau region is therefore no different from that for the creep curve of a vulcanized rubber. It is apparent that the compliance at the plateau can be calculated by using the result obtained in Chapter 2 for the equilibrium elongation of a network, namely,

$$\sigma = (\nu_e k T)(\alpha - \alpha^{-2}) \tag{9.1}$$

where ν_e is the number of network chains per unit volume formed by the entanglements. In terms of M_e, one has $\nu_e = \rho \mathbf{N}/M_e$; thus M_e can be computed from the height of the plateau in Figure 61. A value of about 4500 is obtained. This value is a little lower than the 5000 obtained from viscosity data. Still, in view of the difficulty involved in quantitatively associating $2M_e$ with the position of the break in the viscosity curve, as pointed out in Chapter 3, this agreement is as good as could reasonably be expected. It is also true that the shape of the creep curve leading up to the plateau agrees with that predicted by the theory given in Chapter 6 for network response in the short-time region (38).

When the entanglement network has been stretched, the entanglement points will slip along the chain. This will be somewhat equivalent to the motion of network-junction points as discussed in Chapter 6. The plateau will not be absolutely flat since the network is not permanent. In fact, for very low molecular weights, the chains will slip loose from each other relatively swiftly, and the plateau may actually not appear. At high molecular weights, though, the entanglements near the center of the molecule require a long time to slip free. It is for this reason that one observes the varying length of the plateau with molecular weight.

At very long times, the effect of the entanglement network will be to give rise to the very high viscosity observed for entangled chains that was discussed in Chapter 3. However, even in this region an elastic effect will be observed. This is the result of the stretching of portions of the chain by the surrounding polymer matrix as it flows through the chain. Since superimposed on this elastic effect is the normal viscous flow, special techniques are needed to separate the two effects.

2. The Creep-recovery Experiment

It is possible to separate the elastic and viscous part of the creep deformation by a simple application of the Boltzmann super-position principle. The basis for the method depends upon the fact that, for a linear material, each load application gives rise to a creep curve which is independent of the presence or absence of other loads. This condition is only true at small elongations of course. Consider now the following creep and creep-recovery experiment.

A stress σ_0 is applied to the sample at time $t' = 0$. The creep of the material under this stress can be expressed in terms of the retardation-time spectrum, as discussed in Chapter 7. The elongation of an originally unit-length sample is given by

$$y' = \sigma_0 \int_0^{t'} L(\tau)\, d(\ln \tau) + \sigma_0 t'/\eta \qquad (9.2)$$

The last term in Eq. (9.2) has not appeared in previous equations because it had been assumed that the viscosity was infinite. Such is actually the case for network polymers; but noncross-linked polymers will show true viscous flow, and hence the last term must be present.

If after a time θ the stress is removed, the conditions will be present for a creep-recovery experiment. Consider a new scale of time designated by t that has its zero at time $t' = \theta$; in other words, t is measured from the time of removal of the stress.

According to the superposition principle, the removal of the stress σ_0 at time $t = 0$ is equivalent to the addition of a negative stress $-\sigma_0$ at that time. Hence from time $t' = \theta$ or $t = 0$ onward, the sample elongation will be a combined response to two stresses, σ_0 and $-\sigma_0$. For times $t' > \theta$,

$$y = \sigma_0 \left[\int_0^{\theta+t} L(\tau)\, d(\ln \tau) + \theta/\eta + t/\eta \right]$$
$$- \sigma_0 \left[\int_0^{t} L(\tau)\, d(\ln \tau) + t/\eta \right] \qquad (9.3)$$

The quantity in the first bracket can be split into two portions, the elongation y_θ under stress $+\sigma_0$ at times before $t' = 0$, and the elongation under that stress since $t' = 0$.

$$y = y_\theta + \sigma_0 \left[\int_\theta^{t+\theta} L(\tau)\, d(\ln \tau) + t/\eta \right]$$

$$- \sigma_0 \left[\int_0^t L(\tau)\, d(\ln \tau) + t/\eta \right] \qquad (9.4)$$

where

$$y_\theta = \sigma_0 \left[\int_0^\theta L(\tau)\, d(\ln \tau) + \theta/\eta \right]$$

and is the sample elongation just before the start of the recovery portion of the experiment.

Suppose that one plots two curves on the same graph, the value of y vs. t' during the first portion of the experiment and the value of $(y_\theta - y)$ vs. t during the recovery part of the experiment. These curves are called the "elongation" and the "recovery" curves, respectively, and are shown in Figure 63 for

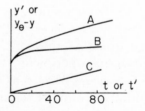

Figure 63.   Curve A is the original elongation of a polymethyl methacrylate with $M = 204,000$ at 140°C. The time scale is in minutes. Curves B and C are the recovery and viscous flow curves, respectively.

one of the polymers used in Figure 61. From Eqs. (9.2) and (9.4), the elongation curve is

$$y' = \sigma_0 \int_0^{t'} L(\tau)\, d(\ln \tau) + \sigma_0 t'/\eta \qquad \text{(Elongation)} \qquad (9.2)$$

and the recovery curve is

$$y_\theta - y = \sigma_0 \int_0^t L(\tau)\, d(\ln \tau) + \sigma_0 \int_\theta^{t+\theta} L(\tau)\, d(\ln \tau) \qquad \text{(Recovery)}$$

$$\text{(9.5)}$$

But since t and t' are plotted on the same axis in Figure 63, they will be identical. Therefore, if the recovery curve is subtracted from the elongation curve, one obtains the result found by subtracting Eq. (9.5) from Eq. (9.2), namely,

$$y' - (y_\theta - y) = \sigma_0 t/\eta - \sigma_0 \int_\theta^{t+\theta} L(\tau)\, d(\ln \tau) \qquad \text{(9.6)}$$

Hence, the difference between these curves will be $\sigma_0 t/\eta$ if the last term in Eq. (9.6) is negligible.

The last term in Eq. (9.6) represents the elastic response of the polymer at times between θ and $t + \theta$. If θ has been assumed very large in comparison with t, the elastic creep during this time interval will be much smaller than the total elastic response. Therefore, if the difference between the elongation and recovery curves is of the same order of magnitude as the elastic recovery, it may be concluded that the last term in Eq. (9.6) is negligible compared with the viscous-flow term. Usually if θ is assumed to be about ten times longer than t, this will be a safe approximation if the viscosity is not extremely high. With this approximation, the difference curve is expressed as

$$y' - (y_\theta - y) = (\sigma_0/\eta)t \qquad \text{(9.7)}$$

Equation (9.7) is that of a straight line having zero intercept and slope σ_0/η; hence the difference curve should be a straight line passing through the origin. This is actually seen to be the case in Figure 63. The polymer viscosity is derived directly from the fact that the slope of the line is σ_0/η. The elastic portion of the elongation curve can now be found by subtracting $\sigma_0 t'/\eta$ from the observed elongation curve. According to Eq. (9.2), the result should be the elastic portion of the elongation.

The above computation points out another fact of interest. In a set of creep experiments one often wishes to use the same piece of material for creep tests at several temperatures; therefore it must be known how long the sample must be allowed to recover before it can be considered to be in its original relaxed state. If the viscous flow—which will never recover, of course—is ignored, from Eq. (9.3) the elongation during recovery is

$$y = \sigma_0 \int_t^{\theta+t} L(\tau) \, d(\ln \tau) \qquad \eta = \infty \qquad (9.8)$$

Obviously the sample will never fully recover, since the integral in Eq. (9.8) will always have a value greater than zero. However, the magnitude of the integral (which is simply the elastic response during the time interval defined by the integration limits) is nearly linear with logarithmic time at long times.

Therefore, if $\theta \ll t$, the integration will cover a negligibly small interval on the log time scale, and the value of Eq. (9.8) will be essentially zero. If the sample is allowed to recover for a time t that is about ten times longer than the load-application time θ, the recovery will usually be essentially complete. The recovery time can be decreased if the temperature of the sample is raised during the recovery period. It should be noted, however, that the above considerations all imply the applicability of superposition. At high elongations of carbon black–filled rubbers, a small portion of the recovery takes much longer than would be predicted from Eq. (9.8) (72).

3. Dynamic Behavior: No Entanglements

Although the qualitative reasons for the creep behavior of a linear polymer are quite simple, the quantitative expression of these ideas is rather complex. Three more or less successful mathematical treatments have been given for the effect. One method is based upon the method for computing chain dynamics that is given in Chapter 6 (38). A second method is based upon an extension of the Rouse computation (82). The third method makes use of mathematical techniques used in electrical circuit analysis (93).

Before consideration of the more complex case where entanglements are important, it is of interest to treat the behavior of linear polymers of very low molecular weight where the number of entanglements is negligibly small. Alternatively, one can consider the case of a highly plasticized polymer having a high molecular weight, since the number of entanglements decreases with increased dilution. In any event, the number of segments per chain (N) will be considered large. To determine the creep behavior of such molecules by the method of Chapter 6 and Appendix 9, the way in which the applied forces act upon the molecule must be known. If no entanglements are present, the forces on the molecule will be due entirely to the friction forces caused by the polymer matrix as it moves past the molecule under consideration.

The question now arises as to whether or not the retardation- and relaxation-time spectra derived in Chapter 6 for network chains apply also to the molecular situation being considered here. It is clear, of course, that the portion of the spectrum resulting from the movement of the network-junction points does not apply here. The rest of the spectrum, however, was concerned with a chain identical to the one now under consideration, except in one respect. In the network case the force is applied directly to the ends of the chain, whereas in the present case the applied forces are distributed along the chain. In principle, this difference should be resolved by carrying out the general computation for this case in the same way as was done in Appendix 9. Now, however, the forces applied to the chain are more complex than those in the case treated there. As a result, only an approximate application of that method has been made. Although the result obtained (73) indicates that a small change in the retardation spectrum occurs because of the distribution of the applied force along the chain, it is not certain that this difference is real. It may merely reflect the approximations made in the application of the general method.

Fortunately, the Rouse method (79), which was also discussed in Chapter 6, has been applied to the case of the free linear polymer with forces distributed along its length; in fact, the method was designed specifically for this case. Accurate computations by means of this method show that the retardation-time distribution is the same as that found for the network chain by the method of Chapter 6 (84,94). Therefore, for both a network chain and a free chain, the following relations are valid [see Eqs. (6.8) and (6.11)]:

$$D_n = (8/3\pi^2 \nu k T) n^{-2} \tag{9.9}$$

$$\tau_n = (f_0 N^2 a^2 / 3\pi^2 k T) n^{-2} \qquad \text{(Retardation)}$$

where $n = 1, 3, 5, \ldots, N$, and D_n is the compliance contribution of the n'th retardation mode. For the relaxation times equivalent to the above retardation times (84,94),

$$E_n = 3\nu k T \tag{9.10}$$

$$\tau_n' = (f_0 N^2 a^2 / 6\pi^2 k T) n^{-2} \qquad \text{(Relaxation)}$$

where $n = 1, 2, 3, \ldots, N$, and E_n is the modulus contribution of the n'th relaxation mode. In this chapter the symbol τ will be used for retardation times, while relaxation times will be designated τ'.

It is now possible to write down at once the behavior of the free-polymer molecule system not only for creep experiments but also for stress relaxation and sinusoidal vibration. This is made possible by the fact that Eqs. (9.9) and (9.10) give the elements of the equivalent Maxwell or Voigt-Kelvin series systems. Since the response of such systems has already been treated in Chapter 7, one need only substitute in the relations found there. For example, the creep response will be

$$D(t) = \Sigma D_n [1 - \exp(-t/\tau_n)] + t/\eta \qquad \text{(for } n \text{ odd)} \tag{9.11}$$

where D_n is given in Eq. (9.9). Similarly, for stress relaxation,

$$E(t) = \Sigma E_n \exp(-t/\tau_n') \qquad \text{(all } n) \tag{9.12}$$

where E_n and τ_n' are given by Eq. (9.10).

Equation (9.11) would be incomplete without the term t/η, since it would not take account of the fact that the system will exhibit true viscous flow. The compliance contribution resulting from viscous flow is t/η; hence this term is added to the right side of Eq. (9.11). After n has been redefined, Eq. (9.11) may be rewritten as

$$D(t) = (8/3\pi^2 vkT) \sum_{n=1}^{N/2} (2n - 1)^{-2}[1 - \exp(-t/\tau_n)] + t/\eta$$

with $\qquad\qquad\qquad\qquad\qquad\qquad\qquad\qquad$ (9.13)

$$\tau_n = (4\eta/\pi^2 vkT)(2n - 1)^{-2}$$

To obtain this latter relation for τ_n, use has been made of Eq. (3.15), the formula for the viscosity of nonentangled polymers. After it has been noted that the tensile viscosity used here is three times as large as the shear viscosity given in Eq. (3.15), that equation becomes

$$\eta = vf_0 N^2 a^2/12 \qquad\qquad (9.14)$$

It is of interest to notice in connection with Eq. (9.13) that when $t = \tau_1$ the elastic response is nearly completed and is about equal to the viscous response. Hence these two effects are intimately related, and both will play equally important roles.

The composite Maxwell model whose behavior is represented by Eq. (9.12) already includes the true viscous flow. This is easily seen from the fact that the long-time behavior of such a system when under constant load will depend primarily upon the motion of the dashpots (see Figure 44). Since in the Maxwell model $\eta_n = E_n\tau_n'$, as was shown in Chapter 6, the viscosity of the system will be

$$\eta = \Sigma E_n\tau_n' \qquad\qquad (9.15)$$

After E_n and τ_n' have been replaced by the values given in Eq. (9.10),

$$\eta = vf_0 N^2 a^2/12 \qquad\qquad (9.16)$$

which is identical to the value previously obtained. Hence, Eq. (9.12) already contains the effect of true viscous flow. It may be written in a form similar to Eq. (9.13), namely,

$$E(t) = 3vkT \Sigma \exp(-t/\tau_n') \qquad n = 1, 2, 3, \ldots, N$$

with $\qquad\qquad\qquad\qquad\qquad\qquad\qquad\qquad$ (9.17)

$$\tau_n' = (2\eta/\pi^2 vkT)n^{-2}$$

Similar relations may also be written for the dynamic compliance D^* and the dynamic modulus E^*. Since $D^* = D' + jD''$,

$$D^* = \Sigma\, D_n(1 + j\omega\tau_n)/(1 + \omega^2\tau_n{}^2) + (j/\omega\eta) \qquad (9.18)$$

and similarly

$$E^* = \Sigma\, E_n(\omega^2\tau_n'^2 + j\omega\tau_n')/(1 + \omega^2\tau_n'^2) \qquad (9.19)$$

Although the retardation- and relaxation-time spectra for the chains treated here are not continuous, the τ_n and τ_n' values are very closely spaced in the region of very large n. Therefore, if the values of t in Eqs. (9.13) and (9.17) are kept small compared with τ_1, then the sums in these equations may be replaced by integrals. That is to say, if concerned only with the short-time response of the chains, Eqs. (9.13) and (9.17) may be written in the form

$$D(t) = (8/3\pi^2\nu k T) \int_{p=1}^{N/2} (2p - 1)^{-2}[1 - \exp(-t/\tau_p)]\, dp + t/\eta \qquad (9.20)$$

$$\tau_p = (4\eta/\pi^2\nu k T)(2p - 1)^{-2}$$

and

$$E(t) = 3\nu k T \int_{n=1}^{N} \exp(-t/\tau_n')\, dn \qquad (9.21)$$

$$\tau_n' = (2\eta/\pi^2\nu k T)n^{-2}$$

From the definition of the retardation-time spectra $L(\tau)$ given in Eq. (7.25), and after comparison with Eq. (9.20),

$$L(\tau) = (8/3\pi^2\nu k T)(2p - 1)^{-2}[dp/d(\ln \tau_p)] \qquad (9.22)$$

Solving for p in the expression for τ_p given with Eq. (9.20) and differentiating gives

$$dp/d(\ln \tau_p) = (\eta/4\pi^2\nu k T)^{1/2}\tau_p{}^{-1/2} \qquad (9.23)$$

After substitution in Eq. (9.22),

$$L(\tau) = (1/3\pi)(\tau_p/\eta\nu k T)^{1/2} \qquad (9.24)$$

Similarly, for the retardation-time spectrum,

$$H(\tau) = (3/\pi)(\eta\nu k T/\tau_p)^{1/2} \qquad (9.25)$$

with τ_p defined by Eq. (9.20). It should be noticed that the values given in Eqs. (9.24) and (9.25) are in terms of longitudinal deformation. The similar quantities in terms of shear are obtained by multiplying Eq. (9.24) by 3 and dividing Eq. (9.25) by 3. In each case, η is the tensile viscosity.

Note that in the short-time deformation region $L(\tau)$ is proportional to $\tau_p^{1/2}$ and $H(\tau)$ is proportional to $\tau_p^{-1/2}$. Hence a

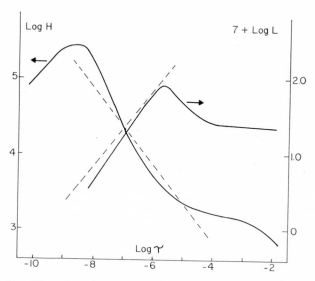

Figure 64.   The relaxation and retardation spectra of Figure 57 are plotted here on a logarithmic scale. Dotted lines of slope ½ and −½ are also shown.

plot of the logarithm of the retardation and relaxation spectra as a function of log τ should show a region at small τ values where the curves will have a slope of $+\frac{1}{2}$ and $-\frac{1}{2}$ for the retardation and relaxation spectra, respectively. Since this conclusion is based upon the same model system as was found applicable to the case of the short-time response of network chains, it should apply to that case also. The $L(\tau)$ and $H(\tau)$ values found for the network polymer shown in Figures 51 and 57 are replotted in Figure 64 on a logarithmic scale. Also in Figure 64 are drawn two dotted lines having slopes $+\frac{1}{2}$ and $-\frac{1}{2}$, respectively. It is apparent that the retardation- and relaxation-time spectra do approximate these slopes at short times.

Further comparison between experiment and theory will be deferred until the effects of entanglements have been discussed.

4. Dynamic Behavior: Effect of Entanglements (38,82)

The previous discussion has been concerned with the effects of viscous flow past a given molecule, with the assumption that all forces are smoothly distributed along the molecule. When cases where entanglements are present are considered, it is clear that certain chain segments—namely, those at the entanglement points—will experience much stronger forces than will the average segment. As was pointed out earlier in this chapter, these entanglement points will act much like crosslinks; hence, the short-time response of the material should closely approximate the response of a polymer network.

After an appreciable time, however, the entanglements will slip loose, and the network will essentially disintegrate. This development does not mean that the number of entanglements in the sample will decrease with time, for, as some entanglements slip loose, others will form as a result of normal Brownian motion. The new entanglements will always be formed in such a way that they will provide a new network which is in equilibrium at the particular state of deformation existing in the sample at that instant. Therefore the entanglement network is never really lost; it is constantly being reformed, but in its relaxed state. These remarks all assume, of course, that flow is not so strong as to preclude essentially equilibrium conditions within the sample.

Since high-molecular-weight chains will normally have hundreds of entanglements along the length of each chain, a myopic or nondetailed view of the chain would not be able to isolate the separate entanglements. For example, consider a chain which has entanglements spaced along the chain about 50 monomer units apart. Any measurement with "resolving power" such that it can distinguish no detail smaller than 50 monomer units along the chain will be unable to detect the presence of the entanglements as separate entities. The observation of the long-time response of a polymer system is likely to be of this low-resolving-power type.

It will be recalled that the high n modes of motion of a chain represent the case where the chain is split into relatively short segments. If the length of these segments is shorter than or of the same general size as the chain length between entanglements, the entanglements will seriously affect the motion of the segments and the response of these modes. However, for the small n (or large τ_n) modes of motion, the segment length characteristic of the mode will be much longer than the distance between entanglements; hence the entanglement points have essentially the same effect on these modes of motion as if they consisted of a uniform force along the chain instead of a highly localized force. The very important conclusion is therefore reached that, for long-time response of a polymer chain, the entanglements have no effect other than to increase the average friction factor for the chain segments.

All these ideas may be incorporated into the previous methods for computing the motion of the chains. The method of Appendix 9 has been extended to include the case of entanglements (38). This amplification has been accomplished by following through the usual computation with segmental friction factors f_0 for most segments; but the segments at the sites of entanglements are assumed to have much larger friction factors associated with them. Unfortunately, the computation cannot easily be carried through, and a solution that is accurate in the plateau region of Figure 61 has not been given. The approximate solution consists of two parts, as would be expected. One set of terms represents the entanglement-network response; the other set of terms represents the long-time response of the chain and is similar in form to the response found in Sec. 9.3. This result may be written

$$D(t) = (8/3\pi^2 \nu k T)\{(M_e/M) \overset{q}{\underset{1}{\Sigma}} \psi(\tau_{1n}) + \overset{N/2}{\underset{1}{\Sigma}} \psi(\tau_{2n})\} + t/\eta \tag{9.26}$$

with

$$\psi(\tau_n) = (2n - 1)^{-2}[1 - \exp(-t/\tau_n)]$$

and

$$\tau_{2n} = (M/M_e)^2(\eta/\eta_0)\tau_{1n} = 4\eta/\pi^2 \nu k T(2n - 1)^2$$

The quantity η_0 will be discussed below. In addition, M is the molecular weight of the polymer; M_e is the molecular weight between entanglements; q is the number of segments between entanglements, which is $N(M_e/M)$; and ν is the number of polymer molecules per unit volume.

It will be noticed that the first sum in Eq. (9.26) represents the usual formula for the network response in a system containing network chains of molecular weight M_e. The second sum plus the last term is identical to the result of Eq. (9.13) and represents the response of linear chains in a medium of viscosity η. Note that the retardation time τ_{2n} for the second term is identical to τ_n given in Eq. (9.13). The effect of entanglements on this term is included in the fact that the viscosity η is dependent upon entanglements.

As far as the network response term in Eq. (9.26) is concerned, it should be noticed that the retardation times do not involve the true system viscosity η. Instead, η is replaced by η_0, which is defined as the viscosity that the system would show if entanglements were not present. In addition, the factor $(M_e/M)^2$ appears in the numerator of the expression for τ_{1n}. This factor appears since $\eta_0(M_e/M)$ is the viscosity that a system of $\nu(M/M_e)$ chains would exhibit if each chain had a molecular weight M_e and if entanglements were not present.

In any event, since Eq. (9.26) is merely a combination of two equations already discussed separately, its general behavior need not be discussed in great detail. Suffice it to say that Eq. (9.26) predicts essentially two distinct responses separated by a time factor of $(M/M_e)^2(\eta/\eta_0)$. Since η is proportional to $M^{3.5}$ and η_0 is proportional to M as shown in Chapter 3, the ratio η/η_0 may then be evaluated. It is equal to $(M/2M_e)^{2.5}$; hence the second portion of the response will occur at a time $4(M/2M_e)^{4.5}$ times longer than the time at which the first portion of the response occurs. For the highest-molecular-weight polymer shown in Figure 61, this factor is about 10^{12}. In the case of the intermediate polymer in Figure 61 the factor is about 10^8, and for the lowest-weight polymer it is about 10^6. The second portion of the response appears to be somewhat closer in time to the first response than this predicts. However, in this regard it should be noticed that the equilibrium compliance given by the second term in Eq. (9.26) is a factor M/M_e larger than that given by the first term. The actual comparison of Eq. (9.26) with experiment is given in reference (38), and the agreement between theory and experiment is found to be only approximate.

A second approach to this problem has been given by Ferry et al. (82), who extended the Rouse theory to include entanglements. Their method is somewhat empirical in form, but it is based on the same general ideas expressed above. In the end, they obtain a result quite similar to Eq. (9.26) but differing in detail. Since neither their method nor the method used to obtain Eq. (9.26) takes proper account of the behavior in the plateau region, both fail to represent the experimental data adequately in that region.

A third method for attacking this problem, which is actually an extension of the previous two methods, has been given by Marvin (93). By setting up a hypothetical electrical circuit nearly equivalent to the molecular picture used to derive Eq. (9.26), he has been able to apply known mathematical techniques to solve the problem rather accurately. In particular, he was able to obtain a better approximation to the behavior in the plateau region than was possible by the other two methods.

Additional comparison between theory and experiment has been made, and the agreement is fairly satisfactory. For example, Eq. (9.26) predicts a retardation- (or relaxation-time) spectrum that shows *two* regions where the $\tau^{1/2}$ dependence discussed in Sec. 9.3 applies. It is relatively obvious that each portion of the response will show the $\tau^{1/2}$ dependence at short times. This prediction has been checked for several polymers and has proved reasonably valid. Typical is the case of a polyisobutylene (95) of very high molecular weight, shown in Figures 65 and 66. The agreement appears good enough to

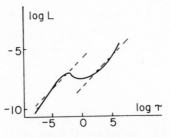 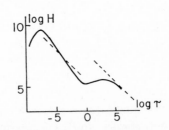

Figure 65. The variation of the logarithm of the retardation-time spectrum (93) with log τ, with τ in seconds, for a polyisobutylene of M = 10^6 at 25°C. Broken lines with slope ½ are drawn for comparison.

Figure 66. The variation of the logarithm of the relaxation-time spectrum (93) with log τ, with τ in seconds, for a polyisobutylene of M = 10^6 at 25°C. Broken lines with slope $-$½ are drawn for comparison.

justify the general picture upon which this discussion has been based.

5. Dynamic Viscosity

The viscosity of a polymer or its concentrated solutions has been discussed in detail in Chapter 3. That discussion assumed a constant small rate of deformation. It is now pertinent to ask how the viscosity behaves if it is measured under an oscillatory force. Viscosity measured under these conditions is designated the "dynamic viscosity," which will be investigated in this section.

If high frequencies of excitation are not involved, the short-time response due to the entanglement network will be small compared with the response of the chains as a whole. Assuming for the present that the long-time deformation of the whole chain will be predominant, it is apparent that in the case of a creep experiment Eq. (9.26) reduces to Eq. (9.20). The viscosity η in these equations will of course be the limiting value at low shear rate and zero frequency. It is the true viscosity of the polymer.

Since Eq. (9.21) applies to this approximation, all the results obtained using the relaxation and retardation times pertinent to that equation will also apply. Equation (9.19) will in particular be applicable to the present problem. Then, from the definition of dynamic viscosity $\eta'(\omega)$,

$$\eta'(\omega) = E''/\omega \qquad (9.27)$$

To check Eq. (9.27), let us consider the case of $\omega \to 0$, for which one should then find that $\eta'(\omega) \to \eta$. However, for $\omega \to 0$ Eq. (9.19) gives the relation

$$\lim_{\omega \to 0} E''/\omega = \Sigma E_n \tau_n' \qquad (9.28)$$

Comparison of Eq. (9.28) with Eq. (9.15) shows that this quantity is indeed the steady-state viscosity η, and thus Eq. (9.27) does prove correct at zero frequency.

If one substitutes from Eq. (9.10) into Eq. (9.19) and in turn substitutes into Eq. (9.27), the result finally obtained is

$$\eta'(\omega) = 3\nu k T \Sigma \tau_n'/(1 + \omega^2 \tau_n'^2) \qquad (9.29)$$

where

$$\tau_n' = (2\eta/\pi^2 \nu k T)n^{-2} \qquad n = 1, 2, \ldots, N$$

The variation of $\eta'(\omega)$ as a function of $\omega \tau_1'$ is shown in Figure 67. Notice that when $\omega \tau_1' = 1$ the viscosity has begun to drop quite rapidly. At high frequencies, the dynamic viscosity becomes very small. This behavior can be interpreted as follows.

Since the viscosity is nothing more than a measure of energy loss, it is apparent that at high frequencies the frictional energy loss must be greatly reduced. At very low frequencies much of the deformation will be due to viscous flow. Such deformation gives rise to a nonrecoverable input of energy. Some of the deformation is due to the stretching of the chains, and this energy is in part, at least, recovered during the compression stage of the cycle. As the frequency is increased, there is less time for viscous flow to occur. Since the elastic deformation occurs more quickly than the viscous flow, the deformation changes from predominantly viscous flow at low frequencies to predominantly elastic stretching at high frequencies. Most of the elasticity energy is

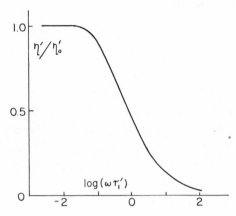

Figure 67.   Variation of dynamic viscosity with frequency according to Eq. (9.29).

recoverable; therefore the energy loss, and hence the viscosity, decreases greatly at high frequencies. This behavior is reasonably well studied and is found to conform at least semiquantitatively with the prediction of Eq. (9.29) (96,97,98).

6. Non-Newtonian Flow

The viscosity of polymers in shear has been assumed independent of shear rate for all the discussions thus far. Equations were derived for the viscosity in Chapter 3, and these equations predicted a constant viscosity. There is overwhelming experimental evidence to show, however, that polymer viscosity actually decreases at high rates of shear. Typical data for a sample of rubber is shown in Figure 68. Here the ratio of observed viscosity η to the zero shear viscosity η_0 is plotted against the shear rate $\dot{\gamma}$.

It is interesting to note that the curve of Figure 67 relating dynamic viscosity to frequency of applied force is of the same shape as the viscosity–shear rate curve. This similarity is apparently more than coincidental. It may be shown in fact that,

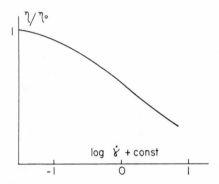

Figure 68. Variation of viscosity with shear rate as found for rubber and several other polymers (103,104).

even though the shear is constant and nonoscillatory, the individual polymer molecules will experience oscillatory forces with frequency $\dot{\gamma}/2$. This may be seen to be true in the following way (100).

Consider the polymer molecule depicted in Figure 69. It is

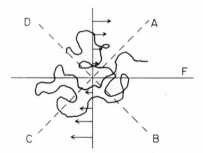

Figure 69. Action of a shear gradient upon a polymer molecule.

considered to be immersed in a viscous matrix, polymeric in nature, which is subjected to the shearing action illustrated by the arrows. Although the molecule may be moving as a whole as well, the translational motion will be of no concern for the present purposes. As pointed out in Chapter 3, the result of the shear gradient $\dot{\gamma}$ illustrated in Figures 69 and A.4 will be to cause the molecule to rotate with average angular velocity $\dot{\gamma}/2$.

As a particular segment rotates with the molecule, it will experience the viscous forces caused by its own motion as well as by the original shearing motion of the matrix. An examination of Figure 69 indicates that a given polymer segment will be pulled away from the center of the molecule as it rotates by A. When it gets to B it will be pushed toward the center. At C it will again be pulled out, and at D again pushed in. Hence the segment experiences an oscillatory force with a frequency that is double the frequency of rotation of the molecule.

It may be shown that if the molecule is considered completely "soft," so that the viscous force discussed above is always balanced by the elastic forces within the molecule, then no change in viscosity results from the alternate stretching and compression of the molecule (100,101). Although a segment moves out from the center and thereby decreases the viscous loss as it rotates from E to A, it will cause an excessive viscous loss as it moves back toward the center in the region from A to F. These two effects exactly cancel; therefore, the molecular distortion by itself does not change the viscosity.

In practice, however, the molecule is not perfectly soft. At high frequencies of rotation especially (i.e. at high shear rates), the molecular segments will not be able to respond instantaneously to the deforming forces. As a result, the above considerations no longer apply.

If the molecule is regarded as stiff and symmetrical enough for each segment to rotate with essentially constant angular velocity $\dot{\gamma}/2$, the viscous force on each segment will be sinusoidal with frequency $\dot{\gamma}$. This problem has been discussed in this way by several authors (100,102). Both the general method outlined in Appendix 9 and the Rouse method have been applied. The latter result appears to make no major approximation other than the one concerning constant rate of rotation. It leads to the following equation for the viscosity as a function of shear rate (102):

$$\eta_s = \nu k T \Sigma \tau_n' / (1 + \dot{\gamma}^2 \tau_n'^2) \qquad (9.30)$$

where τ_n' is the quantity defined in Eq. (9.29).

Since the shear viscosity η_s is $\eta/3$, where η is the tensile viscosity used in the previous equations, Eq. (9.30) is seen to be identical to Eq. (9.29), except that the frequency ω is replaced by the shear rate $\dot{\gamma}$. Tests of this equivalence of shear rate and frequency have been made, and the results indicate the equivalence to be true at least semiquantitatively (97,98). Some experimental data demonstrating this are given in Figure 70.

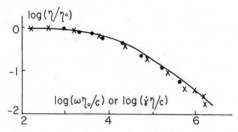

Figure 70.   Variation of viscosity with shear rate ($\cdot$) and frequency ($\times$) for a polyisobutylene of $M = 10^6$ at concentrations of 5 to 22 per cent polymer. The original data (97) contain many more points than shown, but those indicated are typical.

However, the exact form of Eq. (9.30) is apparently not quite correct; but this is not unexpected in view of the rather qualitative assumption of constant rate of rotation. Fairly successful attempts have been made to use the shear-rate variation of viscosity as an absolute molecular-weight method (103,104).

Another approach to this problem has been taken by Pao (105), the essence of whose theory is as follows. He considers the rotating body to be a piece of matter having the same retardation spectrum as the gross polymer. The rotating object need not be reduced to molecular terms; it can just as well be a minute particle of polymer. The relation between the frequency response of the polymer and its response to shear rate is completely obvious in a qualitative way. The polymer particle is clearly undergoing oscillatory distortion, and it will evidence the dynamic viscosity one would predict for an oscillating applied force. Pao's result is not too much different from that given in Eq. (9.30), and the agreement between theory and experiment is relatively good (106).

Although the above results are quite straightforward and encouraging, it should be pointed out that there is still great disagreement about the validity of these results. They are all based upon a uniform rate of molecular rotation, which is an approximation that is not readily assessed. One feels that it is not too bad an approximation for high-molecular-weight, loosely coiled polymers, for in such cases the molecule will approximate a sphere. Both this assumption and the whole idea of a submolecule chain with N large will break down for very stiff rodlike molecules. This qualification has been only cursorily investigated.

More disturbing is the fact that Zimm (107) has tried to apply the Rouse method directly, without making the approximation of constant rate of rotation. In so doing, he must in turn make other mathematical approximations. As an end result he finds that the viscosity should not depend upon shear rate, at least within the framework of his model. Although this answer is not a correct representation of the physical situation, it is impossible at this time to ascertain the exact reason for this failure. Until the correct explanation for this shortcoming is found, a cloud of uncertainty rests over the other results given in this section.

7. Effect of Chain Branching and Polydispersity

It should be stated at the outset that the effects of chain branching on viscoelastic properties are not very well known. Since the distance from chain end to chain end in a branched molecule will be shorter than in a linear molecule of the same molecular weight, it is to be expected that the retardation-time spectrum will be somewhat lacking in the number of very long retardation times. A theoretical examination of certain branched-type molecules actually shows this to be true (108,109); however, the theoretical problem is quite involved and has not been extended to other than the simplest cases.

A little more progress has been made with regard to the zero shear viscosity. In the limit of high molecular weights where entanglements are numerous, on theoretical grounds (110) it appears that the ratio of the viscosity of a branched molecule to that of a linear molecule of the same molecular weight should be equal to $g^{3.5}$. The quantity g is defined as the ratio of the mean square radius of gyration of the branched molecule to the mean square radius of the linear molecule having the same molecular weight. This relation has not yet been subjected to a rigorous experimental check, however. In the region of low molecular weights, theory predicts that the ratio of the two viscosities should equal g, provided that f_0 is not changed by the branching.

It has already been pointed out that a variation of chain lengths in a network polymer will broaden the response curves. This is also true, of course, in the case of linear polymers; however, only the long-time response will be affected by polydispersity in molecular weight. It may be shown that the steady-state elastic compliance, which is proportional to ν^{-1} or M from Eq. (9.26), is actually proportional to $M_{z+1}M_z/M_w$ in the case of a polydisperse polymer (38,111). This indicates that the elastic retardation of linear polymers after extrusion and other viscous flow processes will be proportional to this same quantity. Since the ratio $M_{z+1}M_z/M_w$ severely emphasizes material of very high molecular weight, a polymer having a wide distribution of molecular weights will show more elastic effects than a homogeneous polymer with the same weight-average molecular weight.

Attempts have been made to use the effects of polydispersity upon the observed stress-relaxation behavior for the evaluation of molecular-weight distributions (112,113). Although a measure of success has been attained in this regard, serious objections have been raised to the validity and utility of at least one of these methods (114). It appears that more work is required before these methods can be considered reliable.

PROBLEMS

1. A certain polymer having $M_e = 20,000$, $M_w = 10^6$, and $M_n = 10^5$ is separated into several samples, and these samples are crosslinked to various extents. The molecular weights between crosslink points are ∞, 10^5, 5×10^4, 2×10^4, 5×10^3, and 2×10^3. Sketch on the same graph the creep curves that would be expected for each of these samples. Explain the curves. (You need not put numerical values on the axes.)

2. From the height of the plateau for the curves of Figure 61, compute M_e and show that it agrees with the value given in the text.

3. Consider a single Kelvin element ($E = 2 \times 10^6$ dynes/cm^2 and $\tau = 10^3$ sec) in series with a dashpot ($\eta = 3 \times 10^9$ poise). Compute the response of this system to a constant load of 500 gm.

4. For the system of problem 3, if the load is allowed to remain on the system for 3000 sec and then removed, plot the creep and recovery curves. Use these curves to compute the viscosity of the system. Compare your answer with the viscosity of the dashpot.

5. Suppose a creep experiment was carried out with the load applied for 10^3 sec when the sample was 20°C above its glass temperature. If the temperature of the sample is raised 15°C just after the load is removed, how long must the sample be allowed to recover at this temperature in order for the recovery to correspond to that which would occur in 10^4 sec at the lower temperature?

6. Some polymers (for example, plasticized polyvinyl chloride) tend to form enough very small crystallites so that the polymer is fairly well crosslinked by them. If the crystallites melt out at 120°C and if T_g for the system is about -20°C, what would you expect the logarithmic creep curves to look like at 23°C and 140°C? Explain. (A qualitative answer will suffice.)

7. Derive Eq. (9.25) from Eq. (9.21), showing each step in detail.

8. For the system of problem 3, compute the response to an applied force $\sigma = \sigma_0 \cos \omega t$. Show that, in the limit of small frequencies, the dynamic viscosity of this system reduces to a reasonable value. Explain in words why the dynamic viscosity behaves in the way you find by calculation.

9. Suppose one wishes to compression-mold a plastic dish made from a polymer whose $T_g = 130$°C. Give reasons why there is an upper limit to the molecular weight that the polymer can have if the method is to be practical.

Chapter 10

TENSILE STRENGTH OF RUBBERS

1. Statistics of Rupture

Perhaps the most obvious fact concerning tensile-strength measurements is that they are uniformly irreproducible. By the very nature of the rupture process, the tensile failure will always occur at a flaw in the test sample. No matter how carefully the test piece is prepared, it is absolutely impossible to eliminate all the flaws from it. Although care can be taken to exclude obvious foreign inclusions, bubbles, scratches, etc., it is not possible to exclude these sources of flaws in the sample entirely. In the last analysis, Brownian motion causes density fluctuations within the material which will act as flaws.

Of course, the importance of flaws can be reduced by various techniques. Assuming that reasonable care has been taken to preclude obvious flaws, it is still found that small bubbles, occluded dirt, etc., are always a possibility. The larger the test sample, the more chance of finding such a flaw in the specimen; hence, the average tensile strength should increase somewhat with decreasing sample size. Such behavior has actually been found in certain cases (115). However, a number of small flaws resulting from surface scratches, density and compounding-ingredient fluctuations, occluded bits of particulate matter, and many other causes will always be present even in the smallest practical test sample.

Obviously, then, one can never hope to obtain the "true"

strength of a rubber. The measured tensile strengths will usually be lower than the strength that a perfect sample would show. Many authors have treated the problem of the best method of analyzing tensile-strength data. Since usually the strength of several identical test pieces of a given material are measured, the best procedure for averaging the data should be known. No unanimous verdict has been reached on this question. Most investigators average all the results and discard only those data for samples containing an obvious flaw. Admittedly, this tensile strength will be lower than the strength of a flawless specimen; however, if the strength is always lower by approximately the same factor, this error will only be of minor concern. A rather complete discussion of the effect of flaws on strength has been given in the review article of A. M. Bueche and J. P. Berry (116).

2. Experimental Results

Perhaps there is no physical property of rubber that has been more measured than the tensile strength. This fact is not surprising in view of the obvious importance of this quantity. However, it is surprising to find that, in spite of this great wealth of data, most of it is of little value as an aid to understanding the processes involved. Most of the data have been gathered without proper control of all the many variables that influence tensile strength. In particular, the primary molecular weight of the rubber and the absolute degree of crosslinking are usually unknown and variable. In the discussion that follows, it will be seen that the tensile strength of a rubber is acutely dependent upon these quantities.

Three types of rubbers constitute a very large proportion of total rubber consumption: natural rubber (NR); polyisobutylene containing a small amount of isoprene (so-called "butyl" rubber); and SBR (or GRS), which is a random copolymer of styrene (30 parts) and butadiene (70 parts). Of these three, NR crystallizes slowly at temperatures somewhat below room temperature (see Chapter 11), and butyl crystallizes appreciably only when highly stretched. On the other hand, SBR does not crystallize even in the stretched state. It will be seen that this factor of crystallinity seriously alters the strength behavior.

A. EFFECT OF DEGREE OF CROSSLINKING

One of the primary variables in any vulcanized rubber is the degree of crosslinking. It may be expressed most conveniently in terms of the average molecular weight between crosslinks (M_c), or alternatively in terms of the number of network chains per unit volume (ν). The two representations are of course related through the equation

$$\nu = \rho N / M_c \qquad (10.1)$$

where ρ is the density of the rubber and N is Avogadro's number.

If no chain ends were present in the sample, then ν could be determined directly from the elastic behavior of the rubber at low stresses. From Chapter 2 it is known that

$$\sigma = \nu_e k T (\alpha - \alpha^{-2}) \qquad (10.2)$$

and thus a graph of $\sigma/(\alpha - \alpha^{-2})$ vs. α should be a horizontal straight line with intercept $\nu_e k T$. Therefore, ν could be determined.

In practice, there are two complications involved in this method. First, because it is sometimes difficult to obtain true equilibrium conditions, the plot is not a horizontal straight line. Usually a fair extrapolation can be made, however. The second complication is much more serious. It involves the fact that chain ends are always present; consequently, many chains in the network are broken (i.e., contain a chain end) and are therefore not effective. Equation (10.2) actually gives ν_e, the number of *effective* network chains, which may depart greatly from the total number of network chains.

To relate ν_e to ν, one can proceed as follows. If there were no chain ends in the rubber and if the average molecular weight between crosslinks was M_c, then the number of network chains per unit volume is simply $\nu = \rho \mathbf{N}/M_c$. On the other hand, the original polymer having number-average molecular weight M_n before vulcanization contained $\rho \mathbf{N}/M_n$ chains or $2\rho \mathbf{N}/M_n$ chain ends. To a first approximation, each chain end will cause one of the network chains to be ineffective. Hence,

$$\nu_e = \nu - 2\rho \mathbf{N}/M_n$$

Network chains per unit vol.

or

$$\nu_e = \nu(1 - 2M_c/M_n) \tag{10.3}$$

effective Network chains

Equation (10.3) was first derived by Flory (117). Although it is not exact, subsequent investigators have shown it to be a very good approximation (23,24). Notice that it predicts no effective network chains will be present until the rubber is crosslinked tight enough that $M_c < M_n/2$. Even so, Eq. (10.3) overestimates the number of fully effective network chains, since it makes no correction for the fact that a chain near an ineffective chain will not be fully effective.

A second method for determining M_c is based upon the equilibrium swelling of a vulcanized rubber (1). Since swelling is equivalent in many respects to a three-dimensional stretching of the rubber, it is not surprising that this method yields ν_e rather than ν. Hence it is not possible to obtain M_c from swelling measurements unless M_n for the polymer is known.

Flory investigated the variation of tensile strength of NR with M_c by vulcanizing with a quantitative crosslinking agent (118). His results are shown in Figure 71. It is not surprising that the

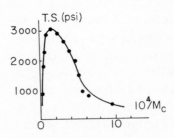

Figure 71.   The tensile strength of natural rubber as a function of molecular weight between crosslinks (118).

strength goes to zero as ν_e approaches zero, since a more or less direct proportionality would be expected between number of load-holding chains and strength. However, the fact that the strength again decreases at high crosslinking density (i.e., large ν_e) is rather surprising. Flory interpreted this in terms of the decreased tendency of rubber to crystallize when a large number of crosslinks are present. Later work on SBR shows a similar behavior, and since SBR does not crystallize, one is inclined to view the previous interpretation with considerable skepticism. Another possible explanation will be given later in this chapter.

Taylor and Darin used a similar procedure to investigate the variation of tensile strength of SBR with crosslinking (119). Their starting material was a somewhat modified SBR in that the low-molecular-weight chains had been removed by an extraction procedure. The data they obtained are shown in Figure 72. Notice that the strength becomes appreciable for ν

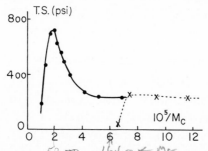

Figure 72. Variation of tensile strength with M_c for SBR which had been extracted (119) (solid line) and which had not been extracted (72) (broken line).

greater than about 10^{-5} mole^{-1}, which corresponds to an M_c of about 100,000. If one uses the rough criterion that appreciable strength occurs only when $M_c < M_n/2$, it is apparent that the material which they used had $M_n \cong 200,000$. This is to be compared with an $M_n \cong 30,000$ for unextracted SBR. Typical data for an unextracted SBR (120) are also shown in Figure 72.

Note that the extracted SBR evidences a behavior quite similar to the natural rubber shown in Figure 71; nevertheless, two differences between SBR and NR are apparent. First, the maximum strength of SBR is only about 700 psi, compared with over 3000 psi for NR. Second, the maximum in the NR curve comes at $M_c \cong 6000$, while the corresponding point for SBR is at $M_c \cong 60,000$. Apparently a part of the reason for the low strength of SBR at the maximum is that only about one-tenth as many network chains are present in the SBR sample at that point.

Obviously the strength maximum for SBR cannot be explained in terms of crystallinity, since this rubber does not crystallize. In this regard, it should be noticed that the unextracted SBR does not show a strength maximum. (The M_c values for this curve were actually computed from measured ν_e values using $M_n = 30,000$.) However, the unextracted polymer must be crosslinked so highly to make a stable network that it appears from Figure 72 that the high-strength portion of the curve may be missing for this reason alone. This possibility will be further investigated later in this chapter.

B. EFFECT OF PRIMARY MOLECULAR WEIGHT

Experiments have been carried out in which the value of M_c was held constant and the molecular weight of the primary uncrosslinked polymer was varied. In a careful study of the tensile strength of butyl rubber by Flory (118), the value of M_c for the vulcanizate was maintained at 37,000. He varied the number-average molecular weight of the primary molecules by using fractionated samples of butyl and mixtures thereof. His data show that the tensile strength is dependent upon M_n rather than on some other average of the molecular weight. The data are shown in Figure 73.

If chain ends had no effect whatsoever, one would expect no variation of tensile strength with M_n. However, as discussed earlier, the presence of chain ends will decrease the number of effective network chains, and thereby will also decrease the strength. It is not surprising, then, that the strength is very low for small M_n and rises to some nearly constant value at high M_n. Since it was shown in the last section that the number of effective network chains is negligible unless $2M_c < M_n$, the strength might be expected to drop to zero at $M_n = 74,000$. Actually, as seen in Figure 73, the strength does not become appreciable until M_n is somewhat higher than this value. In view of the fact that an effective network chain close to an ineffective chain will not be fully effective, this discrepancy is perhaps not too surprising.

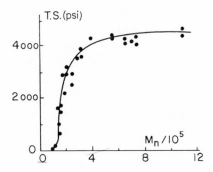

Figure 73.   Tensile strength (118) of butyl rubber as a function of M_n, with M_c being held constant at 37,000.

Flory analyzed the data of Figure 73 in terms of the fraction of the total number of chains tied to the infinite network. Since many of these chains will not be effective chains at low molecular weights, serious doubts arise concerning the exactness of such a comparison. In any event, this fraction is $1 - 2M_c/(M_n + M_c)$, which becomes zero for $M_c = M_n = 37,000$ in this case. This is much too low a value for M_n when compared with the data of Figure 73. However, if the tensile strength is proportional to this fraction, then a plot of strength vs. $(M_n + M_c)^{-1}$ should be a straight line with ratio of slope to intercept equal to $2M_c$. The experimental scatter is large, as is always found for tensile-strength data, but within reason it does lie on a straight line. However, the slope-to-intercept ratio is equal to about 130,000 rather than the predicted 74,000.

C. EFFECT OF FILLER

A distinction must be made between so-called "reinforcing fillers" and "nonreinforcing fillers." As pointed out in Chapter 2, the nonreinforcing fillers increase the hardness of a rubber somewhat and change the tensile strength only slightly. On the other hand, reinforcing fillers greatly increase the modulus and wear properties of the rubber. This is the primary reason for adding filler to natural rubber and other rubbers that crystallize upon stretching. In the matter of tensile strength, filler presence is relatively ineffective in changing the tensile strength of crystallizable rubbers. On the other hand, the strength of SBR and other noncrystallizable rubbers is enormously increased by the addition of carbon black and various silicas, the two most important reinforcing fillers.

The effect of carbon black filler on the tensile strength of SBR (120) is shown in Figure 74. Notice that the addition of

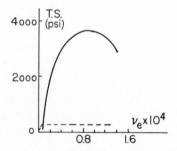

Figure 74. Tensile strength of SBR gum stock (broken curve) and SBR containing 30 parts HAF black (full curve) as a function of number of effective network chains (120).

30 parts of filler by weight to 100 parts of SBR (i.e., about 12 volume per cent) has raised the strength by a factor of about 15. Note also that the filled material shows a maximum strength at an M_c not too much different from that true for natural rubber. This effect is of great importance from a practical standpoint, since it changes SBR from a weak, nearly useless rubber to a rubber having strength comparable to natural rubber.

It should be pointed out that the maximum in the curve of Figure 74 is not a result of chain breakdown at prolonged cures. Convincing data are available to show that the decrease in strength at high ν_e values is the result of the small M_c rather than any other effect. Although the data shown are for sulfur cures, peroxide and other cure systems exhibit similar behavior. One is therefore led to the conclusion that low M_c values are, in themselves, detrimental to tensile-strength properties. A possible explanation for this statement will be given later in this chapter.

D. EFFECT OF TEMPERATURE

The tensile strength of all rubbers is of the order of several thousand psi when they are at temperatures below T_g. In this temperature range they are, of course, no longer rubbers but glasses. A discussion of the strength of glasslike materials will be given in Chapter 11. For the present, the discussion will be concerned with rubbers at temperatures appreciably above T_g. It is obvious that rubbers at low temperatures must exhibit high strengths, since they are making the transition from the high-strength characteristic of a glass to the moderate-strength characteristic of a rubber. As the temperature is raised, the strength behavior of crystallizable rubbers is found to differ greatly from that of SBR and other noncrystallizable rubbers. In general, one observes that temperature ranges which favor the proper formation of crystallites also favor high strength. This is shown (119) in Figure 75.

The interpretation for the data shown in Figure 75 is usually given somewhat as follows. At low temperatures the strength is high because the material is approaching the glass state. As the temperature is raised, the strength decreases because of the decreasing glass effect. In addition, near $-20°C$ natural rubber crystallizes quite rapidly, and the effect of crystallinity becomes important. The crystallinity at these low temperatures is dependent upon two competitive processes. If the temperature is low enough, the crystals will nucleate and begin to grow from

the amorphous polymer. Lowering the temperature aids nucleation at least in this temperature range. However, if the temperature is too low, the polymer is so viscous that the chains
cannot move readily to positions where they align themselves
properly for crystal growth. Hence, if the temperature is too
high, the crystals will not nucleate well, while at too low a
temperature the crystals cannot grow. The tensile-strength maximum is presumably a reflection of the high crystallinity in this
temperature range.

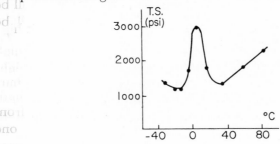

Figure 75.   Strength of vulcanized natural rubber as a function of
temperature (119).

At temperatures of zero and higher the nucleation process
decreases, and thus the strength also decreases. However, rubber crystals form at much higher temperatures than this, and
natural rubber will actually crystallize slowly over a period of
years at room temperature. The melting point of such crystals
is near 40°C. Stretched rubber will actually crystallize at temperatures much higher than this, however. This fact is used to
explain the increase in tensile strength with temperature that is
observed at temperatures near room temperature. It is thought
that the crystals which form at the higher temperatures will be
better aligned in the direction of stress and will therefore contribute more to the strength. Because all crystallinity disappears
at very high temperatures, the strength again falls at temperatures beyond the range shown in Figure 75.

The tensile-strength behavior of SBR, both filled and gum
stocks, with temperature (120) is shown in Figure 76. Notice

that the gum stock shows relatively constant strength above about 20°C. The rise in strength at low temperatures is a reflection of the fact that the material is approaching the glass state.

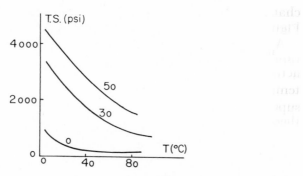

Figure 76. Variation of tensile strength of SBR with temperature. The numbers on the curves give the concentration of HAF black in parts per hundred of rubber (120).

From Figure 76 it is observed that the strength of carbon black filled stocks decreases rapidly over the whole temperature range as the temperature increases. At high temperatures, the effect of the black is nearly all lost. Similar behavior is noticed for silica filled stocks. There is some reason to believe that the adhesion of the filler to the rubber decreases with increase in temperature and that this is the cause of the observed tensile-strength decrease. This decrease is far from certain, however. The possible causes for this effect will be discussed more fully in a later portion of this chapter.

E. EFFECT OF TEST RATE

Until now it has been assumed in this chapter that the tensile test rate (i.e., the rate of elongation of unit length of test sample) was constant. Since most practical testing machines are usually operated in the same general test-rate range, the results quoted in previous sections of this chapter are comparable. There is, however, marked variation in tensile strength if the test rate is changed by a large factor (121), a situation that is shown in Figure 77.

As shown in Figure 77, the strength of an SBR gum stock rises rapidly at high test rates. The data shown in Figure 77 were actually taken at several temperatures and reduced to a single temperature by using a modification of the temperature-time superposition method. The WLF equation seems to apply to these data. This stock had a strength of 230 psi at 25°C and an

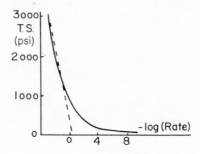

Figure 77.   Tensile strength of SBR as a function of test rate (121).

extension rate of 2 in. per in. per min. Similar measurements have been made on other gum stocks of other noncrystallizing rubbers, and all reveal a behavior much like that shown in Figure 77. An interpretation of this behavior will be given in a later section after the general molecular basis for tensile strength has been discussed

Another means for investigating the strength variation with time consists of measuring the time the rubber will take to break under a constant stress. In this type of test, the rubber is able to hold a small stress for a much longer time than it can hold a large stress. Typical data for SBR containing carbon black (122) are shown in Figure 78. To a rough approximation at least, the methods used in obtaining the data of Figures 77 and 78 give results that reflect the same molecular phenomena (121). It will be pointed out later that the variation in strength observed is intimately related to the viscoelastic response of the polymer chains.

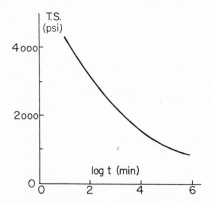

Figure 78. Time taken to break at the indicated load for an SBR vulcan-izate containing 30 parts HAF black (72). The data were taken at 32 and 68°C and are here reduced to 32°C.

3. Theoretical Considerations: A Simple Model

To gain insight into the molecular parameters that influence tensile strength, it is of value to consider a particularly simple model. As a first approximation, the tetrahedral network will be replaced by the model network whose structure is shown in Figure 79. The network chains are assumed to point in three perpendicular directions as shown. Furthermore, the applied stress is assumed to be applied in the same direction as one of the

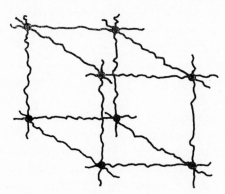

Figure 79. Schematic network model.

three sets of chains. The one-third of the total chains that points in this direction will hold all the applied stress.

Notice that the load is held by a set of strands of chains which extend completely through the sample in the direction of the stress. If the unstretched sample is assumed to be a unit cube, then there will be ν chains in it. On the other hand, the number of chains in a strand will be taken as n. In addition, there will be n^2 strands holding the applied load and these constitute only one-third of the total number of strands. Hence,

$$(3n^2)(n) = \nu \tag{10.4}$$

or

$$n = (\nu/3)^{1/3}$$

If each chain in each of the n^2 load-bearing strands is assumed to hold the same load, then all the stressed chains will break at once. If the strength of a chain is taken as F_c, the tensile strength will be given as

$$\text{T.S.} = n^2 F_c$$

which after use of Eq. (10.4) may be rewritten as

$$\text{T.S.} = (\nu/3)^{2/3} F_c \tag{10.5}$$

This result is surprising in some ways. In the first place, it predicts that the tensile strength is proportional to the two-thirds power of the number of network chains rather than to the first power. This variation with $\nu^{2/3}$ is the result of the fact that the chains act as strands of chains. There are $(\nu/3)^{2/3}$ of these strands traversing the sample in each of the three perpendicular directions. Each set of the $(\nu/3)^{2/3}$ strands can only hold a load F_c times the number of strands, no matter how many chains exist in each strand.

It would appear that the two-thirds dependency is not peculiar to the molecular model used in this simple computation. Even a tetrahedral network will act as a set of strands. Of course, the numerical constant may change from model to model, but the dependency on ν should not change. This requires a reanalysis of Flory's data shown in Figure 73. Since ν should be replaced by ν_e for any real network, the tensile strength would be proportional to $(1 - 2M_c/M_n)^{2/3}$ if M_c is held constant. A plot of Flory's data for tensile strength versus $(1 - 2M_c/M_n)^{2/3}$ approximates a straight line rather closely, as it should. Hence the experimental data do not disagree with the prediction of Eq. (10.5) as far as the $\nu^{2/3}$ dependency is concerned, provided that M_c is held constant.

The variation of tensile strength with M_c is not correctly given by Eq. (10.5). While Eq. (10.5) would predict a monotonic increase in strength as the degree of crosslinking is increased, the data quoted earlier in this chapter show a decrease in strength at very high degrees of crosslinking. Obviously the computation is in error.

Perhaps the most suspect assumption for the simple model used in the above computation is the unrealistic view that each chain holds the same load. In a real rubber, the loads held by various chains would be expected to vary widely. The actual rubber network cannot be considered a uniform geometric structure. Since the chains are presumably vulcanized while in their random configurations, some of the chains will already be highly extended even before the stress is applied to the sample. In addition, some of the chains will be much shorter than others. Since the ratio of the extended length of a freely orienting chain to its random length is $N^{1/2}$, where N is the number of freely orienting segments per chain, it is clear that the shorter chains will be fully elongated first and will therefore break first.

It may be shown (123) by rather complex computations that the effect of this uneven distribution of load becomes more serious at high degrees of crosslinking than it is at low degrees of crosslinking. Basically this is a result of the fact that the percentage deviation from the average for the number of segments per network chain increases as the number of segments per average network chain decreases. Therefore, when the network chains contain, on the average, only a few segments, the chance of finding a chain with only half the average number of segments is greater than if the average chain contained a large number of segments. As a result, the number of very highly stressed chains increases as the degree of crosslinking increases.

It is reasonable to assume that a break will propagate through the sample when conditions are such that the breaking of one chain causes a second to break and this causes a third to break, and so on. If one network chain breaks, the load that it held must now be held by its neighbors. In the event that one of these neighbors is already highly stressed, it too will break under the additional stress. Obviously, as the number of very highly stressed chains increases, the break will propagate more easily. One is therefore led to conclude that too high a degree of crosslinking can be deleterious as far as tensile strength is concerned, since it results in wide variations in stress applied to the network chains.

A very approximate theoretical treatment has been given for this nonuniform sharing of load at high degrees of crosslinking and the resulting decrease in tensile strength. It predicts the general behavior found by experiment (123); however, it, as well as the other current theories for tensile strength, leaves much to be desired (119,124). These theories have recently been reviewed in detail (125).

4. Interpretation of Filler and Crystallite Action

The manner in which filler particles and crystallites increase the strength of rubbers can be explained in the following way. Assuming that the break proceeds in a stepwise manner—the breaking of one segment causing its neighbors to break, and so on—it becomes apparent that load-sharing mechanisms are very important in determining tensile strength. Any means by which the additional load thrown onto a group of chains by the breaking of one of its number may be more equally distributed among the group will lessen the chance for propagation of the break. One such way of sharing the load is by addition of reinforcing fillers.

Consider, for example, the portion of a network between filler particles schematically illustrated in Figure 80. If the central chain were to break at A without the filler particles being present, the ends of the broken chain would retract a sizable distance. Most of the load held by chain A would be thrown onto chains B and C. However, with the filler particles in the positions shown, the broken chain will only retract a short distance, and most of the load held by chain A will be distributed over all the chains that are attached to the filler particles. Hence the filler particles act effectively as a means of distributing the load more

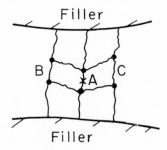

Figure 80. Diagram explaining the action of filler particles on strength.

equitably. They will therefore decrease the chance for a break to propagate, and consequently the strength of the sample will be increased.

The above discussion has assumed that the chains are tightly held against the filler surface. As pointed out in Chapter 2, there is substantial reason to believe that reinforcing fillers are strongly bonded to rubber chains at various sites on the filler surface. However, if the strength of the rubber-filler bond decreases as the temperature is raised, the filler action can be decreased. This is one possible explanation for the decrease in strength of filled rubbers as the temperature is increased (120). Other possible explanations of this effect might be based upon the decreased resistance of the chains to oxidative scission at higher temperatures.

The above remarks concerning the load-sharing action of fillers can be applied equally well to crystallites. Obviously the filler particles in Figure 80 could be replaced by crystallites and the same arguments would hold. Of course, the temperature effects would be different in the two cases; the effect of temperature on crystallites was discussed in Sec. 10.2D. Rudimentary theoretical work embodying the above ideas has been carried out (120). It indicates that reasonable agreement can be obtained between experiment and a theory based upon the concepts discussed in this section. Much more work needs to be done in this regard, however, before the theoretical treatment of this problem can be considered satisfactory.

5. Interpretation of Rate Effects (126)

As pointed out in the discussion of the data for SBR shown in Figure 77, tensile-strength data as a function of test rate at various temperatures can be combined by a temperature-time superposition. It is found that the shift factor a_T needed to superpose the data is the same as that used to superpose visco-elastic data for this polymer. In particular, the values of a_T needed agree quite well with the predictions of the WLF equation (121). This observation leads to conjecture that the variation of tensile strength with rate is merely a reflection of the fact that viscous forces retard the motion of the chains. This may easily be shown to be true.

At low strain rates the molecular network chains need only move very slowly as the sample is extended. The viscous forces, being proportional to the speed of the chains, will be very small. In addition, the chains will not lag far behind their equilibrium elongation for the stress present at any given instant. The chains will therefore exhibit the strength that is characteristic of their extended, essentially motionless state. This is exactly the condition which has been presupposed in previous sections.

It is clear from this that the tensile strength should be constant at all low rates of test, provided the rubber is warm enough so that the chains are reasonably free to move. Exceptions to this general condition can usually be traced to true viscous flow within the rubber or to crystallization phenomena. Fortunately, the usual strain rates employed in the testing laboratory are low enough to be near this insensitive range at least in the case of the common rubbers. This would not be true, as will be seen, if the testing temperature were 20°C lower or if the rubber had a glass temperature 20° higher.

As the speed of the test is increased, or as the temperature is decreased, the chains will have increasing difficulty in elongating as fast as the test requires. This is true since at higher strain rates the chains must move faster, and therefore the viscous retarding forces will be larger. Similarly, at lower temperatures the viscous forces will be larger. One would intuitively guess that at some rate of test the energy expended by the testing machine in overcoming these viscous forces will become comparable to the elastic energy it furnishes to the rubber. At this and higher strain rates, the elongation forces will be greatly increased, and the rubber will show a higher tensile strength.

These ideas may be expressed in mathematical terms. Actual calculations have been made for small to moderate strain rates, and the expected behavior is found (126). It is also found that the temperature-time superposition should be valid. In simplest terms, this means that an increase in strain rate would change the tensile strength in the same way as a decrease in temperature. Unfortunately, the theory breaks down at higher strain rates because of the mathematical approximations made.

At very high test rates or at temperatures approaching the glass temperature, a somewhat different way of looking at the molecular processes proves convenient. Under these conditions, the network chains are far from being fully extended at the instant of break. The fracture is brittle in nature and is much as would be expected for a glassy plastic. Upon referring to Figure 81, it is seen that in a slow test near break the chains traverse a given cross section of the sample only once. They have had time to become fully elongated, and this would be the condition in a slow test.

During a fast test, however, the chains are still rather coiled and traverse the sample cross section several times. Since there are several times more bonds holding the load across a given cross section in a fast test than in a slow test, the strength in a fast test should be much larger than in a slow test. This reasoning can be expressed mathematically and a quantitative result obtained for the tensile strength (126). It predicts that the tensile strength at high test rates should rise almost linearly with the logarithm of the test rate. Since the chains will not have ex-

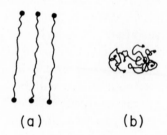

(a)   (b)

Figure 81. Typical network chain configurations just before break in (a) a slow test and (b) a fast test.

tended far enough in such a test for the crosslinks to be of much importance, the reasoning should be the same for all polymers. In fact, the tensile strength of a material such as molten polystyrene evidences much the same behavior as rubber under fast tests. The broken line in Figure 77 shows the slope of the tensile-strength curve for polystyrene, and it is noticed here that the behavior is essentially the same as that for SBR.

The above lines of thought indicate clearly that the tensile strength at a fixed temperature is intimately related to the glass temperature of the rubber. For example, if tests are carried out at room temperature, the tensile strength of a rubber having $T_g = -60°C$ should be much lower than for a similar rubber having $T_g = -20°C$. In the first case the frictional forces experienced by the network chains will be very low, and all ordinary test rates will be slow enough for the chains to elongate readily as the test proceeds. In the second case the frictional forces are large, and the chains will respond only very sluggishly to the applied force. Hence the usual rates of test will be too fast for the chains to elongate as rapidly as the test requires. This expected relation between tensile strength and glass temperature is actually found to be in accordance with the experimental data (127). These aspects will be discussed more fully in Sec.11.4.

PROBLEMS

1. Eq. (10.5) implies that the tensile strength is proportional to $\nu^{2/3}$. If this were the only factor involved and if an NR sample has a strength of 3000 psi for $M_c = 6000$, what should its strength be for $M_c = 48,000$.

2. As a very crude approximation, represent a vulcanized rubber sample by a Kelvin element with $E = 1000$ psi and $\tau = 0.10$ sec. Suppose the sample breaks when the tension in the spring is 3000 psi. Plot the stress-strain curve to break for such a model at each of the following test rates: 1.0 sec^{-1}, 10 sec^{-1}, and 100 sec^{-1}. What is the magnitude of the tensile strength in each case?

3. A noncrystalline, unvulcanized polymer of high molecular weight behaves in many ways like a rubber if the temperature is high enough. The entanglements provide an unstable crosslinked network. What would you predict for the tensile strength of such a molten polymer as a function of test rate? Give particular attention to the approximate absolute magnitude of the strength at moderate to very slow test rates.

4. A very lightly crosslinked natural-rubber sheet is subjected to a tensile force in the plane of the sheet. While the sheet is highly extended in the direction of the force, it is crosslinked to an M_c of about 6000. Discuss the strength properties of the resultant sheet.

Chapter 11

PROPERTIES OF POLYMERIC GLASSES

1. Introduction

The viscosity and elasticity properties of a rubbery or fluid polymer are dependent primarily upon the chainlike nature of the molecules. Although the absolute rate at which the chains move about is a function of the exact chemical nature of the chains, this variation in rate of motion can be readily expressed for all chains in terms of the WLF equation. Hence, the viscoelastic response of various polymers can be expressed in such a way that, when properly corrected for variations in glass temperatures, the response is nearly independent of the chemical structure of the molecules. This is a strong unifying factor that permits discussion of the viscoelastic behavior of all polymers without delving into the exact constitution of each molecule concerned. It makes possible the description of polymer behavior in terms of the submolecule model used so extensively in the previous chapters.

Even so, it was noticed from time to time in the preceding chapters that certain short-time phenomena could not be handled adequately by using the submolecule approach. In particular, all modes of motion of the chain that split the chain into very small sections are not reliably described by the submolecule or freely rotating segment approximation. These modes of motion are important for responses that occur in times comparable to the retardation times of such modes. It was shown in Chap-

246

ter 6 that the response time or retardation time of the n'th mode is

$$\tau_n = 4\eta/\pi^2 \nu k T n^2 \tag{11.1}$$

The n'th mode of motion splits the chain into essentially equal sections. If these sections become so small that the section can no longer be considered a freely orienting segment, then responses of the polymer system that take a time less than τ_n cannot be described well by use of the submolecule and freely orienting chain-segment approximations. Then the actual structure of the polymer segments must be considered.

It was pointed out in Chapter 4 that the segmental jump frequency at the glass temperature is of the order of one jump every 10 sec. From this information it is inferred that the retardation time associated with a chain segment will be of the order of 10 sec. This is not an exact correspondence, of course, but the order of magnitude must be correctly given by such reasoning. With this fact in mind, it is clear that near the glass temperature of a polymer one will be unable to properly describe the polymer response that requires a time of a few seconds or less, unless account is taken of the actual structure of the segments. At temperatures below the glass temperature, all but the extremely long-time response of the plastic will be the result of movements within the individual segments. Long-range motion of the chains will take such a long time that most practical measurements will not be influenced by it.

From these considerations it is apparent that the mechanical response of plastics in the glassy state is primarily dependent upon the internal motion of the chain segments. It is expected that regularity of response between chemically different chains will not be nearly so common as was found for chains above the glass temperature. Although this will generally be the case for the materials and properties discussed in this chapter, certain correlating features will be found that give a common basis to the behavior of all glassy polymers. This characteristic is especially true in the case of the ultimate properties.

2. Creep Behavior

The response of plastics to constant tensile stress has been quite widely studied. Since the elongations of plastics below their glass temperatures are usually only 1 or 2 per cent, even if relatively large stresses are applied for fairly long times, a formidable problem arises. If low stresses are used so that linear behavior is assumed, then the elongations are so small that there is great difficulty in carrying out the measurements. For this reason, most creep investigations have been carried out at relatively high stresses. Even though such measurements are of marked practical importance, they are not too useful from a purely scientific standpoint unless some knowledge is available concerning nonlinearity in the system.

A. POLYSTYRENE

A typical, fairly well-studied plastic is polystyrene. It should be remembered while analyzing data on this polymer that commercial polystyrene has $T_g = 83°C$ rather than the 100°C characteristic of purified polystyrene. The difference in values is apparently the result of the plasticizing action of residual monomer and other low-molecular-weight molecules. In any event, creep measurements under various applied stresses have been carried out for polystyrene, and some of the excellent data of Sauer, Marin, and Hsiao (128) are shown in Figure 82.

From Figure 82 it is clear that a comparatively large and nearly instantaneous deformation occurs when the load is applied. At the lower stresses at least, the deformation that has occurred during the first few minutes of the test is much larger than the creep that takes place during the next thousand hours. From such data alone it is not possible to say whether or not this nearly instantaneous deformation is the result of elastic stretching of bonds or whether it also involves some viscous motion as well. To settle this point, measurements are needed as a function of temperature. The elastic response should be essentially instantaneous and, being nonviscous in nature, should depend only slightly on temperature. The viscous response, on the other hand, should be temperature-sensitive, and the nearly instantaneous portion of this response should decrease with decreasing temperature. There is reason to suspect that a sizable portion of this initial response shown in Figure 82 is viscous response. (Note that "viscous response" as used here is not synonymous with "viscous flow." In this context the term merely infers that the elastic response is viscosity-controlled in so far as its rate is concerned.)

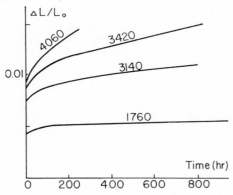

Figure 82.   Creep of polystyrene (128) at 77°F. The numbers on the curves give the applied stress in psi.

A second feature apparent from Figure 82 is the fact that the material does not obey Hooke's law in the region of stresses shown there; that is to say, the strain does not vary linearly with stress. This observation is not surprising since the stresses are really quite large. It is not a simple matter to express exactly this nonlinearity between stress and strain, since different portions of the same curves exhibit different nonlinear effects when comparing two curves. However, because this effect is not extremely large, a rough measure of the nonlinearity can be obtained by comparing the slopes of the creep curves at long times. It will be appreciated from the discussions of previous chapters that this nearly straight-line form of the curves at long times is more apparent than real. A plot extended over a much larger time scale would almost surely not be a straight line.

Be this as it may, an investigation of the long-time slopes as a function of stress is still of some value. Findley (129) has analyzed the slopes of the curves in Figure 82, as well as those for some of his own data at lower stresses. He finds that the slopes of the creep curves 1000 hours after the load is applied give the curve for creep rate versus stress shown in Figure 83. Notice

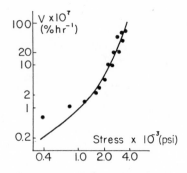

Figure 83.   Creep of polystyrene at 77°F as found from experiment (128, 129) (points) and as predicted by Eq. (11.2) (solid line).

that the data shown there extend down to 400 psi, where one would expect Hooke's law to begin to apply. Findley attempted to accommodate these data by a relation of form

$$v = 26 \times 10^{-7} \sinh (\sigma/540) \qquad (11.2)$$

where v is the relative creep rate in per cent per hour, and σ is measured in psi. This equation is shown as the solid curve in Figure 83, and the agreement is reasonably good.

Equation (11.2) is interesting in several respects. First, it reduces to a Hooke's law form in terms of stress-strain at low stresses, since sinh (x) is approximately x at small values of x:

$$10^7 v = (2\%_{540})\sigma \qquad \text{for } (\sigma/540) \ll 1 \qquad (11.3)$$

The relation given by Eq. (11.2) is also noteworthy in that it is of a form often encountered when Eyring's theory of rate processes is applied to highly nonequilibrium conditions. To show how this comes about, consider the following molecular situation. Suppose that an atom or small group of atoms along a chain is subject to a rather large force σ_0 in a certain direction. Furthermore, suppose that the unit under consideration is constrained by surrounding atoms to remain fixed in the position in which it finds itself. If the unit is to move to a new position, it is assumed that it must pass through a nonequilibrium transition state which has a higher free energy than the normal state of the unit.

As a crude picture of the situation, it can be said that the unit must exert large forces and do substantial work to move from one position to another. In the absence of an applied force, this movement can only occur if the unit obtains much more than the average amount of thermal energy. According to Boltzmann's relation the probability that the unit will acquire enough energy to move to a new position is proportional to $\exp(-E_0/kT)$, where E_0 is the energy needed by the unit if it is to move.

Consider the case of a unit that experiences an external force σ_0 in the x direction. The problem is greatly simplified if one assumes the unit can only move in two directions, parallel or antiparallel to the direction of σ_0. Refer to the energy-distance diagram shown schematically in Figure 84. The unit under consideration oscillates about the point 0 as a result of its thermal motion. At low temperatures only a very few of these identical units in the sample have enough thermal energy to surmount the potential barrier of height E_0 and move into a new equilibrium position. In the absence of external forces, equal numbers of units will move in both the plus and minus x directions; hence the sample as a whole remains unchanged.

When an outside tensile force is applied to the sample, each unit will experience an average force σ_0 in the x direction. If now a unit attempts to cross the energy barrier in the $+x$ direction, it need only possess a thermal energy $(E_0 - \sigma_0\delta)$, as shown in Figure 84. This is a result of the fact that the force σ_0 does

$\sigma_0\delta$ work on the unit as it moves through the distance δ from the equilibrium position to the peak of the energy barrier. It is clear that the applied force lowers the amount of thermal energy which the unit must possess to reach a given point on the energy barrier. The actual thermal energy needed by the unit to reach

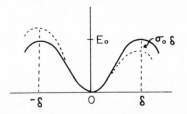

Figure 84.   Energy diagram for a polymer segment in the presence of an applied stress.

any given point away from the equilibrium position is shown by the dotted curve in Figure 84. Then the probability that a unit will move in the $+x$ direction to a new equilibrium position is

$$P_+ = P_{00} \exp\left[-(E_0 - \sigma_0\delta)/kT\right] \tag{11.4}$$

where P_{00} is a frequency factor. Similarly, the probability that a unit will move in the $-x$ direction is

$$P_- = P_{00} \exp\left[-(E_0 + \sigma_0\delta)/kT\right] \tag{11.5}$$

If there are n such units in the sample, the net flow of units in the $+x$ direction is

$$\text{Net flow} = n(P_+ - P_-) \tag{11.6}$$

Substituting in Eq. (11.6) from Eqs. (11.4) and (11.5),

$$\text{Net flow} = nP_0[\exp\left(\sigma_0\delta/kT\right) - \exp\left(-\sigma_0\delta/kT\right)]/2 \tag{11.7}$$

where

$$P_0 = 2P_{00} \exp\left[-E_0/kT\right]$$

But from the definition of the hyperbolic sine, in place of Eq. (11.7) one has

$$\text{Net flow} = nP_0 \sinh\left(\sigma_0\delta/kT\right) \tag{11.8}$$

which is identical in form to Eq. (11.2). Although Eq. (11.8) is couched in terms of molecular quantities, it is clear that σ must be proportional to σ_0. One could, of course, speculate that the ratio of σ_0 to σ would be about the same as the ratio of the cross section of a unit to unity; hence σ_0 would be equal to $A\sigma$, where A is the cross-section area of a unit. Since $A\delta$ would be of the order of the volume of a unit (V), Eq. (11.8) would be replaced by

$$\text{Net flow} = nP_0 \sinh (\sigma V/kT) \qquad (11.9)$$

Moreover, the work done on the units in the sample must equal the work done by the applied stress. This work will be proportional to net flow times σ_0 or to $v\sigma$, depending upon whether the problem is viewed from the molecular or from the laboratory measurement standpoint. Therefore, in place of Eq. (11.9), one has the relation

$$v = (\text{constant}) \sinh (\sigma V/kT) \qquad (11.10)$$

which is very similar to Eq. (11.2).

By comparing Eq. (11.2) with Eq. (11.10) it is apparent that

$$V/kT = \text{constant}/540 \qquad (11.11)$$

where the constant is needed to change the units of σ from psi to dynes/cm^2. Solving for V, one finds that V is equal to $(6 \times 10^{-8} \text{ cm})^3$. Hence the unit used for this discussion, if it were cubical in form, would be about 6 Å on a side. This is of the same order of magnitude as the size of a monomer unit and is therefore not an unreasonable value. In spite of this agreement, the reasoning leading to Eq. (11.10) was extremely crude, and thus not too much reliance should be placed upon it. However, the model used to obtain Eq. (11.10) is not completely unreasonable, and it has the advantage of furnishing a physical reason for the observed stress dependence of the creep at low temperatures. At temperatures much above T_g, the motion of the chain segments will be rather fast. In this region $\sigma_0\delta/kT$ will be smaller not only because T is larger but also because the applied forces will usually not be as large as in the glassy state;

hence, the hyperbolic sine can be replaced by its argument and Hooke's law will apply.

B. POLYMETHYL METHACRYLATE

The creep behavior of polymethyl methacrylate (PMMA) has also been measured (38). Once again the commercial polymers made from methyl methacrylate often are not pure. Although the presence of monomer is not a problem for this polymer, different grades of the commercial polymers have T_g values substantially different from each other and from the value of 105°C characteristic of the pure polymer. These differences are, in some cases at least, the result of copolymerization with other acrylates or methacrylates. For this reason, there is some difficulty associated with the comparison of data from different sources.

Two rather complete investigations of pure PMMA have been made, one using creep methods (38) and the other using stress relaxation (48,55). Both experiments worked in the region of low stress, so that the stress-strain behavior was essentially linear. Data were taken in the rubbery as well as the glassy region and were reduced by using the temperature-time superposition. These data are shown in Figures 85 and 86.

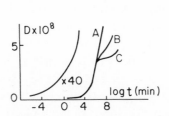

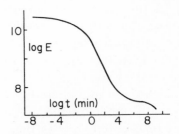

Figure 85. Tensile creep D of polymethyl methacrylate (38) at 110°C. Curves A, B, and C are for molecular weights of 2.0, 6.5, and 41 × 10⁵, respectively. The units of D are cm²/dyne

Figure 86. Stress relaxation of a polymethyl methacrylate (48) at 110°C. The units of E are dynes/cm².

It is apparent that even at the shortest times reached experimentally that the elongation is still being retarded by viscous forces. For this reason one would suspect that a temperature-time superposition procedure would be valid even in the glass state. The available experimental data indicate that this is at least approximately true; nonetheless, one complication is apparent.

If one refers to Figure 20 in Chapter 4, the apparent energy of activation for the viscoelastic behavior of PMMA is seen to behave rather queerly below T_g, which is about 105°C. The data shown in Figure 20 were obtained in the course of the measurements leading to the curves of Figure 85. A similar behavior was found from the variation of stress relaxation with temperature when the data of Figure 86 were obtained (48,55). Although the discussion in Chapter 4 explained the reason for the increase in apparent activation energy as the temperature is lowered to T_g, no reason was given there for the rapid *decrease* of activation energy with decreasing temperature below T_g. The explanation for this behavior will now be given.

In order to understand why the apparent energy of activation decreases rapidly below T_g, one must first be aware of the physical meaning of the term "apparent activation energy." Although the mathematical definition of this quantity has been given in Chapter 4, a qualitative statement concerning it may not be out of place here. The activation energy is a measure of the way in which the rate of deformation changes with temperature. If the creep behavior of a material was identical at two different temperatures, the rate of deformation would be independent of temperature, and the apparent activation energy would be zero. On the other hand, the apparent activation energy will be very large if a temperature increase of a few degrees changes the rate of elongation by a large factor. Hence, the decrease in apparent activation energy below T_g is equivalent to the observation that the rate of molecular motion does not decrease very fast as the temperature is lowered.

Actually, this is exactly the behavior which would be predicted from the very nature of the glass temperature. It was pointed out in Chapter 4 that the glass temperature was the temperature at which the molecules were moving so slowly that they could not equilibrate during the time of the test measurement. If it were true that *no* change in free volume and mobility could occur below T_g (which would be equivalent to shock cooling with no opportunity allowed for equilibration), then the rate of elongation should remain constant at all temperatures below T_g. As a result, the apparent energy of activation would be zero at temperatures below T_g.

This behavior is not actually observed, because the system really does equilibrate somewhat even below T_g. However, true equilibrium is generally not reached at these lower temperatures, and consequently the rate of elongation will not decrease as rapidly with decreasing temperature as might be expected. It should be also noted that the exact values of apparent activation energy at these low temperatures will depend somewhat on how long the sample is allowed to equilibrate. A comparison of the activation energies found from creep and stress relaxation by different investigators shows decided differences in the values below T_g (38,48). Apparently the methods for conditioning the samples in the two cases were different.

3. Response to Oscillatory Measurements

The application of sinusoidal vibration techniques to the study of soft polymers has been discussed in some detail in earlier chapters. It was found that the loss tangent, tan δ, or the ratio of the imaginary portion of the dynamic modulus to the real portion of the modulus was indicative of molecular motion processes. In particular, if a molecular mode of motion had a retardation time near the period of the applied driving force, the dynamic loss and tan δ were large. Because of this fact the loss tangent can be measured and used directly as an indication of the presence of molecular retardation times. For example, in Chapter 8 it was shown that a system with a single retardation time will show a maximum loss when the period of the applied force equals the retardation time. Actual molecular processes, of course, show wide loss maxima since more than a single retardation time is involved.

To illustrate the general response of glassy polymeric materials to sinusoidal excitation, use will be made of the rather extensive data of Deutsch, Hoff, and Reddish (130) for polymethyl methacrylate (PMMA) and polymethyl-α-chloroacrylate (PMCA). These polymers have essentially the same structure, except that the methyl group on the chain in PMMA is replaced by a chlorine atom in PMCA as shown by the structural formulas below:

$$
\begin{array}{cc}
\underline{\text{PMMA}} & \underline{\text{PMCA}} \\[4pt]
\text{CH}_2 & \text{Cl} \\
| & | \\
-\text{C}-\text{CH}_2- & -\text{C}-\text{CH}_2- \\
| & | \\
\text{C}=\text{O} & \text{C}=\text{O} \\
| & | \\
\text{O}-\text{CH}_3 & \text{O}-\text{CH}_3
\end{array}
$$

The glass temperature of the PMMA used was about 105°C, and that for the PMCA was about 135°C.

Although these authors acquired data over a frequency range from 10^{-2} to 50 cycles/sec, the most interesting features of their results can be seen by plotting the observed losses as a function of temperature for one frequency. Such a plot is shown in Figure 87. The frequency of the applied force in this case is 50 cycles/sec. Although data for the higher temperatures is not

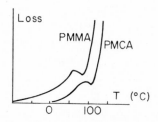

Figure 87.   Mechanical loss at 50 cps for polymethyl methacrylate and polymethyl-α-chloroacrylate (130).

shown, the curves rise to about five times the height shown and then drop once again at still higher temperatures. Since these extremely high loss peaks occur somewhat above the glass temperature in each case, they represent the losses due to the chain retardation times discussed in earlier chapters. These retardation times correspond to long-range motion of the polymer chains. This peak in the loss spectrum is called the "alpha peak" or "relaxation."

A second loss peak is noticed at temperatures below the glass temperature. This is the so-called "beta peak." As pointed out above, a loss peak means that the frequency of some molecular mode of motion is close to the applied frequency. Since it is clear that the segmental motion of the chain backbone will be much slower than the 50 cycles/sec of the driving force, the loss peak at low temperatures cannot be explained by chain-backbone motion. It is necessary to look for a molecular motion that is still relatively free even at these reduced temperatures.

The only obvious possibility for a fast molecular motion at low temperatures in these materials appears to be motion within the pendant side groups. Three possibilities exist. The motion of the —CH_3 group about the bond between it and the oxygen atom as axis is obviously quite free and would therefore persist well below the glass temperature. This motion does not involve the rotation of any sizable dipole and should therefore give rise to no sizable dipolar dispersion. As will be discussed in more detail in Chapter 12, the dielectric data for both of these polymers (130) indicate the presence of a dipole dispersion associated with the beta loss peak. Hence, the rotation of the —CH_3 group by itself does not appear to be the cause of this loss peak.

A second alternative would be the rotation of the O—CH_3 bond on the valence cone. This motion would involve the rotation of the O—CH_3 dipole and would give rise to a dipole dispersion such as observed; hence, this motion is a possible source of the beta dispersion.

The third possibility would be the rotation of the whole side group about the C—C bond as axis. Once again, the rotation of a dipole is involved, and thus the dielectric data would be explainable. It appears that this latter type of motion will be the slowest of the three motions discussed, since it involves the motion of the largest group of atoms. Since no other loss peak occurs between the alpha and the beta loss peaks, this third type of motion must be responsible in part at least for the beta dispersion.

One cannot be absolutely sure that the second mechanism, the O—CH$_3$ bond rotation, is not also the cause of a portion of the beta dispersion. It would appear that the rotation of this bond would be a higher frequency, and hence a lower temperature, dispersion than that for the side group as a whole. However, these two types of motion might well be close enough in frequency to give rise to a single loss peak. This view is made plausible by the fact that no further loss peaks occur at lower temperatures at least down to −100°C. [Certain investigators (131) have recently reported a third loss peak at very low temperatures, but the exact cause of this peak is still in doubt.]

The dynamic storage modulus also reflects these various molecular motions. However, data for the same polymers as were used to obtain Figure 87 are shown in Figure 88, and it is seen

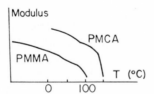

Figure 88. Dynamic modulus at 50 cps for polymethyl methacrylate and polymethyl-α-chloroacrylate (130).

that the dispersions are not nearly so readily discerned. It is therefore apparent that loss measurements in the glassy state are more easily used for interpretation purposes than are data for the storage modulus alone. However, it is noteworthy that the storage modulus is still less than 10^{11} dynes/cm^2 even at very low temperatures. This is still a factor of 10 less than the modulus of the diamond lattice. One therefore infers that motion is still somewhat free even at these temperatures. However, it would not be safe to conclude that these polymers should show the same modulus as the diamond lattice if all motion ceased, since the lattice structure is tighter in the case of diamond than in the polymers treated here.

An apparent activation energy for both the alpha and beta processes can be obtained from oscillatory measurements over a frequency range at each of several temperatures. Depending upon the temperature range of the measurements, the value of the apparent activation energy for the alpha process may be anywhere from about 30 to 200 kcal/mole, as is shown in Figure 20 of Chapter 4. It is not surprising then that the value quoted by Deutsch and his associates for PMMA is about 80 kcal/mole.

The beta process, however, should not require the same energy for activation as does the alpha relaxation. In particular, a lower activation energy should be disclosed for the beta process. Actually, for PMMA the value is found (130) to be about 20 kcal/mole, while for PMCA it is about 28 kcal/mole. This difference in values in the two cases is not too easily interpreted since the rotating groups are the same in each case. However, in view of the fact that the surroundings of the pendant side groups are not the same in the two cases because of the presence of the Cl atom in PMCA, it is perhaps not too surprising that a small difference does exist.

It is important to notice that the difference in activation energy between the alpha and beta processes makes the temperature-time superposition invalid in these regions. This is true for the following reason. The superposition procedure assumes that, for example, the loss curve as a function of log frequency will appear the same at one temperature as at another, except that the log-frequency scales will be displaced. A set of two loss peaks, such as the alpha and beta peaks, that have a frequency separation of six decades at one temperature should show this same separation at any other temperature if the superposition is valid.

In the present case, however, the molecular motion responsible for the alpha process has a higher activation energy than that for the beta process, at least in certain temperature intervals. Hence, if the beta-process response is six decades faster than the alpha response at one temperature, it will actually be less than six decades faster at a higher temperature. For this reason the loss peaks will not have the same log-frequency separation at two different temperatures, and the data cannot be superposed. The temperature-time superposition is therefore not applicable to a range of measurements that includes visible evidence of both processes. Fortunately, at temperatures above T_g the observed response is so fast that the beta relaxation occurs almost instantaneously. Since the longer-time portions of the response all have the same activation energy, the superposition procedure will apply to them. The fact that the essentially instantaneous response does not superpose properly is of no consequence, since the details of this portion of the response cannot be resolved by the common methods of measurement. Some light has been shed on these questions by a systematic study of a large series of methacrylates (132).

Near and below T_g, however, the beta response will become slow enough so that it can be resolved in detail by using ordinary measuring techniques. Under these circumstances one will observe anomalies when applying the superposition precedure to a wide range of frequencies or measurement times. Nevertheless, it is still possible to apply the temperature-time superposition procedure to a given portion of the response curve; for example, the alpha response region and the response at longer times will be susceptible to superposition. Since it is these responses which presumably give rise to most of the observed creep and stress-relaxation behavior even appreciably below T_g, the superposition procedure is still valid at long times. Some uncertainty exists, however, as to the respective contributions of the alpha and beta mechanisms to creep response at very low temperatures.

4. Tensile Strength of Plastics

Glassy plastics characteristically exhibit tensile strengths of several thousand pounds per square inch and ultimate elongations less than about 5 per cent. Since plastics are rubbers which have been cooled below T_g, there must be a gradual transition from a strong, brittle (i.e., low ultimate elongation) plastic to a more or less weak, soft rubber as the temperature of the material is raised from below T_g to well above it. Crosslinked polystyrene at 170°C would be expected to behave much the same as SBR at 20°C, since these temperatures are about 70° above the glass temperature in each case. This expectation is actually true, of course, and it is known that crosslinked polystyrene behaves like any other noncrystallizing rubber provided that the temperature is high enough. Therefore it is not possible to distinguish completely between the strength behavior of rubbers and plastics.

As pointed out in the last chapter, rubbers acquire a strength very close to that of a glass if the rate of test is very high. This development was a result of the fact that at high test rates the chains were unable to elongate fast enough under the combined action of the viscous and applied forces. Since each chain was still quite coiled even at the instant the sample broke, there were several bonds from each chain holding the load on a given cross section. Under slow tests, because the chains were nearly fully elongated upon breaking, each chain furnished only one bond to hold the load on a given cross section. It is this factor which causes a polymer to have much higher strength at low temperatures (where it is a glass) than it has at high temperatures (where it is a rubber).

It follows, of course, from the above reasoning that a plastic below its glass temperature will act like a rubber as far as its ultimate strength and elongation are concerned, provided that the test rate is very slow. In practice, the test rate is not nearly slow enough to show this effect. However, it is well known that if a stress somewhat below the ultimate stress is applied to a sample, the sample will eventually break under this stress. This is merely a reflection of the fact that, at the time of the break, the chains have elongated so much that the number of load-holding bonds remaining on a given cross section is not sufficient to support the stress. These ideas may be put on a semiquantitative basis as follows (133).

Consider the coiled polymer chain shown in Figure 89. It coils through the cross section of the sample marked by the dotted

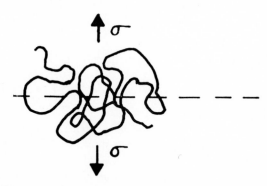

Figure 89.   Diagram of a molecule in the position it might occupy at the instant a stress is applied to the sample.

line in that figure at a number of places. At the instant the stress σ is applied to the sample, each segment that passes through the cross section helps to support the stress. As time goes on and the chain elongates more fully, it will pass through the cross section less often and will furnish fewer segments to hold the stress on that cross section. Finally, at long times the chain will be fully elongated as in Figure 90a, and only one of its segments will be holding the load on the cross section under consideration.

To put these ideas in quantitative terms, it is observed that the time taken for the chain to reach the situation pictured in Figure 90a is approximately equal to τ_1. The quantity τ_1, the longest retardation time of the chain, is given by Eq. (9.9), which is rewritten here as

$$\tau_1 = f'N^2a^2/3\pi^2kT \qquad (11.12)$$

The reason for the use of f' instead of f_0 will be explained below. Since $\tau_2 = \tau_1/2^2$ is the time taken for half of the chain to adjust under the applied forces (i.e., it is the retardation time of the second mode of motion), the configuration shown in Figure 90*b*

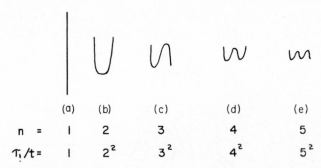

	(a)	(b)	(c)	(d)	(e)
n =	1	2	3	4	5
τ_1/t =	1	2^2	3^2	4^2	5^2

Figure 90. Schematic diagrams showing the general outline of chain configurations at various times after the application of a large stress.

will be typical of the chain at a time $\tau_1/2^2$ after the load is applied. Similarly, the diagrams of Figure 90*c*, *d*, and *e* show in a schematic way the chain configurations at times of $\tau_1/9$, $\tau_1/16$, and $\tau_1/25$ after the stress was applied. Hence at any time τ_1/n^2 after the load is applied to the sample, the number of segments of a given chain that are holding the stress across a given cross section will be proportional to n. However, since there are only N segments in the chain, n has a maximum value equal to N.

These considerations lead to the following picture. At very short times, there will be $1/A$ chain segments holding the stress σ on a given unit cross section, where A is the cross-sectional area of a segment. This will still be approximately the case at a time equal to τ_1/N^2 after the load is applied. At a slightly longer time, $t = \tau_1/(N-1)^2$, each chain will fold only $(N-1)$ times instead of N times, and the number of chain segments holding the load on the original unit cross section will also be reduced to a new value, $(N-1)/AN$. This process may be extended as shown below to give the number of segments holding the load as a function of time.

Time	Number
τ_1/N^2	$(1/A)$
$\tau_1/(N-1)^2$	$(1/A)(N-1)/N$
$\tau_1/(N-2)^2$	$(1/A)(N-2)/N$
$\tau_1/(N-3)^2$	$(1/A)(N-3)/N$
$\cdot$	$\cdot$
$\cdot$	$\cdot$
$\cdot$	$\cdot$
$\tau_1/2$	$(1/A)(2/N)$
τ_1	$(1/A)(1/N)$

Therefore one has the following relation for the number of segments holding the load on a given cross section at any time t:

$$\text{Number} = (1/A)(\tau_1/N^2 t)^{1/2} \qquad (11.13)$$

If it is assumed that all segments are equally stressed and that each can hold a load F_0, the sample will break when F_0 times the number of segments is equal to the stress on the sample. The relation between stress and break time is therefore

$$\sigma = (F_0/A)(\tau_1/N^2 t_c)^{1/2} \qquad (11.14)$$

where t_c is the time at breaking. After substitution from Eq. (11.12),

$$\sigma = (F_0/A)(f'a^2/3\pi^2 k T t_c)^{1/2} \qquad (11.15)$$

However, to the accuracy of the present computation, one can set $A = a^2$, in which case the expression becomes

$$\sigma = (f'/3\pi^2 k T t_c)^{1/2}(F_0/a) \qquad (11.16)$$

It would appear at first glance that Eq. (11.16) predicts the time to break would vary inversely as the square of the stress. This prediction is not true, however. Since f', the segmental friction factor, is related to the jump frequency ϕ by the relation [see Eq. (3.8)]

$$f' = 6kT/a^2\phi' \qquad (11.17)$$

Eq. (11.16) can be rewritten as

$$\sigma^2 = (2/\pi^2)(F_0^2/a^4\phi')(1/t_c) \qquad (11.18)$$

But ϕ', the jump frequency, becomes dependent upon stress at very high stresses. The primes on ϕ' and f' were placed there to indicate that these quantities were not the same as found under low stresses. This dependence of ϕ on stress has already been considered in Sec. 11.2A, where it was found that the probability of a segment jumping in the direction of the stress was higher than its probability for jumping in the opposite direction. Since the jump frequency in the absence of the stress in the case of a plastic is usually very small, the large stresses needed to break the sample will usually cause the reverse-direction jump rate to be negligibly small in comparison to the jump rate in the direction of the stress. Hence, one has from Eq. (11.4) the fact that the jump rate without stress (ϕ) is related to the jump rate with stress by

$$\phi' = \phi \exp (\sigma_0 \delta / kT) \qquad (11.19)$$

The quantity σ_0 is the stress on a segment. At the instant the stress is applied to the sample, $\sigma_0(1/A) = \sigma$. Since the elongation of most plastics at the instant of break is only a few per cent, this relation between σ_0 and σ can be considered to be nearly true independent of time. With this assumption Eq. (11.18) becomes

$$\phi \sigma^2 t_c = (2/\pi^2)(F_0^2/a^4) \exp (-\sigma V / kT) \qquad (11.20)$$

where $V = A\delta$ is essentially the volume of a segment. Taking logarithms, one has

$$\sigma = -(kT/V) \ln (\phi t_c) + \psi \qquad (11.21)$$

where

$$\psi = (kT/V) \ln (2F_0^2/\pi^2 \sigma^2 a^4)$$

Although the function ψ is not strictly a constant, the range of strengths to which Eq. (11.21) will be applicable is from about 10^4 to 10^3 psi. It is obvious from the form of Eq. (11.21) that the major portion of this change in σ must come from the term involving t_c. With this fact in mind, the second term in Eq. (11.21) can be considered nearly constant. Equation (11.21) is then the equation of a straight line when σ is plotted against $\ln (t_c)$. The slope of the line is negative and is equal to kT/V.

Typical data showing the time taken for a plastic to break under various constant loads are shown in Figures 91 and 92 (133). The data shown in Figure 91 are for polystyrene, while the data in Figure 92 are for polyethyl methacrylate. In

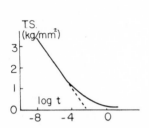

Figure 91. Time taken for polystyrene to break under various constant loads (133) at 120°C. The time units are minutes.

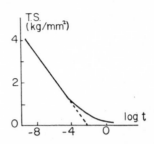

Figure 92. Time taken for polyethyl methacrylate to break under various constant loads (133) at 102°C. The time units are minutes.

each case the data were acquired at various temperatures and then superposed by shifting the data along the log-time axis in the usual way. Since a nearly straight-line dependence is observed in the glassy, high-strength region in each case, the quantity V can be evaluated by use of Eq. (11.21); it turns out to be about $(13 \text{ Å})^3$ in both cases. This is also the value obtained from the straight-line portion of Figure 77 for SBR, which was obtained from rate-of-test measurements. In view of the simplifications used during the computation, this value for V is quite reasonable.

Another check on the meaningfulness of Eq. (11.21) can be obtained by noticing that it predicts the straight-line will yield zero strength when

$$\phi t_c = 2F_0^2/\pi^2\sigma^2a^4 \tag{11.22}$$

Some difficulty presents itself here, since an average value must be used for σ. Noticing that the extrapolated strength is zero for $t_c = 1$ sec in both Figures 91 and 92, and taking $F_0 = 5 \times 10^{-4}$ dyne and $a = 13$ Å together with $\sigma = 2000$ psi, the jump frequency ϕ is found to be about 10^{+4} jumps/sec in both cases. Since the reference temperatures for these graphs are much above T_g in both cases, this jump-frequency value is not unreasonable. Of course, it is quite approximate because of the latitude of choice for σ and F_0. In any event, the general behavior of Eq. (11.21) appears correct.

The above considerations have not been detailed enough to demonstrate the effects of segment orientation upon strength. An interesting and practical case arises if a polymer is stretched when rubbery, thereby orienting the chains, and then cooled to a glass. The resultant material should show exceptionally high strength for stresses in the direction of the previous stretching but should show poor strength in the perpendicular directions. Measurements showing this effect have been carried out, and a theory giving quantitative agreement with the data has been worked out (134,135). Typical data are shown in Figure 93, where the theoretical prediction is shown by the solid curve.

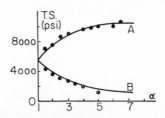

Figure 93.   Tensile strength of oriented polystyrene (134). Curve A is the theoretical prediction for the strength in the direction of orientation, and curve B is for the perpendicular direction.

Although the theory of this effect is comparatively straightforward, since only the ratio of the strength oriented to the strength unoriented is of interest, the computation is far from trivial. Essentially, it amounts to the determination of the number of chain bonds holding the load at any given degree of chain orientation. No suppositions need be made concerning rate effects since identical test conditions are assumed in all cases. The agreement between theory and experiment is quite good, as can be readily seen.

5. Flaws, Cracks, and Crazing

A plastic that has been under tensile load for a long time will often evidence a phenomena called "crazing" (136). The surface of the plastic is covered with multitudes of almost infinitesimal plateletlike cracks. These cracks always appear to lie with their planes perpendicular to the stress and apparently result from the pulling apart of small regions of the plastic under the action of the stress. It is probable that the surface is most susceptible to the craze cracks because of the fact that strains are highest in that region, although this is not known for certain. Extensive investigations have been made concerning the effects of the crazing on strength, etc. It has been found that even the highly crazed regions still possess great strength, although these regions are somewhat less strong than the noncrazed polymer (136).

From this type of behavior, however, it is apparent that the plastic is far from homogeneous. In particular, the stress will be largest near the edges of the cracks, and the sample fracture should thus start at a highly stressed region near a crack. Of course, the presence of these flaws in the plastic will decrease the strength below its theoretical limit; still, it appears that the functional relation between load and break time will not be affected by the presence of cracks.

The dynamics of fracture in terms of the rate of propagation of the crack and the exact locus of the first catastrophic event during the fracture process have been studied to some extent. It has been found that meaningful patterns are discovered on the fresh surfaces of the fractured plastic. There is also evidence that an oriented layer of molecules exists on the fracture surface (137).

Recently Berry (137) carried out an interesting study of the effect of cracks on the strength of polystyrene and polymethyl methacrylate. His investigation made use of the Griffith crack theory for tensile strength. This theory has found wide applicability in phenomenological treatments of strength. It is based upon the concept that the sample will fail when the increase in surface energy resulting from the growth of the crack is exactly equal to the loss in stored elastic energy as the crack grows. That is to say, enough elastic energy is stored near the crack to provide the energy needed to propagate the growth of the crack.

It may be demonstrated that it follows from the Griffith criterion that the tensile strength is related to the elastic modulus E, the specific surface energy γ, and the crack length $2c$ by the relation

$$\text{T.S.} = (2E\gamma/\pi c)^{1/2} \tag{11.23}$$

Hence, the tensile strength of the plastic should vary in proportion to the inverse of the square root of the crack length. By introducing artificial cracks into the plastic, Berry showed that this inverse relation appears to apply; in fact, he was able to predict that the natural cracks have c values of about 0.043 and 0.002 in. in polystyrene and polymethyl methacrylate, respectively. However, the quantity γ determined from experiment turns out to be much larger than would be expected on the basis of the energy required to break bonds as the crack grows. The energy needed to break bonds along the fracture surface is in the order of 10^2 ergs/cm^2. Berry found the experimental value of γ to be a factor of 10^4 larger than this and concluded that the energy required to propagate the crack was largely expended doing viscous work. This conclusion is to be expected from the theoretical considerations of the previous sections. It also fits quite well with the idea that an oriented molecular layer exists at the fracture surface.

PROBLEMS

1. At 217°C, polystyrene with $M = 10^5$ has a viscosity of about 3000 poise. What is the n value for the mode of motion of this chain which splits the chain into segments one monomer long? What is the retardation time for this mode of motion?

2. It has been suggested that the true equilibrium value for the free volume

in a glassy polymer could be more easily attained if the polymer were first swollen in the vapor of a good solvent and then dried. This swelling-drying operation is to be carried out isothermally at the temperature below T_g in question. What do you think about this idea? Give reasons for your answer.

3. Would you expect the Boltzmann superposition principle of Sec. 7.8 to apply to the creep data for glassy plastics discussed in Chapter 11? Explain your answer.

4. A very crude way of representing a material having both an α and β dispersion would be to represent it by two Kelvin elements in series. As an example, let the constants for these elements at a particular temperature be $E_1 = 10^{10}$ dynes/cm^2, $\eta_1 = 10^3$ poise, $E_2 = 10^6$ dynes/cm^2, and $\eta_2 = 10^5$ poise. Plot the D' and D'' vs. log ω curves for this system when excited by a force $\sigma = \sigma_0 \cos \omega t$.

5. For the system of problem 4, suppose the energy of activation for the α process is 80 Kcal/mole and that for the β process is 20 Kcal/mole. (Assume η varies with temperature but E does not.) Replot the curves of problem 4 for a temperature 20°C lower than the temperature for which the parameters of the elements are given.

Chapter 12

DIELECTRIC AND NUCLEAR MAGNETIC
RESONANCE BEHAVIOR

1. Measurement of Dipole Moments of Polar Polymers

It is well known that the dielectric constant ϵ of a polar liquid is
much larger than that for a nonpolar liquid. This is a reflection
of the fact that dipoles in the liquid tend to line up in the direction of any applied electric field and thereby contribute additional polarization to the liquid. Such will also be the case in
molten polymers and even in solid polymers if the dipoles are
able to orient with the applied electric field. The exact magnitude of the polarization due to the dipole orientation of molecules
with average dipole moment $\bar{\mu}$ is

$$P_0 = 4\pi\bar{\mu}^2\mathbf{N}/9kT \tag{12.1}$$

where $\mathbf{N}$ is Avogadro's number, and P_0 is called the "orientational polarization."

Another contribution to the total molecular polarization comes
from the dipoles induced in the molecules by the applied electric field. This induced polarization P_I and the orientational
polarization P_0 are related to the observed dielectric constant of
the material through the relation

$$[(\epsilon - 1)/(\epsilon + 2)](M/d) = P_I + P_0 \tag{12.2}$$

where M and d are the molecular weight of the molecule and
the density of the material, respectively.

Although the frequency dependence of the dielectric constant will be considered in more detail later in this chapter, it is of interest to examine this behavior qualitatively at this point. If the applied electric field is impressed upon the liquid by placing it between two plates of a condenser, the charge on the condenser, and hence the field in the dielectric liquid, will depend upon the voltage impressed on the condenser. If a direct current voltage source is used, the dipoles in the liquid will have a long time in which to line up with the field. Unless they are actually frozen in place in the liquid (in this case it would be a solid), the dipoles will tend to line up under the action of the electric field, thereby making P_0 large. Also, of course, the molecules will polarize under the action of the field and give rise to a finite value for P_I. From the form of Eq. (12.2) it is evident that the larger $P_I + P_0$ is, the larger will be the dielectric constant ϵ of the material.

If the voltage applied to the condenser is alternating, then the electric field will reverse itself $\omega/2\pi$ times per sec, where $\omega/2\pi$ is the frequency of the alternating voltage source. The dipoles must therefore reverse their direction $\omega/2\pi$ times per sec if they are to remain aligned with the electric field. The induced polarization P_I of the molecules is the result of small displacements of electrons within the atoms, and these displacements will also alternate with frequency $\omega/2\pi$. As long as the movements giving rise to P_I and P_0 can keep up with the alternating electric field, the values of P_I and P_0 will remain constant. The dielectric constant will also remain constant as long as this is true.

Since it is known that the electrons can move extremely rapidly within the atoms, P_I would not be expected to change with frequency. The induced polarization is able to follow fluctuating electric fields even as high as the optical frequency range. The orientation polarization, being the result of the rotation of groups of atoms that form a dipole, will not be able to follow extremely high-frequency oscillations of the electric field. As the dipoles rotate to keep alternating in step with the electric field, they experience viscous forces proportional to the velocity of rotation. If the frequency of the applied voltage becomes too high, the dipoles will be moving too sluggishly under the action of the viscous and electric forces to respond well to the electric field. In fact, at very high frequencies, the dipoles will be completely unable to keep up with the alternating field, and their contribution to the polarization drops to zero.

Even at high frequencies, however, the induced polarization is essentially unchanged. From electromagnetic theory it may be demonstrated that the dielectric constant at optical frequencies is equal to the square of the index of refraction (more correctly, the index at very long wavelengths, n_∞), so that

$$P_I = [(n_\infty^2 - 1)/(n_\infty^2 + 2)](M/d) \qquad (12.3)$$

Therefore, if the refractive index is known, one can substitute from Eq. (12.3) into Eq. (12.2), and the orientation polarization can be computed from a knowledge of the dielectric constant. If the dipoles are able to follow the applied electric field, then Eq. (12.1) applies, and the average dipole moment for the molecules can be computed.

All the above considerations are based upon the premise that the molecular dipoles are not interacting with each other in such a way as to cause molecular association or other types of intermolecular restrictions to dipole alignment. This assumption would be true if the dipolar molecules were infinitely dilute in a nonpolar liquid. Generally, measurements on dilute solutions of dipolar molecules are extrapolated to infinite dilution in order to compute the dipole moment. For the present, however, these complicating features will be ignored. Actual experimental techniques for the measurement of dipole moments are given in several textbooks on the subject.

2. Computation of Dipole Moments of Polar Polymers

The molecular orientational polarization P_0 is a measure of the dipole contribution to the dielectric constant. This quantity is in turn given by Eq. (12.1), which shows that it is proportional to the square of the dipole moment. More precisely, upon combining Eqs. (12.1) and (12.2) and after making use of the fact that $\mathbf{N}d/M$ is the number of molecules n, then

$$(\epsilon - 1)/(\epsilon + 2) = (nP_I/\mathbf{N}) + (4\pi/9kT)\bar{\mu}^2 n \qquad (12.4)$$

It is of interest to consider the variation of the last term (the dipole term) in Eq. (12.4) as Z monomer units are polymerized to form a polymer containing Z units. Each monomer unit is assumed to have a dipole moment μ_0 that is unchanged by polymerization. To begin with, before polymerization, the contribution of the Z monomers to the last term in Eq. (12.4) is proportional to $\mu_0^2 Z$.

When the monomers are polymerized, three general limiting cases are possible. First, the polymer can be completely stiff, with all the monomeric dipoles lined up and aiding each other as illustrated in Figure 94a. Since the molecule has a dipole

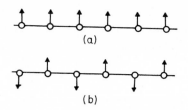

(a)

(b)

Figure 94.   Two simple models for polymer chains carrying dipoles.

moment $\mu_0 Z$, the contribution of the original Z monomer units to the last term in Eq. (12.4) will now be proportional to $\mu_0^2 Z^2$. However, if the dipoles exactly cancel each other as in Figure 94b, the contribution will be zero. On the other hand, if the dipoles are completely free to rotate in all directions with respect to each other, even though they are in the polymer molecule, their contribution will be the same as before polymerization, namely, $\mu_0^2 Z$.

Hence it is clear that the dipole-moment contribution of a polymer molecule containing Z dipoles, each of magnitude μ_0, can range all the way from zero to $\mu_0^2 Z^2$. The contribution of the free monomers was $\mu_0^2 Z$. These various values are dependent upon the way in which the polymer molecule is constructed.

Since the range of possible values is so wide, the polymer dipole moment should provide a key to its structure, an approach that will now be explored further.

It is shown in the literature that the average dipole moment $\bar{\mu}$ of a polymer containing Z identical dipoles μ is given (138) by

$$\bar{\mu}^2 = \left\langle \sum_{n=1}^{Z} \sum_{m=1}^{Z} \boldsymbol{\mu}_n \cdot \boldsymbol{\mu}_m \right\rangle_{\mathrm{av}} \tag{12.5}$$

As usual, the symbolism $\langle \boldsymbol{\mu}_n \cdot \boldsymbol{\mu}_m \rangle_{\mathrm{av}}$ means the average value of the product $\mu_n\mu_m \cos \theta$ over all chain configurations, where θ is the angle between the n'th and m'th dipoles.

Note that the problem of evaluating Eq. (12.5), and in particular each term such as $\langle \boldsymbol{\mu}_n \cdot \boldsymbol{\mu}_m \rangle_{\mathrm{av}}$, is essentially identical to the problem of finding the average projection of one chain bond upon another, that is, $\langle \mathbf{a}_j \cdot \mathbf{a}_k \rangle_{\mathrm{av}}$. This type of problem was solved for several different chain types in Chapter 1. Similar computations have been made to evaluate Eq. (12.5), but they will not be reproduced here. The answers for two cases that are easily obtained, however, will be given here.

First, consider the free-rotation case. In that instance, since dipole positions parallel and antiparallel to each other are equally probable, for free rotation

$$\langle \boldsymbol{\mu}_n \cdot \boldsymbol{\mu}_m \rangle_{\mathrm{av}} = 0 \qquad n \neq m$$
$$\langle \boldsymbol{\mu}_n \cdot \boldsymbol{\mu}_n \rangle_{\mathrm{av}} = \mu^2 \tag{12.6}$$

Substitution of these values in Eq. (12.5) yields

$$\bar{\mu}^2 = Z\mu^2 \qquad \text{(Free rotation)} \tag{12.7}$$

Therefore, the dipole contribution per monomer unit of the chain ($\bar{\mu}^2/Z$) is just equal to the dipole moment of a monomer unit. Hence, tying monomer units into a freely orienting chain does not change the dipole contribution to the dielectric constant.

Another fairly simple case to evaluate is the case of a polymer such as polyvinyl chloride with the assumption of no steric hindrance to rotation on the valence cone. Each chain bond is assumed to rotate freely on its valence cone so that, although the valence angles are preserved, no other steric factors are considered. This computation follows the general lines obtained for a similar case in Chapter 1, but the details are available in the literature (138) and will not be given here. The answer turns out to be

$$\bar{\mu}^2/Z = \mu^2(^{11}\!/_{12}) \tag{12.8}$$

provided that Z is large.

Even in this more realistic case, it is apparent that the dipole contribution is essentially unchanged by polymerization. This is perhaps not too surprising since the dipoles are not extremely tightly coupled in such a chain. However, free rotation is probably a very poor approximation even though the valence angles are preserved. This is seen to be the case from the fact that actual measurements give (138,139)

$$\bar{\mu}^2/Z = 0.75\mu^2 \qquad \text{(Polyvinyl chloride)}$$
$$\bar{\mu}^2/Z = 0.56\mu^2 \qquad \text{(Poly-}p\text{-chlorostyrene)}$$

The second polymer listed is essentially identical to polyvinyl chloride as far as dipole position is concerned. The only difference is in the added steric hindrance provided by the bulky benzene-type ring. Obviously, the assumption of free rotation that leads to Eq. (12.8) is not valid.

Some work has been done to relate the observed dipole moment of polymer molecules to steric hindrance along the chain. Such work, unless coupled with other measurements such as the determination of molecular size, has not been especially useful. It has been found that copolymerization behavior can be elucidated to some extent by the study of the dipole moment of a copolymer of a monomer containing a rigid dipole together with a monomer without a dipole (140). It should not be overlooked that the dipole moment of a polymer chain is one of the few ways in which reliable data can be obtained concerning the freedom of internal motion of a chain.

3. Dielectric Dispersion; Theory for Small Molecules

If a dipole system is subjected to an alternating electric field, the contribution of the dipoles to the dielectric polarization will depend upon the frequency of the applied voltage. As shown in Sec. 12.1, the dipoles are unable to rotate fast enough to keep up with the field at very high frequencies, and the orientational polarization drops to zero. This effect may be described in several nearly equivalent ways. A detailed discussion is given in the excellent book by Frohlich (141). It will be sufficient for the present purposes to discuss a simplified model that has been used by several authors.

Suppose a dipole can only orient in two positions, one parallel and one antiparallel to the x axis. This dipole, of moment μ, will for the present be assumed rigidly fixed to a small molecule. Furthermore, it will be assumed that for the molecule to rotate from its one equilibrium position to the other, an activation energy E_0 is required. The chance that a given molecule has enough energy to rotate is given by the Boltzmann distribution and is proportional to $\exp\left(-E_0/kT\right)$.

If an electric field is applied to the material and if it is directed along the $+x$ axis, the dipoles will preferentially rotate so as to line up with it. In particular, if the potential energy of the dipole because of the electric field is taken as zero when the dipole is perpendicular to the field and $\pm V$ when parallel to it, the chance of a molecule rotating so as to be parallel to the field is proportional to $\exp\left[-(E_0/kT) + (V/kT)\right]$. The chance for the antiparallel rotation is proportional to $\exp\left[-(E_0/kT) - (V/kT)\right]$. If a 180° rotation is designated a jump and if the result is expressed in terms of the jump frequency ϕ, the average number of molecules jumping to the positive or parallel position per second is

$$n_2\phi_0 \exp\left(V/kT\right) \tag{12.9}$$

and for the reverse direction

$$n_1\phi_0 \exp\left(-V/kT\right) \tag{12.10}$$

In these expressions, n_1 and n_2 are the number of molecules parallel and antiparallel to the field, respectively. The quantity ϕ_0 is the average jump or rotation frequency in the absence of an applied field. Clearly, the sum of n_1 and n_2 must equal the total number of molecules.

It is now possible to write an expression for the quantity dn_1/dt, the rate of change of the number of molecules aligned with the field. This quantity will be the difference between the number of molecules rotating into the positive direction and the number rotating out of the positive direction into the negative direction:

$$dn_1/dt = n_2\phi_0 \exp{(V/kT)} - n_1\phi_0 \exp{(-V/kT)} \qquad (12.11)$$

Also, from the same reasoning,

$$dn_2/dt = -n_2\phi_0 \exp{(V/kT)} + n_1\phi_0 \exp{(-V/kT)}$$

For essentially all applications, the quantity V/kT will be much less than unity. This is easily seen from the definition of V, which shows it to be just μF where F is the electric field. Since F is seldom larger than 10 ergs/esu/cm and since μ is of order 10^{-18} esu-cm, V/kT will be of order 10^{-2}. Hence it will be allowable to expand the exponentials of Eqs. (12.11) and (12.12) to give

$$dn_1/dt = \phi_0[(n_2 - n_1) + (n_2 + n_1)(\mu F/kT)]$$

and $\qquad\qquad\qquad\qquad\qquad\qquad\qquad\qquad\qquad (12.13)$

$$dn_2/dt = \phi_0[(n_1 - n_2) - (n_2 + n_1)(\mu F/kT)]$$

After subtraction of Eqs. (12.13) and upon realization that the net number of dipoles aligned with the field ν is $n_1 - n_2$,

$$d\nu/dt = 2\phi_0[-\nu + n(\mu F/kT)] \qquad (12.14)$$

where n is the total number of molecules. If the field F is oscillating sinusoidally according to the relation $F = F_0 \sin{(\omega t)}$, the solution of Eq. (12.14) is

$$\nu/\nu_0 = (1 + \omega^2\tau^2)^{-1}[\sin{(\omega t)} + \omega\tau \cos{(\omega t)}] \qquad (12.15)$$

where

$$\nu_0 = n\mu F_0/kT \qquad \text{and} \qquad \tau = 1/2\phi_0$$

It is clear from this result that the polarization possesses two components, one in phase and one 90° out of phase with the applied field. The component in phase gives rise to the ordinary dielectric constant, the so-called "real part" of the dielectric constant, which is termed ϵ'. Since the in-phase portion of the polarization varies as $(1 + \omega^2\tau^2)^{-1}$, it is essentially constant at low frequencies and then drops rapidly near $\omega \approx 1/\tau$ and eventually becomes nearly zero at very high frequencies. This is exactly the variation predicted in Sec. 12.1. At low frequencies the dipoles can follow the oscillating field, but at very high frequencies they are unable to keep up with the rapid alternation. A plot of the variation of the real part of the dielectric constant (ϵ'), as predicted by the behavior in Eq. (12.15), is shown in Figure 95. Of course, the dielectric constant will not drop to

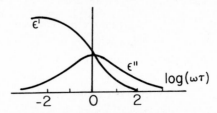

Figure 95.   Variation of the real and imaginary parts of the dielectric constant with frequency according to the Debye equations.

zero as shown, since the induced polarization will still be present. The curve shown is only the dipole contribution to the dielectric constant.

The portion of the polarization out of phase with the field gives rise to the so-called "imaginary part" of the dielectric constant, which gives rise to dielectric energy losses in the test material. This is easily seen from the following considerations. Since the force on an average dipole is proportional to $F_0\mu \sin \omega t$, the energy loss per cycle will be the integral over one cycle of this force times the rate of change of the net number of aligned dipoles. Hence,

$$\text{Loss} = \oint (d\nu/dt)\mu F_0 \sin \omega t \, dt \qquad (12.16)$$

After carrying through the indicated operation, one has

$$\text{Loss} = (\text{const})\omega\tau/(1 + \omega^2\tau^2) \qquad (12.17)$$

Hence the loss is proportional to the out-of-phase portion of the polarization. It is very low at both high and low frequencies and goes through a maximum at the frequency where ω is equal to $1/\tau$. The variation of loss with frequency is also shown in Figure 95.

The curves of Figure 95 are the "Debye dispersion curves," so named because they were first obtained by Debye. Notice the great similarity between the curves of Figure 95 and the mechanical dynamic-compliance and loss curves shown in Figure 42. As in the case of the mechanical loss curve, the maximum in the electrical loss curve appears at a characteristic frequency for the system. In the present case, the frequency at which the loss maximum occurs is twice the jump frequency of the molecules. Of course, since the picture used to describe the actual molecular system was quite crude, it is not surprising that the curves of Figure 95 do not always agree with experiment. Many simple polar molecules in dilute solution show dispersion curves much like those shown in Figure 95. However, as the dipole-dipole and dipole-solvent interactions become more complex, the actual dispersion curves become much wider in frequency range than those shown in Figure 95. Frohlich has given a very critical review of the range of validity of the Debye curves (141).

4. Dielectric Dispersion in Polar Polymers

Two different approaches may be taken to compute the dipole dispersion for polar polymers. One of these would start from the generalized picture of the polymer chain in terms of the submolecule or some other more realistic model. If the geometry of the dipoles is known, the instantaneous forces on them can be computed. The problem then reduces to solving for the motion of the chain under the electric and viscous forces. Such an approach has actually been carried out, but drastic approximations must be made if the problem is to be at all manageable (107,142). In particular, it must be assumed that the dipole direction is coincident with the direction of the end-to-end vector of the segment or submolecule. After some disagreement in the literature, it is now agreed that these computations lead to the result that the dispersion curves should be essentially the same as the Debye curves. In addition, the frequency at the maximum in the loss curve should be given by (107,142)

$$\omega_{\max} = 12kT/l^2 f_0 \qquad\qquad (12.18)$$

where l is the length of the springlike segments used in the computation, and f_0 is the segmental friction factor. This result is, of course, only true for chains containing many freely orienting segments.

The result quoted in Eq. (12.18) is not very satisfying for two reasons. First, it is based on the fact that the chain dipoles are directly in line with the freely orienting segments; yet it would be difficult to imagine a polymer for which this is true. Second, the computations leading to Eq. (12.18) are so involved that great chance for error exists in the computation process. This is particularly serious since results other than that of Eq. (12.18) have been obtained by essentially the same method of computation. For these reasons, one is ready to consider simpler—perhaps less detailed, but inherently safer—methods for computing the dispersion curves for polar polymers. One such method is outlined below (143).

Although the absolute dipole moment of the chain used for the computation will depend stringently on the exact way in which the dipoles are attached to the chain, this property is of no concern for the present purposes. It will be assumed for the present that the dipole is attached rigidly to the chain segment, as in polyvinyl chloride, for example. In addition, it will be assumed that the chain segments move with jump frequency ϕ but that dipole orientations parallel and antiparallel to the applied field are the only ones allowed. Of course, this latter restriction is essentially the same as was made in Sec. 12.3 for nonpolymeric molecules. Such limits do not constitute a serious simplification.

The chain segments may conveniently be taken as freely orienting segments. Although internal motion is always present in a segment this large, the dipole moment of the segment will move at essentially the same rate as the segment itself, provided that the dipoles are rigidly attached to the chain backbone. It is true that the motion of one freely orienting segment will influence the motion of its adjacent neighbors; however, from the definition of this type of segment, there will be no preferred orientation of one segment with respect to another. Hence, the dipoles themselves are essentially freely orienting, and the same computational methods can be applied to them as were used in Sec. 12.3 for small, independent dipoles. From that computation it is at once evident that the Debye dispersion relations apply and that the frequency at the maximum in the dielectric loss curve is given by

$$\omega_{max} = 2\phi \tag{12.19}$$

where ϕ is the segmental jump frequency defined in previous chapters.

In Chapter 4 it was shown that the segmental jump frequency was related to the segmental friction coefficient by the relation

$$\phi = 6kT/\delta^2 f_0 \tag{12.20}$$

where δ is the jump length for a freely orienting segment. After substitution of Eq. (12.20) in Eq. (12.19),

$$\omega_{max} = 12kT/\delta^2 f_0 \tag{12.21}$$

This result is to be compared with that given in Eq. (12.18). The two relations are identical; however, this is rather fortuitous in view of the differences in the basic molecular models used for the computations. Other models would lead to different numerical constants in Eq. (12.21).

It is noticed that the method of computation leading to Eqs. (12.19) and (12.20) was applicable to any long polymer chain, provided that the dipole was rigidly attached to the chain backbone. The method shows clearly that the molecular weight of the chain, if it is high, does not influence the dipole dispersion. In addition, it appears obvious that the Debye dispersion curves will be obtained by any method of computation that assumes a chain of freely orienting segments and ignores complications involving the structure of the material about the chain in question. Particularly, it should be noted that the mere fact that the dipole is attached to a long chain does not mean that the Debye relations are invalid.

Equation (12.19) is of great value for purposes of relating theory to experiment; in particular, it gives a direct means for measuring the segmental jump frequency. Although the factor of 2 in Eq. (12.19) should not be taken as quantitative, it is nevertheless true that the frequency at which the loss maximum is found should be reasonably close to twice the jump frequency. It is by this method (50) that it is found that the segmental jump frequency in polystyrene is near 0.10 sec^{-1} at the glass temperature, as stated in Chapter 4.

Actually, the experimentally observed dispersion curves for polymers are rarely as sharp as the Debye curves predict. The loss peak is in general much wider than would be expected. A few typical examples are given in Figure 96. It should be pointed

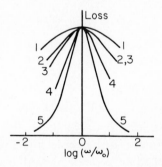

Figure 96. Variation of dielectric loss with frequency for (1) polyvinyl chloride; (2) polyvinyl chloride + 20 per cent diphenyl; (3) polychlorostyrene + 20 per cent diphenyl; (4) polyvinyl chloroacetate; (5) Debye equation prediction. [Data of R. M. Fuoss and J. Kirkwood, *J. Am. Chem. Soc.*, **63**, 369 (1941).]

out, however, that the loss peaks usually narrow somewhat when nonpolar plasticizer is added to the polymer. Although the cause of this broadening of the dispersion curves is not known with certainty, it appears safe to say that it is a result of rather strong interactions with the surrounding fluid as well as to the nonisotropic nature of the polymer segments. The reader is referred elsewhere for further discussion of this matter (143,144).

The treatment of the case of a dipole that is not rigidly held to the chain backbone is not too much different from the case already discussed. Obviously, the same reasoning as pursued before can again be used to show that the Debye curves still apply. The loss maximum will still come at twice the dipole jump or rotation frequency; however, the jump frequency for a group not attached rigidly to the chain backbone will be different from the segmental jump frequency. For a better understanding of the consequences of this fact, consider the dipole dispersion that would be expected for poly-m-chlorostyrene, whose structure is given below.

The portion of the molecule under consideration, which is shown above, has its dipole moment directed along the C—Cl bond. This vector dipole can be split into two parts, a vector parallel to AA′ and one perpendicular to AA′. In order for the parallel component of the dipole to reverse its direction, the whole chain backbone must move. This component of the dipole should behave as if it were rigidly attached to the chain backbone; hence it should give rise to a loss maximum at a frequency of 2ϕ, where ϕ is the segmental jump frequency for the polymer. This maximum is called the "alpha loss peak" or "alpha dispersion."

The perpendicular component of the dipole can rotate much more freely. It will reverse its direction each time the pendant ring rotates about AA'. This should be a much more frequent occurrence than a rotation of the whole chain segment; hence it should give rise to a loss maximum at much higher frequencies than are found for the alpha process. This loss region is called the "beta dispersion."

It is seen at once that the situation here is essentially identical to the case treated in the last chapter dealing with the mechanical loss maxima. There, too, rigidly attached groups and chain segments gave rise to an alpha dispersion; and loosely held side groups gave rise to secondary beta dispersions at higher frequencies. Careful studies of mechanical and dielectric properties of the two methacrylates discussed in the last chapter show that, to within experimental error, the beta dispersions occur at about the same frequency for both dielectric and dynamic mechanical measurements (130,132,144). Hence, the discussions given there apply to the present case as well (145).

The above discussion has been based upon the assumption that the polymer chain was many freely orienting segments in length. If the chain is very short or very stiff, this premise will not be true. In such cases, the friction factor for a freely orienting segment will be identical to the friction factor for the whole molecule. As the size of the molecule increases, so too will its friction factor; hence its alpha dispersion frequency will decrease with increasing molecular weight. As soon as the chain has become a few freely orienting segments in length, the alpha dispersion frequency will no longer be a function of molecular weight. In the case of the very stiff cellulosic molecules, it is actually found that the alpha dispersion frequency does vary somewhat with molecular weight at moderate molecular weights (146).

5. Nuclear Magnetic Resonance: The Method (147)

The dielectric dispersion of polar polymers is a valuable tool for determining the rate of motion of the dipoles. Nonetheless, the method is restricted to cases where the polymer chain contains judiciously placed polar groups. Polymers such as polyisobutylene, polyethylene, etc., that do not contain dipoles are not amenable to study by this method. It is in cases such as these that nuclear magnetic resonance measurements are of most value. This method consists of measuring the response of a material to a small radio-frequency magnetic field while the sample is maintained in a strong steady magnetic field. In many ways it is analogous to dielectric dispersion measurements in that they both measure a resonance phenomenon between the dipoles and an applied field. The dielectric case makes use of electric dipoles and electric fields, while the magnetic case uses magnetic dipoles and magnetic fields. Both methods measure the energy loss, and in each case a loss peak is observed at the resonance frequency. Although the two methods are similar in this respect, they do differ in many other important respects. One of the most important differences concerns the dipole rotation which is brought into resonance with the applied oscillatory field.

In the case of the dielectric measurements, the dipole oscillating under the action of the electric field consists of a group of atoms. Its rotation is restricted by the viscous contacts with the neighboring molecules. The characteristic features of the dipole dispersion curve are determined almost entirely by these viscous forces.

The situation is far different in the case of nuclear magnetic resonance. Since the dipoles are the nuclei of the atoms, rotation of a nuclear dipole can take place through the rotation of the nucleus of the atom. In general, the atom itself does not move. Since no viscous forces are involved in this case, the rotation frequency of the dipoles is controlled by entirely different mechanisms. These mechanisms will not be discussed in detail here. Suffice it to say that the resonance frequency ω_m is related to the strength of the applied constant magnetic field H through the relation

$$\omega_m = (g\beta/h)2\pi H_0 \qquad (12.22)$$

In the above equation, h is Planck's constant, β is a known constant called the "nuclear magneton," and g is a constant characteristic of the nuclear dipole under consideration. All the quantities entering into Eq. (12.22), except ω_m and H_0, are constants that do not vary with temperature, viscosity, or any other experimental factor. Hence the resonance frequency for a given nucleus is essentially dependent upon only one factor, the strength of the constant magnetic field within the region of the nuclear dipole. Furthermore, if the magnetic field in the sample is not exactly the same for all like nuclei, the resonance frequency for these nuclei will not all be the same.

For example, if the nuclear dipoles are reasonably close to each other, each nuclear magnet will give rise to a magnetic field. This small field ΔH will be in addition to the strong constant applied field H_0. The total field in the region of a given nuclear dipole will therefore be given by $H_0 + \Delta H$, and the resonant frequency will be

$$\omega_m = \omega_0 + \Delta\omega = (g\beta/h)(H_0 + \Delta H)(2\pi) \qquad (12.23)$$

Since ΔH may have many different values, both positive and negative, depending upon the exact environment in which the nuclear dipole finds itself, the various nuclei of the same type will not all resonate at the same frequency. Hence the resonance loss peak will be observed to be more or less wide, depending upon the homogeneity of the dipolar magnetic fields.

It is possible to compute an average value of ΔH for nuclei in a crystalline lattice. As a result, it becomes possible to predict the width of the resonance curve in such a material. Usually the width of the resonance peak is characterized in terms of the so-called "second moment." The precise definition of this term will not be needed for the present discussion. To a rough first approximation, it is equal to the square of the width of the resonance peak at the two points on each side of the main resonance where the loss has dropped to half its maximum value. The general orders of magnitude are as follows: $\omega_m/2\pi$ is about 20 Mc/sec, H_0 is of order 5×10^3 oersteds, and the average ΔH is of the order of 10 oersteds. It is common practice to plot the resonance curve as a function of H_0 rather than ω, since it is usually easier experimentally to change the field strength than it is to change the frequency ω. The two quantities are equivalent, of course, since they are related by a constant as shown in Eq. (12.22). A typical resonance curve is shown in Figure 97.

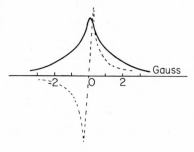

Figure 97.   Typical nuclear resonance line (solid curve) plotted as a function of difference in magnetic field strength between the applied field and the maximum-resonance field. Experimentally, the derivative curve is usually observed, and this is shown as the broken curve.

It should be pointed out that the usual isotope of carbon has no nuclear dipole and does not give a resonance curve. Hydrogen, however, does possess a nuclear dipole and is the nucleus most commonly monitored in nuclear magnetic resonance studies.

Nuclear magnetic resonance measurements of the type under consideration are of importance, for they permit evaluation of ΔH in Eq. (12.22) from the width of the magnetic resonance peak. If ΔH resulting from surrounding nuclei is very small, the width of the resonance peak is determined by the inhomogeneity of the impressed magnetic field H_0. For a properly built magnet, this inhomogeneity in the magnetic field will be only a very small fraction of an oersted over the region of the test sample and may usually be neglected.

The utility of the measurement of ΔH is greatly increased by the fact that ΔH can be used as a measure of molecular motion. This is a result of the fact that the value of ΔH measured by ordinary techniques is an average value over a time of order 10^{-4} sec. As a result, in a liquid somewhat above its glass temperature, the molecules will rotate and translate fast enough for all to experience very nearly the same average magnetic field in a time of 10^{-4} sec. Hence, ΔH, the nuclear magnetic resonance line width, will be nearly zero. On the other hand, in a liquid below T_g, the molecules move very slowly and thus will have moved only slightly in a time interval of 10^{-4} sec. In this case, ΔH will not be averaged out to zero, and the nuclear magnetic line width will be wide. Therefore, it is clear that the width of the nuclear magnetic resonance peak is a means for detecting molecular motions. This value will be more fully understood after a consideration of the examples given below.

6. NMR Measurements on Polyisobutylene

It will be recalled that, since polyisobutylene is a nonpolar polymer, dielectric measurements are of only limited value in this case. Since the polymer contains many hydrogen atoms, it will show a nuclear magnetic resonance curve. The width of the resonance curve (ΔH) has been measured over a wide range of temperature (148). This variation, together with the mechanical dynamic loss (149), is plotted in Figure 98.

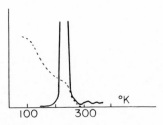

Figure 98.   Mechanical loss (149) (solid curve) and nuclear resonance second moment (148) (broken curve) for polyisobutylene as a function of temperature.

The large mechanical loss peak occurs in the temperature range near the glass temperature ($-70°C$), as outlined in previous chapters. Since the structure of this polymer is

$$-CH_2-\overset{\displaystyle CH_3}{\underset{\displaystyle CH_3}{\overset{|}{\underset{|}{C}}}}-$$

the α loss mechanism that gives rise to this large mechanical loss is the usual one, motion of the chain backbone. This is also confirmed by the variation of the NMR line width, which is essentially zero above about $280°K$. The very narrow magnetic resonance line at these temperatures means that the chain rotation frequency (more specifically, the segmental jump frequency) must be in excess of 10^4 per sec, in order that local structural variations in H_0 might be averaged out to zero.

The variation in resonance line width at very low temperatures is also of interest. It appears that near $100°K$ the line width approaches the value that would be predicted for a rigid lattice. However, as the temperature is raised, the line width decreases, thereby indicating that the polymer is showing some motion. This cannot be motion of the chain backbone at temperatures so far below T_g. Thus, it can only be concluded that the CH_3 groups are beginning to rotate about their axes. This rotation apparently requires a temperature of nearly $200°K$ to become sufficiently fast to show its total effect on the line width.

It is interesting to notice that the NMR line width shows the α resonance region to occur at a higher temperature than does the mechanical dispersion. This relationship is usually found to be the case and is easily understood. The mechanical loss maximum was shown in previous chapters to occur near the place where the dynamic test frequency equals the segmental jump frequency. This test frequency is seldom in excess of 100 cycles/sec. On the other hand, the NMR line width narrows when the segmental jump frequency is greater than about 10^4. This will understandably occur at a much higher temperature than the temperature at which the mechanical loss maximum occurs.

7. NMR Measurements on Polyvinyl Chloride

Although polyvinyl chloride contains a small amount of crystallinity, it is usually so minute as to be of no consequence for dielectric and NMR measurements. Since this polymer contains no side groups that are not fastened rigidly to the chain, one would expect to find no appreciable resonances other than the alpha resonance. The NMR line width (150), together with the dynamic mechanical loss curve (149) for this polymer, are shown in Figure 99. Unfortunately, because the samples used for the

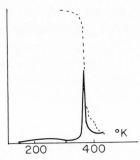

Figure 99. Mechanical loss (149) (solid curve) and nuclear resonance line width (150) (broken curve) for polyvinyl chloride as a function of temperature.

two sets of measurements were not identical, quantitative comparisons are difficult. It is noted, however, that the expected behavior is observed. Although measurements of the line width ΔH do not extend to very low temperatures, the line width at the lowest measured temperature is already 11.0 oersteds, compared with the computed maximum value for this material of 12.7 oersteds.

The reason for the low, broad resonance in the mechanical loss curve is not well understood. It could possibly be associated with the presence of HCl or other impurities often found in this material. There is also some possibility that it may be related to the small amount of crystallinity.

8. NMR Measurements on Other Materials

There are various data available for the nuclear magnetic resonance behavior of other polymers, as well as for the two given here. These data have been the subject of recent review (147). In general, the line-width versus temperature curves show very clearly the alpha resonance region associated with T_g. The line width is also very effective in demonstrating the onset of rotational motion in the glass state in certain cases. A case in point is that of polyisobutylene, as discussed above. The method has also been effectively applied to the study of crystalline polymers, and this application will be discussed further in the next chapter.

A second method for using nuclear magnetic resonance for the study of molecular motion involves the measurement of the nuclear magnetic relaxation times, T_1 and T_2. The precise measurement of T_1 and T_2 is a more complicated experimental problem than the measurement of line widths. For this reason, most investigators have not measured these quantities but have restricted themselves to line-width measurements. It would appear, however, that knowledge of T_1 and T_2 would be of even more value than the line width. It is to be expected, therefore, that these measurements will be of more importance in the future; however, since they have not been widely used as yet for the study of polymers, no discussion of this method will be given here. The interested reader is referred to the paper of Powles for an example of the capabilities of this method (151).

PROBLEMS

1. Consider a molecule such as polyvinyl chloride, but one in which all the bond angles (except hydrogen) are 90°. Compute the average dipole moment for such a chain (as a result of the C—Cl dipole), assuming free rotation on the valence cone. Compare your answer with that for the case where the true bond angles are used.

2. Qualitatively and by means of graphs showing dielectric loss plotted

against log frequency, discuss the dielectric dispersion behavior of the following three systems: (*a*) poly-*p*-chlorostyrene, (*b*) poly-*m*-chlorostyrene, and (*c*) polystyrene plasticized with about 10 per cent chlorobenzene.

3. How large is the fraction of excess dipoles oriented with the field (ν_0/n) if the field strength F_0 is 1000 volts/cm and the dipole moment is 2.0 Debyes? Use the two-position model discussed in the text and assume the temperature to be 27°C.

4. What would you predict for the NMR line-width variation with temperature for the following systems: (*a*) polyisobutylene, (*b*) a random 50–50 copolymer of isobutylene-*p*-chlorostyrene, and (*c*) a random 50–50 copolymer of isobutylene–vinyl chloride? Show the approximate position of T_g for each system on the line-width vs. temperature plot.

5. For the systems listed in problem 4, compare the mechanical loss at 1 cps., dielectric loss at 1000 cps., and NMR line width as a function of temperature. Identify the mechanism for each prominent feature of the curves involved.

Chapter 13

CRYSTALLINITY

1. Comparisons between T_g and T_m

High polymers are unique in that each has two important "melting" temperatures. The "melting" region that occurs at lowest temperatures is not a melting point at all, but merely a softening temperature. This is the glass temperature T_g, which has been discussed in great detail throughout the previous chapters. It is the temperature range in which the thermal motion of the molecules becomes so slow that they are unable to respond within a reasonable time to the action of an applied force; consequently the material is observed to change from a soft to a hard substance as the temperature is lowered through this region. But since the molecules are still in a random, liquidlike state even below T_g, the glass temperature cannot be called a thermodynamic melting temperature. For this reason one avoids calling T_g a "melting" temperature, since this can only lead to confusion with the true thermodynamic melting temperature T_m.

The most obvious change that occurs at a true melting point is best observed by X-ray diffraction. Below the melting temperature T_m, the semicrystalline material gives a typical crystal powder picture such as the one shown in Figure 100. One notices a series of sharp diffraction rings that indicate the sample contains randomly oriented crystals. The diameter of the circular rings may be used as a measure of the atom spacings within the crystals. Their presence proves that the material is composed, partly at least, of essentially perfectly ordered arrays of atoms.

295

Something can be learned about the size of these ordered arrays or crystallites from the sharpness of the diffraction lines. It is found that the dimensions of the crystallites are of the order of a few hundred angstroms in most cases. These are relatively large sizes from the atomic view, the diameter of a carbon atom being less than 2 Å. From a macroscopic view, however, they are extremely small and cannot even be resolved in an optical microscope, except for uncommon cases to be pointed out later.

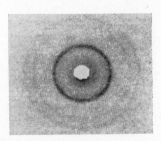

Figure 100.   X-ray diffraction pattern for unstretched silicone rubber at $-60°C$. Above $-50°C$ the sharp diffraction rings disappear, indicating that the crystals melt out at that temperature (152).

At a certain temperature T_m, and above, the X-ray pattern no longer shows the sharp diffraction rings of Figure 100. This indicates clearly that at T_m the crystallites break up and melt. No longer are there ordered three-dimensional arrays of atoms in the substance; the material is now liquidlike. Although there may be some very short-range order still present, the ordering is essentially nonexistent over dimensions larger than a few atomic diameters. Even this very short-range order does not persist but keeps changing rapidly as thermal motion takes place in the liquid; hence, molecular diffusion is many times faster above T_m than below. To a first approximation, it can be said that below T_m the molecules, or portions thereof, which are in crystalline regions are unable to translate. They can vibrate about their equilibrium positions and can even rotate to a small extent in certain exceptional cases; but they are locked into place within the crystal, and translation is to a first approximation impossible.

This statement is not precisely true, however, and it will be qualified later in this chapter.

Most low-molecular-weight liquids evidence only one of these characteristic softening temperatures, the true thermodynamic melting point T_m. The liquid is very fluid at temperatures only a fraction of a degree above T_m, and thus the material is obviously far above its glass temperature. At a fraction of a degree below T_m the material is completely crystalline, and the molecules are locked in place within the lattice. Hence, there is no opportunity whatsoever to observe a glass temperature as the crystallized liquid is cooled further.

Very rarely, a low-molecular-weight liquid that does not crystallize readily is encountered. A case in point is that of diethyl phthalate (153). This liquid is composed of molecules that apparently have some difficulty in arranging themselves into a crystalline array; hence, as the liquid is slowly cooled down to $-60°C$, it becomes very viscous, indicating that the glass temperature is being approached. It shows no X-ray diffraction rings indicative of crystals even when the material becomes a glasslike substance at about $-65°C$. One has here, then, a low-molecular-weight liquid which does not readily crystallize and which may therefore be cooled low enough as a liquid to show the glasslike behavior of liquids of very low thermal energy. Other substances that behave in this way are known and are discussed in the literature (49).

The interesting feature about diethyl phthalate is that it may also crystallize and disclose a true melting phenomenon under certain conditions. If the liquid is held at about $-53°C$ for several hours, it will suddenly begin to crystallize and will crystallize fully in a comparatively short time. The resultant needlelike crystals may then be slowly warmed. They do not melt until the temperature is about $-8°C$, at which point they all melt at a well-defined melting temperature T_m. Thus it is possible, in certain cases at least, to observe both T_g and T_m for a low-molecular-weight liquid. There are many low-molecular-weight liquids which can be cooled so swiftly through the melting point to temperatures below T_g that crystals do not have time to form. These materials will not form crystals in any reasonable length of time once they are in the glassy state, since the molecules cannot move freely enough to arrange themselves in a crystalline array.

Two factors are responsible for the fact that the glass temperature is observable in essentially all high-molecular-weight materials. In the first place, most polymers do not crystallize. As will be seen later in this chapter, most polymer chains are not regular enough to allow the formation of reasonably perfect crystals. The more imperfect a crystal is, the less stable it will be. As a result, the material is unable to form stable nuclei for crystal growth, and growth may be impossible even when a crystal nucleus is formed. The second factor derives from the impossibility of crystallizing all the polymer in a given crystallizable polymer sample. Even if the sample were composed of a single perfectly uniform molecule, it is doubtful if the polymer could ever be 100 per cent crystalline. Although small single crystals of polymer can be grown under exceptional circumstances, a bulk polymer that crystallizes usually contains many very small crystallites. It is likely that one polymer chain may sometimes crystallize partly in one crystallite and partly in another. Since the two crystallites generally will not lie in proper juxtaposition to allow the chain to pass directly from one crystal into another, part of the chain will not be in any crystal. This effect will naturally be most serious if the number of crystallites is very large. This situation is encountered in the case of rapidly cooled crystalline polymers, as will be seen later.

Since most polymers contain a sizable portion of amorphous material even at temperatures well below the glass temperature, the polymers will give evidence of T_g as well as T_m. A noncrystallizable polymer such as thermally polymerized styrene will show no exceptional change in properties at T_m. It will remain more or less liquidlike down to the glass temperature $T_g = 100°C$, where it becomes hard and brittle. However, a crystallizable polymer such as low-density polyethylene will partially crystallize at $T_m = 110°C$. Below this temperature it is no longer liquidlike and does not flow under low stresses, but it is still relatively soft and flexible. However, at approximately $-110°C$, polyethylene becomes very hard and brittle—behavior that is characteristic of a material at its glass temperature. Hence, both characteristic temperatures, T_g and T_m, are important for such a material.

2. Factors Determining Crystallizability (154,155)

Basically the criterion for crystallization is that the free energy of the crystalline phase must be lower than the free energy of the liquid phase. Even when this is true, however, the polymer may not crystallize except under very special conditions. For example, even in the low-molecular-weight liquid diethyl phthalate mentioned above, kinetic conditions governed whether or not crystals would grow, even though the crystalline phase was the more stable. Similar behavior is noticed for polymers. Many crystallizable polymers are easily supercooled. If the free energy of the liquid is higher than that of the crystal, however, the polymer should crystallize under the proper conditions.

The basic problem to be solved in determining whether a given polymer will crystallize is essentially the problem of relating the free energy of the liquid polymer to that of the crystal. Several factors contribute to the change in free energy as a polymer goes from liquid to crystal. First, the putting together of a group of molecules originally in a liquid to form a crystal gives rise to the evolution of heat, the heat of fusion. This will be represented by the symbolism ΔH_f and will be measured in calories per mole of chain repeating units. Since this change in energy is the result of the tighter association bonds between the molecules in a crystal than those in a liquid, it is clear that ΔH_f will be large whenever strong intermolecular bonding is possible. For example, hydrogen bonded materials should show large heats of fusion. In addition, ΔH_f should depend upon structural factors that influence the closeness with which the molecules can pack. In any case, the change in ΔH will be positive when going from liquid to crystal and will favor crystal formation.

The second basic factor entering into the free-energy change between liquid and crystal is the entropy of fusion per mole of chain repeating units, designated ΔS_f. A polymer molecule in the molten polymer has very few restrictions on its possible positions. Although a small amount of ordering with respect to its neighbors is expected, a polymer molecule in the melt will be able to assume nearly all configurations possible for a chain of its structure without regard to the orientation of surrounding chains. This lack of order in the liquid will give rise to a high entropy. In the crystalline material, however, the molecules are constrained in many ways. Not only are the chain atoms constrained to occupy certain sites in the crystal lattice, but they must also have the proper orientation in these sites. Obviously the state of order in the crystal is much higher than in the liquid, thereby giving rise to a lower entropy for the crystal. It is clear that, since a system seeks the state of highest entropy, entropy alone would favor the liquid state.

For the present, the rather small energy and entropy effects of chain ends, crystal surface regions, and possible diluent will be ignored. To that approximation, which is equivalent to assuming a perfect crystal, the change in free energy as liquid changes to crystal is given as

$$\Delta F_f = \Delta H_f - T\,\Delta S_f \tag{13.1}$$

At the melting point T_m, crystals and liquid are at equilibrium, and hence $\Delta F_f = 0$. The melting temperature is therefore given by

$$T_m = \Delta H_f / \Delta S_f \tag{13.2}$$

Equation (13.2) states the simple fact arrived at above. The melting temperature of a polymer crystal will be high if the heat of fusion is large (i.e., high intermolecular attraction) or if the entropy of fusion is small. As may have been surmised from the above discussion of the entropy change, it is a very difficult quantity to estimate a priori. No satisfactory way of relating this quantity to the exact details of molecular structure is known. In general, however, it is felt that a very flexible chain will show a higher value for ΔS_f, since it can take up more configurations in the liquid than would be possible for a stiff chain. A discussion of this whole problem, along with typical values for ΔS and ΔH, is given by Mandelkern in an excellent review article (154).

3. Effect of Imperfections on T_m

As pointed out above, a precise discussion of the melting phenomena would have to consider the complicating effects of surface energy, chain ends, and diluent. The qualitative effect of each of these variables is easily seen; they all lead to a lowering of T_m below the value expected for a perfect crystal (156).

Small crystallites will possess a higher energy per unit volume of crystalline material than will a single perfect crystal. This is essentially obvious from the fact that the surfaces between crystallites will be regions of poor packing; hence, the chains at the surface will not contribute their full value to the heat of fusion. It is expected, then, that in a polycrystalline material containing crystallites of various sizes the smallest crystallites will melt at a lower temperature than the large crystallites. This probability is actually observed to be the case, and a typical example (157) of this is seen in Figure 101, which shows the

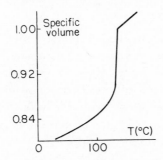

Figure 101.   Variation of specific volume (gm/cc) with temperature for polymethylene (157).

variation of specific volume for polymethylene as a function of temperature. Since the crystals have a higher density than the amorphous material, the melting of crystallites gives rise to an increase in specific volume. It is seen from the figure that about 80 per cent of the crystalline material melts out in the 5° temperature interval below T_m, the temperature at which all crystallinity is gone. There is, however, continued melting over a wide temperature range below T_m. It is not supposed that all these low melting regions are made unstable by the surface-energy effects, since the other factors mentioned above also contribute to this effect, as well as inherent crystal imperfections.

The effects of chain ends and diluent also contribute to lowering of the melting point. Chain ends actually restrict the growth of crystallites, if one assumes they cannot exist inside the crystal. Or if they actually do enter into the crystal, they decrease the perfect packing within the crystal and hence decrease ΔH and T_m. On the other hand, diluent probably does not enter into the crystallites and therefore does not change the value of the heat of fusion. Nevertheless, the entropy of the liquid (regarded as a measure of disorder) is certainly increased by the presence of diluent. As a result, ΔS_f is increased and T_m is lowered. Flory has shown (158) that if T_{m0} represents the melting point of the perfect crystal, the melting point in the presence of a volume fraction v_1 of diluent is reduced as follows:

$$1/T_m = 1/T_{m0} + (RV/V' \, \Delta H_f)(v_1 - \chi v_1^2) \qquad (13.3)$$

In this relation, V and V' are the molar volumes of the polymer repeat unit and diluent, respectively, and R is the gas constant. The quantity χ is a polymer-solvent interaction parameter.

An expression similar to Eq. (13.3) applies also for the effect of chain ends. In particular, if one considers a heterogeneous polymer having the most probable molecular-weight distribution, it is found that (158) for a chain system having a number-average degree of polymerization Z_n,

$$1/T_m = 1/T_{m0} + 2R/\Delta H_f Z_n \qquad (13.4)$$

If attention is confined to $v_1 \ll 1$ in Eq. (13.3), it is apparent that the equation can be rewritten as

$$1/T_m = 1/T_{m0} + (R/\Delta H_f)X \qquad (13.5)$$

where X is the mole fraction of impurity. In addition, since $2/Z_n$ is essentially the mole fraction of chain ends, Eq. (13.5) can also be used to represent Eq. (13.4).

4. Effect of Copolymerization

The effect of copolymerization upon crystallinity and melting point is not simple. At the outset it is impossible to say exactly what assumption is proper when picturing the crystallites. If the comonomers are very similar in structure, there is a possibility that they may easily fit into the same crystal lattice. In such a case, the crystal may be only slightly disrupted by the copolymerization. On the other hand, if the comonomers are very dissimilar, the crystal may be unable to tolerate even a small number of foreign monomer units within it. A further point of concern is that the exact distribution of the comonomers along the chain will be of importance.

Perhaps the only really safe prediction that can be made concerning the effect of copolymerization with monomer B upon the melting point of a polymer composed predominantly of monomer A is that the melting point will be lower than that for pure A. An approximate theory for this has been given by Flory (158,159), who finds

$$1/T_m = 1/T_{m0} - (R/\Delta H_f) \ln X_A \qquad (13.6)$$

In this relation it is assumed that X_A, the mole fraction of the parent polymer, is interspersed randomly along the chains with the comonomer of mole fraction X_B. When the polymerization kinetics preclude random copolymerization, X_A should be replaced by the probability that an A unit is followed by another A unit as the chain grows. Clearly, if X_A is near unity, then $\ln X_A$

is equal to ln $(1 - X_B)$, which is approximately equal to $-X_B$. Hence Eq. (13.5) applies to this case also in this limit.

Although experimental data for random copolymers appear to conform to Eq. (13.6), it is found that ΔH_f computed by this relation is not the same as found by other approaches; in general, it is much smaller than one would expect (154). This may be a reflection of the inadequacy of the theory. It is also possible that it represents an experimental error, since the measurement of T_m for copolymers is not an easy matter.

The difficulty encountered with measurements on copolymers is associated with the fact that Eq. (13.6) gives the melting point of only the most stable crystallites. It is observed that the melting range of copolymers is exceedingly wide, and it is very difficult to determine exactly where the last bit of crystallinity disappears. Even in the case of low-density polyethylene, which has a relatively high number of short chain branches, a great deal of widening of the melting range is observed in comparison with the data for polymethylene as shown in Figure 102. In this case,

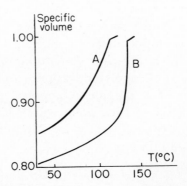

Figure 102.   Variation of specific volume (gm/cc) with temperature for linear polyethylene (B) and low-density, slightly branched polyethylene (A) (157).

the short chain branches may be considered equivalent to a comonomer.

If two monomers whose individual pure polymers form crystalline material are copolymerized, the copolymer will usually exhibit a sort of eutectic point. This phenomenon follows from the fact that addition of a comonomer to either one of the pure polymers will lower the melting point; hence, T_m as a function of comonomer concentration will show a minimum value at some intermediate concentration. Not much can be said about the exact position of the minimum from the present state of crystallization theory. A typical experimental plot (161) for the variation of T_m with composition is shown in Figure 103.

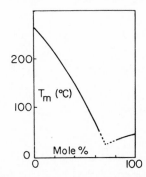

Figure 103.   Melting point of polyethylene adipate–polyethylene terephthalate copolymers as a function of mole percentage of adipate (161).

The case of block and graft copolymers is also of interest. If the blocks or grafts are quite long, the two types of units will separate into two phases, which will disclose crystallization properties quite similar to the homopolymers. Although the melting temperature of the two phases will depend somewhat on the size of the blocks or grafts, this effect is essentially equivalent to the behavior expected for crystallites of this size in a homopolymer. Of course, when the blocks or grafts are quite short, the separation into two phases will no longer occur, and one has in effect a normal copolymer. It is clear that a great range of crystallization behavior is possible in the case of copolymers.

5. Effect of Crystallization Temperature

It is usually possible to supercool a crystallizable polymer without much difficulty; therefore the rate of crystallization of a polymer can be recorded merely by cooling it quickly from the melt to the required temperature and recording its specific volume as a function of time. Typical plots obtained during the crystallization of polymethylene at several temperatures are shown (154) in Figure 104. In this figure the ratio of the specific

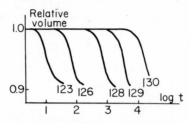

Figure 104.   Crystallization as a function of time for polymethylene at the centigrade temperatures indicated on the curves. The time is measured in minutes (160).

volume at time $t = t$ to that at time $t = 0$ is plotted against the time the sample had been cooled. This ratio is a rough measure of crystallinity. It should be noted that the value of T_m for this polymer is about 137°C. Notice further that, while it only takes about 20 min for crystallization to become nearly complete at 123°C, a time of over 20,000 min is required at 130°C for the same extent of crystallization.

Two distinct processes occur as the polymer crystallizes. First, a crystalline nucleus for crystallization must form. Second, the crystal must grow out from this nucleus. These two processes involve quite different factors, and it will be seen that each has a temperature dependence which is quite different from the other.

If the polymer is assumed to be pure, the nucleus for crystallization will be a very small crystalline region within the melt. This region will be formed by a coincidental alignment of several small sections of polymer chains into a crystalline array; such arrangements must occur very frequently within a molten polymer. Usually, however, thermal motion of the chains is sufficient to break up the incipient crystallites before they have a chance to grow. The question as to the condition for stability of a nucleus is therefore important.

Earlier in this chapter it was shown that crystallization occurs when the entropy loss in the process is exactly compensated by the energy loss. For large crystals the surface energy is a negligible part of the whole energy change and can therefore be neglected. Such is not the case when one is considering crystal nucleation. Since the volume of the crystal is small, the surface energy is comparable to the bonding energy within the crystal. At the melting point for large perfect crystals, a small crystal will actually have a significantly higher free energy than the molten polymer. This property is the result of its high surface energy; hence, such a crystal will be unstable.

Even though a small crystallite is thermodynamically unstable at temperatures several degrees below T_m, it is possible under certain conditions for this crystallite to grow large enough to become stable. This is a result of the fact that the surface energy is a decreasing fraction of the total energy as the crystal grows. At infinite crystal size, the surface energy is a negligible fraction of the total, and the perfect crystal will melt at T_m. For a smaller crystal, the surface energy must equal $\Delta H_f - T \Delta S_f$ at the melting point for this crystal; therefore the usual condition, $\Delta H_f - T \Delta S_f = 0$, does not apply at the temperature where this crystal becomes unstable. This means the small crystal becomes unstable at a temperature somewhat below T_m. It follows from this discussion that a polymer will not, in practice, crystallize at T_m. All crystal sizes below an infinitely large one are unstable at this temperature. At a temperature a degree or so below T_m, crystals larger than a certain fairly large critical size will be stable; however, the chance that thermal fluctuations in the melt would give rise to such a large perfectly ordered region is very small. Hence the rate of crystal growth at this temperature will be essentially zero because of the exceedingly low number of stable nuclei available for growth.

As the temperature is lowered further below T_m, the smallest stable crystal size will decrease; hence it will be easier to form a stable nucleus in the melt, and the number of growing nuclei will increase. As a result, the over-all observed rate of crystallization will increase as the temperature is lowered. This is the explanation of the behavior shown in Figure 104. The long induction period at temperatures close to T_m is merely a reflection of the difficulty in obtaining stable nuclei at these temperatures.

A typical curve showing the rate of crystallization as a function of temperature is shown in Figure 105. This particular

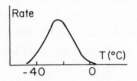

Figure 105.   Crystallization rate of natural rubber at various temperatures (162).

curve is for natural rubber (162), but a similar curve would be found for the material of Figure 104. As pointed out above, the rate is very low at temperatures just below T_m. Natural rubber is a well-studied material in this respect, and it has been found to crystallize very slowly at room temperature; but crystallization does occur at this temperature over a period of years. The crystallites formed at these temperatures are apparently very large and perfect, since they have a very high melting point. Whereas crystallized natural rubber is usually considered to melt at about 28°C, one sample of rubber that crystallized over a period of about thirty years (163), so-called "stark" rubber, has been found to have $T_m = 40°$C.

In any event, the increasing rate of nucleation as the temperature is lowered accounts for the rise in rate shown in Figure 105. However, below $-25°$C the rubber begins to show viscous effects characteristic of a material approaching its glass temperature. The molecular motion is decreasing rapidly with decreasing temperature in this region. As the molecular motion slows down, both the rate of nucleation and rate of growth from the nuclei will begin to decrease.

The nuclei are formed by the occasional appearance of ordered regions as a chance occurrence under thermal motion. If the molecules were at rest, only those nuclei present at a given instant would ever exist; hence the nucleation rate would be zero. This will almost be the case near and at T_g. At $-25°C$ this effect is beginning to be felt and is partly responsible for the decrease in rate at this and lower temperatures. In addition, if molecular motion does not exist, the molecules near a growing nucleus cannot move into proper orientation to be added at the surface; therefore the growth of nuclei already present will decrease at low temperatures. This also contributes to the decreased rate below $-25°C$. Obviously, rubber can be supercooled to $-50°C$ and held there indefinitely with very little crystallization taking place.

6. Influence of Crystallization Temperature on T_m

As pointed out in the last section, very high melting points can be obtained for a rubber crystallized very slowly just below its melting point. This characteristic must be the result of the extraordinary perfection and size of such crystals. Since the growth occurred very slowly, great opportunity existed for defects in structure to be eliminated by alternate "melting" and "freezing" of a chain as it was added to the crystal growth surface. In addition, since the number of nuclei would be very small in this temperature range, each nucleus can grow into a very large crystal before encountering interference from other growing nuclei. As a result of the high perfection and large size, the crystals thus formed have nearly the melting point of a perfect crystal.

If the polymer is cooled from the melt to a point greatly below T_m, both the crystal growth rate and nucleation rate will be rather large. Many nuclei growing simultaneously will result in great interference between the various crystallites. The size of the crystallites will be reduced, since their volume of growth is restricted by the surrounding crystallites. Furthermore, it is possible that the region of contact between growing centers will result in a poorly ordered, strained, or perhaps even an amorphous region. Both of these factors will cause the resulting crystals to be unstable at temperatures greatly below T_m, the melting point for the perfect crystal.

This variation of crystallite melting temperature with the temperature at which crystallization took place has been observed by many investigators. The observed variation for natural rubber (162) is shown in Figure 106. Notice that melting usually

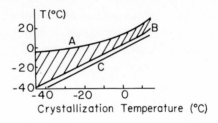

Figure 106.   Natural rubber crystallized at the temperature indicated by curve C begins to melt when the rubber is heated to the temperature shown by curve B. Melting continues as the temperature is raised further, but all crystallites have melted when the temperature indicated by curve A is reached (162).

begins at a temperature about 5° above the temperature of crystallization. An interesting feature of this type of data, however, is the fact that the variation in melting point with crystallization temperature depends upon the way in which the data are taken. If the crystalline sample is warmed very slowly, the small imperfect crystals melt at lower temperatures but then recrystallize into more perfect forms. Hence, if the measurements are taken slowly enough, the same melting curve will be obtained no matter how the crystals were formed, as long as the total fraction of crystalline material is the same at the start of the measurements.

7. Effect of Stretching on Crystallinity

An interesting polymer to consider is polyisobutylene. This material does not crystallize at temperatures near room temperature and is essentially noncrystalline at all temperatures. However, upon stretching, the rubber shows a rather high degree of crystallinity from X-ray diffraction measurements. It is apparent in this and in many other cases that stretching of the rubber has increased its ability to crystallize.

The reasons for this effect are quite obvious. When the rubber is stretched, the chains are placed in a much more ordered state than they occupied in the unstretched rubber. They are, in fact, arranged much in the same way as they would have to be if they were in a crystallite. Consequently, the loss in entropy as the chain is removed from the oriented amorphous region to the crystal will be much lower than would have been the case if the amorphous region had not been oriented. Since T_m equals $\Delta H_f/\Delta S_f$, with a decrease in ΔS_f upon orientation it is clear that T_m will increase.

It is possible to put the above concepts on a semiquantitative basis. Flory has done this (164) and has found that the melting temperature depends upon the extension ratio α in the following way:

$$1/T_m - 1/T_{m0} = (R/\Delta H_f)[(6/\pi n)^{1/2}\alpha - (\alpha^2/2 + 1/\alpha)/n]$$

$$(13.7)$$

The quantity n is the number of chain units between crosslinks. Equation (13.7) is not quite correct, since it does not predict $T_m = T_{m0}$ at $\alpha = 1$; however, it does appear to satisfy experimental data for natural rubber at large α values. Since this is the region of importance, the deficiency of the equation at low extension is not too serious.

A stretched rubber should also crystallize faster at a given temperature than would the unstretched rubber. Experiments by Treloar (22) on natural rubber show this effect very clearly.

Some of his data are shown in Figure 107, where density change, which is roughly proportional to change in crystallinity, is plotted as a function of time. The temperature used for the measurements shown there was 0°C. Notice that the crystallization proceeds exceedingly slowly in the unstretched rubber. At 700 per cent elongation, however, the crystallization took only a relatively short time. It was also observed that crystallization was much more rapid at 50°C than at 0°C. Essentially all the crystallization took place during the first few seconds after stretching.

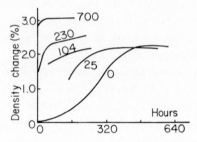

Figure 107. Crystallization of natural rubber (unvulcanized) at various percentages of elongation, as indicated on the curves (22). Percentage change in density is used as the measure of crystallinity.

Another interesting feature involves the decrease in tension necessary to hold the rubber at a fixed elongation as crystallization proceeds. This effect arises from the fact that a portion of a chain which becomes part of a crystallite will be elongated far beyond its average length under random thermal motion in the amorphous state. As it elongates, with the sample elongation remaining constant, the portion of the chain still remaining in the amorphous region will be compressed. Since the chains in the amorphous region were under tensile stress to begin with, this compression effect will decrease the tension needed to hold the sample at fixed length. At sufficient extents of crystallization the tension will actually drop to zero. Careful measurements of this effect have been made by Gent (165), and he has compared his results with the approximate theory of Flory. Fairly reasonable agreement is obtained in spite of obvious deficiencies in the theory.

8. Morphology of Crystallization

For many years the accepted picture for crystallinity in polymers was that shown in Figure 108. The idea was that individual

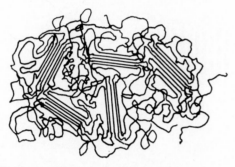

Figure 108.   Schematic diagram showing the idea of polymer crystallinity generally accepted before 1959.

chains run straight through a crystallite, then into an amorphous region and back into another crystallite, and so on through several crystallites. The crystallites were considered to be more or less cylindrical in shape, with the chains running through the crystallite parallel to the cylinder axis. X-ray diffraction measurements indicated these crystallites to be of the order of a few hundred angstroms in size. Recently, however, it has been possible to form rather perfect single crystals of polymers in dilute solution. Unexpectedly, these crystals did not conform to the type that would be expected from extrapolating the model of Figure 108 to dilute solution conditions. The crystals are observed to be composed of folded chains, as indicated in Figure 109. The crystal itself is usually similar to the one shown in Figure 110. As indicated, the crystals are flat plates with a thickness of a few hundred angstroms, and the chains run through the crystals perpendicular to the flat faces. The other two dimensions are much larger. It is observed that the crystals are somewhat like playing cards in the way they rest upon each other. There is evidence, however, that the crystals are not completely flat but have a slightly pyramidal shape. None-

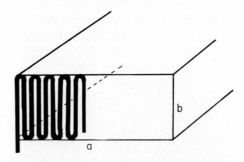

Figure 109. Schematic diagram showing how folded polymer chains form a platelike crystal. The chain axis is perpendicular to the large surfaces of the plate. An actual crystal would have a thickness b much smaller than the distance a.

theless, to a first approximation, they are essentially flat (169).

It is rather interesting to notice that in polyethylene, for example, a given chain must be folded about ten or twenty times within a crystal. In spite of this, the crystals grown from dilute solution are remarkably uniform in thickness. Attempts have been made to compute the thickness of such crystals by balancing the surface fold energy against the usual energy and entropy contributions to the free energy (167,168). Such computations appear to give reasonable results but must in reality be viewed with great reservations as a result of the following observations.

When a crystal grown from solution at a given temperature is annealed at a higher temperature, the crystal becomes thicker (170). Its new equilibrium thickness is essentially the same as that found for a crystal actually formed at the higher temperature. Hence, the crystals appear to possess great internal mobility, and one surmises that the chains can "snake" their way through the crystal in such a way as to increase the num-

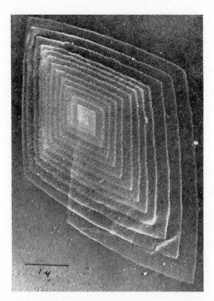

Figure 110. Electron micrograph of a multilayered single crystal of linear polyethylene grown from dilute solution (166). Each layer is about 100 Å. thick, and the chain axes are perpendicular to the page.

ber of units between folds. Naturally, this all occurs without actual melting of the crystal; in fact, in certain cases at least, the annealed crystal has been found to have developed a series of holes within itself in order to furnish material for the growth in thickness. This phenomenon is depicted in Figure 111, which shows the crystal to take on a sort of Swiss cheese appearance. From this it is clear that any computation involving surface-energy balance is not as straightforward as it might seem at first sight.

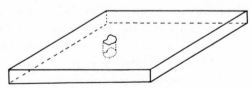

Figure 111. Schematic diagram of a platelike crystal with an annealing hole in it.

The fact that the chains within the crystal are able to move quite easily, both by translation and rotation, is demonstrated by nuclear magnetic resonance line-width studies (171). Even at temperatures far below the crystalline melting point. the line-width characteristic of the crystalline chains has narrowed somewhat, indicating motion of these chains. An attempt has been made to relate this motion within the crystal to the free energy and size of the crystals (170). Preliminary results are encouraging, but the theory for these effects is still far from complete.

One is interested, of course, in what these observations on single crystals mean when growth of crystals from the melt is considered. Although there is a great deal of difference between crystallization from dilute solution and formation of crystals in the melt, there appears to be good reason to think that even in the latter case the crystals form as rather irregular platelets. For example, overgrowth upon a single crystal laid down in dilute solution appears to show much the same structure as is frequently observed in melt crystallization. These more complicated structures, which are many times larger than individual crystallites, are called "spherulites."

Spherulites are aggregates of small crystallites that usually have grown until the aggregate size has become of the order of a few hundredths of a millimeter. They are readily seen under the light microscope and in this respect are unlike the individual crystallites, which are often smaller than the wavelength of light and thus cannot be resolved in a light microscope. The spherulites are, as the name implies, approximately spherical in shape. They appear to grow within a mass of small crystallites by addition of the crystallites to the surface of the enlarging sphere. In highly crystalline materials, the spherulites eventually collide with each other as they grow and hence lose their characteristic spherical perimeter as they grow about each other. A typical case is illustrated in Figure 112. Since the crystallites will not coalesce into spherulites unless the mobility of the system is quite high, shock cooling favors small spherulites, while long anneal-

Figure 112. Spherulites of polytrimethylene glutarate enlarged 185 times and observed between crossed polaroids (172). The material was prepared by cooling the molten polymer between two glass plates.

ing favors very large ones. Since the large spherulites scatter light much more than the very small crystallites arranged at random, an annealed polymer will appear much more cloudy than a shock-cooled polymer.

9. Molecular Parameters Affecting Crystallinity (155)

It goes without saying that the more regular and symmetrical a polymer is, the better will be its chances of crystallizing. Thus, it is not surprising that polymethylene is highly crystalline, since it has a very regular structure. The fact that polyethylene crystallizes well is also to be expected, since it is identical to polymethylene in structure except for occasional branch points along the chain. However, since the branch points disrupt the chain perfection needed in a crystal, it is reasonable that highly branched polyethylene has a melting point greatly below that for polymethylene.

The structure of polyisobutylene is very similar to that of

polyethylene, and it would be expected to crystallize as well; however, the hydrogen atoms on alternate carbons have been replaced by methyl groups. This difference will prevent polyiso-butylene from packing into a crystal as well as polymethylene. Not only are the methyl groups larger than the hydrogen atoms, but they also cause great steric hindrance along the chain back-bone. The net result of this is to make polyisobutylene a poorly crystallizing material unless it is stretched; in the stretched state it crystallizes fairly well.

If the methyl groups on polyisobutylene are replaced by chlorine to form polyvinylidine chloride, the bulk of the side group is somewhat smaller, and crystallization should improve for this reason. More important, though, the polarity provided by the chlorines increases the association energy between adja-cent chains in the crystal. As a result, this polymer has a melting point of 210°C, which is about 80° above that for polyethylene.

Even more striking is the case of polytetrafluoro ethylene, in which all the hydrogens in polymethylene are replaced by fluo-rines. This polymer has the symmetry properties of polyethylene plus the cohesive properties attributable to the C—F bond. It is not surprising, therefore, to find that this polymer has a very high melting point, namely, 327°C.

For many years it was believed that polymers such as poly-styrene and polymethyl methacrylate would never be crystal-lized. This conviction was a result of the fact that these chains were so-called "atactic" polymers. In an atactic polymer the chain monomer unit, such as styrene, adds to the chain in such a way that the phenyl groups occur at random on either posi-tion A or B shown in Figure 113. As a result, the large phenyl group could not be fitted easily into any simple crystalline lat-tice. By use of suitable catalysts, it is now possible to polymerize so-called "isotactic" polystyrene, in which the phenyl group always appears in the A position. As a result, the chain is very regular, and the phenyl groups can be packed into a reasonable lattice. This polymer, unlike the noncrystallizable atactic form,

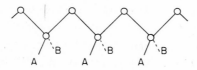

Figure 113. Diagram for the polymer chain used to describe atactic, isotactic, and syndiotactic forms.

crystallizes to give a polymer with a melting point of about 250°C.

Many other polymers have recently been prepared by special catalysts in isotactic form. Polymethyl methacrylate, for example, has been obtained in both isotactic and syndiotactic forms that are quite unlike the common atactic polymer. Whereas the atactic polymer has never been crystallized, the isotactic and syndiotactic forms are both rather highly crystalline. The term "syndiotactic" refers to the chain whose side group alternates in a regular way between the A and B position.

Perhaps the most important example of the effect of chain geometry on crystallinity occurs in the case of natural rubber and gutta-percha. Natural rubber is an all-*cis* polymer of isoprene whose structure is shown in Figure 114*a*. This material is well

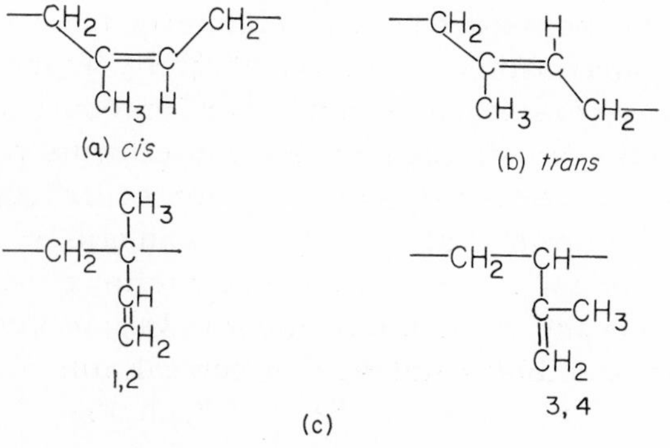

$$-CH_2 \quad\quad CH_2- \\ C=C \\ CH_3 \quad H$$

(a) *cis*

$$-CH_2 \quad\quad H \\ C=C \\ CH_3 \quad CH_2-$$

(b) *trans*

$$ CH_3 \\ -CH_2-C- \\ CH \\ \| \\ CH_2$$

1,2

$$-CH_2-CH- \\ C-CH_3 \\ \| \\ CH_2$$

3, 4

(c)

Figure 114. Three isomeric forms of polyisoprene: (*a*) natural rubber, *cis*-1,4-polyisoprene; (*b*) gutta-percha, *trans*-1,4-polyisoprene; (*c*) 1,2- and 3,4-polyisoprene.

known and crystallizes very slowly at room temperature. Its geometric isomer, *trans*-polyisoprene, is known as gutta-percha and is highly crystalline at room temperature. Its structure is shown in Figure 114*b*. Note that the sole difference in structure between these two cases involves the two possible ways in which the chain can continue beyond each double bond. In the *cis* configuration, the chain approaches and leaves the double bond thus:

The *trans* configuration has the chain enter and leave the double bond in the following way:

This change in geometric configuration is sufficient to produce a marked effect upon crystallinity.

Until recently, laboratory-produced polyisoprene was essentially noncrystalline. This is a result of marked structural irregularity in the synthetic polymer. While isoprene can polymerize in the ways shown in Figure 114*a* and *b*, called "1,4 addition," it can also polymerize as shown in Figure 114*c*, so-called "1,2 and 3,4 addition." Obviously, a polymer containing a mixture of these various forms will not crystallize readily. Since ordinary synthetic polyisoprene is a mixture of these forms, it is essentially noncrystalline. However, recently, by means of special catalyst systems, it has been possible to produce large quantities of synthetic polyisoprene having essentially the same structure as natural rubber. Polybutadiene, being very similar to polyisoprene in possible structural forms, can also be synthesized in crystallizable form by using these new techniques. The general problem of the geometric relations in various polymer crystal structures has been discussed by several authors (173,174).

10. Fiber Formation

Although a detailed discussion of the properties of fibers is beyond the scope of this book, it is advantageous to examine a few features of interest concerning them at this time. Basically, a fiber is a crystallizable polymer that has been highly oriented. To be practical, it must be able to crystallize in the highly oriented state and retain the orientation and crystallinity to rather high temperatures. In order to do this, the material must have a high melting point, a property that immediately places sizable restrictions upon the substance.

As ordinarily prepared, the fiber-forming material is a partly crystalline, nonoriented polymer. It must next be oriented or "drawn." In the drawing process the chains must elongate to a large extent as the material is subjected to a tensile stress. This action requires several qualities in the base material. First, the polymer must be well above its glass temperature at the drawing temperature (preferably not too far from room temperature). If this were not true, the material would be hard and brittle, and the chains could not elongate easily under the applied force. This requirement may be mitigated to a certain extent if the polymer can be handled in a suitable solvent. Second, enough crystallinity must be present in the material at the start of the drawing procedure so that the polymer will not simply pull apart. The crystallites must act as crosslinks so that the resultant polymer network can be oriented. Third, the stretched, oriented polymer must become rather highly crystalline in the oriented state. The crystallites cannot be so perfect as to impart great rigidity to the polymer, however, or the material will be too brittle to be useful. It is important, nevertheless, that the crystallites be stable to rather high temperatures so that they will not melt out during normal handling of the fiber.

Perhaps the most stringent of the above requirements is that the material have a high melting point. This requirement is not even satisfied by highly crystalline polyethylene. Obviously, high symmetry of the base molecule must be coupled with high intermolecular forces if the requisite melting points are to be attained. It is not strange, therefore, that the successful fibers are based upon polar chains.

Other factors such as chain stiffness, alternation of copolymer constituents, branching, and crosslinking are also important in determining the nature of a fiber. The whole process of fiber production is a highly specialized and intricate operation. For example, the elementary property of dye acceptability is a very involved problem that is concerned with the chemical reactivity of the chain, as well as with its extent of crystallinity. Even the proper shape and size of an effective fiber are not simple problems. Needless to say, the field of fibers has a very wide compass. The interested reader is referred to the book by Billmeyer for an introduction to the subject (175).

PROBLEMS

1. The heat of fusion for polyethylene (154) is about 1.6 Kcal per mole of monomer units. How large is the depression of the melting point caused by chain ends for degrees of polymerization (a) 6, (b) 10, (c) 30, and (d) 1000, as predicted by Eq. (13.4)? Compare these values with handbook values where possible. Assume T_m for the pure polymer to be 135°C.

2. The heat of fusion per mole of monomer units for natural rubber (154) is about 1.0 Kcal/mole. If 28°C is taken as the melting point of the unstretched rubber, compute T_m for the rubber at $\alpha = 4.0$, assuming $M_c = 6000$.

3. The brittle points of polydecyl methacrylate and polydecyl acrylate are both about -30°C. On the other hand, the hexadecyl methacrylate and acrylate polymers have brittle points of about 15 and 35°C, respectively (175). Discuss these values in terms of the glass temperatures of the polymers of the methyl esters and in terms of the melting points of the straight-chain paraffins, decane and hexadecane.

4. When taking creep or stress-relaxation data for natural rubber, the fact that natural rubber crystallizes makes measurements in the range -35 to -15°C very difficult. How would the presence of crystallization manifest itself in such measurements? Why is it that measurements outside this temperature range present no serious difficulty? What special precautions must be taken in carrying out measurements even outside this temperature range if crystallinity is not to be a serious problem?

5. It has been reported (*Chem. Abstr.*, **55**, 14965g) that 95 per cent *cis*-1,4-polybutadiene has a glass transition, measured at 10 Kc/sec, of -95°C as compared with -50°C found by the same method for the usual random polybutadiene. Compare these values with the $T_g = -85$°C usually quoted for the latter polymer and try to explain the discrepancy. Give a reason why the transition temperatures for the two polymers differ in the way one observes.

Chapter 14

TEAR AND MOLECULAR BREAKDOWN OF RUBBERS

1. Nature of the Tearing Process

When a rubber fails under excessive forces in a practical situation, it usually fails because of the development of a tear. Hence, it is important to know what factors give rise to high tear strength, so that rubbers possessing this desirable quality may be prepared. But before one can ascertain the importance of various molecular properties of a rubber in providing tear resistance, it is necessary to examine the actual mechanics of the tearing process. This must be done in order to see how the rather complex tear phenomena is related to the more basic rubber properties such as tensile strength, modulus, and dynamic loss.

It is rather obvious that the physical condition at the tip of a tear is not simple. Since the material there is under very high strain, it is impossible to compute the stress and strain distribution by using the methods of simple linear viscoelasticity. The situation is concerned with that portion of the stress-strain curve where the stress rises very rapidly as a function of strain. At the same time, since the stress will decrease very rapidly outside the vicinity of the tear tip, there is also a concern with material possessing stresses from the very smallest up to the breaking stress. The fact that motion is also involved as the crack grows indicates that the dynamic response of the rubber at high strains is also of importance. With such a complex situation existing at

323

the tearing surface, it is not surprising that a detailed solution of the tearing problem has never been presented.

In order to circumvent the complicated distribution of forces near the tear tip, Thomas (176,177) and his associates have treated the whole problem from the standpoint of energy rather than force. They have designed experimental situations for which the geometry is simple enough so that certain simple relations may be shown to apply to the tearing rubber. Since they find agreement among the various physical methods used, they are reasonably sure that their results will apply to tears when the geometry is more complicated. For the purposes of the discussion here, only one of their methods will be described.

If a sheet of rubber of thickness h is cut in the typical trousers shape shown in the top of Figure 115, it may then be subjected

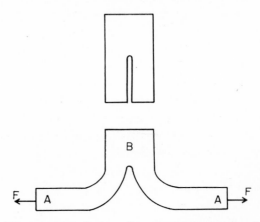

Figure 115. The standard "trousers" tear experiment showing the sample before stretching and when under stress.

to stress in the manner shown in the lower part of that figure. The tip of the tear can be made of known diameter d by the use of a circular cutting tool. When a stress is applied to this as shown, the stress behavior near the tip is rather complex. However, if the legs are made long, the stress distribution about the tip of the tear will be independent of the depth of the tear as long as essentially equilibrium conditions apply.

If the sample tears a distance ΔC under the force F, the force F will move a distance Δs. This distance is composed of two parts. First, the length of the unstretched tear has increased by an amount ΔC, and thus F must move through this distance. However, since the length ΔC added to the legs (indicated as sections A in Figure 115) came from region B of Figure 115, where it was in the unstretched condition, the increase in length of the legs is not merely ΔC; instead, the increase in length will be $\alpha_l \Delta C$, where α_l is the extension ratio of the material in the legs. Hence the work done by the two forces F is equal to

$$\Delta W = 2F\alpha_l \Delta C \qquad (14.1)$$

It is now important to determine how much of this work went into energy loss at the tear. At first sight, it might be thought that all the energy of Eq. (14.1) was lost in the tear. Such is not the case, however, because some of this energy is stored in the extra rubber of length ΔC added to the legs of the test sample. Since this incremental length was unstretched prior to the small increase in the tear length, it had a length ΔC. When it ended up, it was in the leg and had been stretched to a length $\alpha_l \Delta C$. Since work is the integral of force times incremental distance, this extra stored energy will be

$$\int_{\alpha=1}^{\alpha_l} 2\sigma a(\Delta C) \, d\alpha \qquad (14.2)$$

where a is the cross-section area of the leg piece, and σ is the stress at elongation α.

Notice that σa is not equal to F, except when $\alpha = \alpha_l$. In addition, the integral will give a factor $(\alpha_l - 1) \Delta C$ to a rough first approximation, instead of the factor $\alpha_l \Delta C$ in Eq. (14.1). It is apparent from this that if the legs are taken rather wide so that the tear will propagate at a small value of α_l, then the term in Eq. (14.2) will only be a small fraction of the energy expended.

Hence the energy given by Eq. (14.1) will nearly all be lost in the tear. This approximation will be assumed valid in that which follows; therefore the energy loss in the tear as it increases by a length ΔC is given directly by Eq. (14.1).

It is now convenient to introduce a characteristic tearing energy per unit of tear area, designated T. This energy is defined as the loss in energy within the tear as the tear produces unit area and will be called the "tearing energy." Therefore,

$$\Delta W/(h\,\Delta C) = T \qquad (14.3)$$

where h is the thickness of the test sheet. By use of Eq. (14.1) and upon assuming $\alpha_l \cong 1$, the following relation between tearing force and tearing energy is found:

$$T = 2F/h \qquad (14.4)$$

One therefore has an energy characteristic of the tearing process that is related by Eq. (14.4) to easily measured experimental quantities.

2. Factors Influencing the Tearing Energy

If the tearing energy T is to be related to structural constants of the rubber such as tensile strength and modulus, the situation at the tip of a tear must be examined in detail. The most striking observation is that the strain drops extremely rapidly as a function of the distance from the slit or tear point. For example, the variation of the extension ratio α as a function of the distance y from the edge of a tear with tip diameter d in a typical trousers test piece (178) is shown in Figure 116. This particular sample was still below the tension at which the break would propagate. Other investigators using different geometrical arrangements also confirm the fact that the strain rises exceedingly rapidly near the edge of the tear (179). Although an exact theoretical treatment of the dynamics of this situation would be very complicated, a rather simple picture can be used to illustrate the predominant behavior.

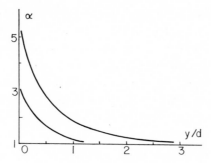

Figure 116. The variation of extension ratio near the tip of a "trousers" tear piece in terms of the ratio y/d, where y is the distance from the tear point and d is the diameter of the tip of the tear (178).

Represent the tip of the tear by the model shown schematically in Figure 117. The V-shaped portion of the diagram is meant to be the tip of the tear. One of the lines making the V will move to the right as the tear propagates, the other to the left. It is convenient to replace the rubber near the tip of the tear by

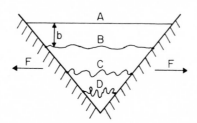

Figure 117. Schematic model for the behavior of rubber strands near the tip of a tear.

strands indicated by A, B, C, and D in the figure. Let each strand have a thickness b, equal to the distance from the highly strained edge of the tear to a point ahead of the tear where the strain is a small fraction of the strain at the edge. The volume of rubber in strand A will therefore be approximately hbd, where h is the sample thickness, and d is the diameter of the tip of the tear.

Strand A is highly elongated, and when it reaches a critical elongation, it will break. Designate the energy per unit volume stored in this strand at break as ϵ_o. It should, if the present model is meaningful, be equal to the stored elastic-energy density in a simple tensile sample at break. When strand A breaks, it is apparent that most of the energy it contains will be lost as heat. A certain amount of its energy will be transferred to strand B by viscous and other forces as it aids in the stretching of strand B while A is retracting. This energy transfer to B cannot be large unless the crosslinking is very tight or if viscous forces between the rubber layers are very high. For the moment, it will be assumed that all the energy in strand A is lost.

By the time strand B has reached its breaking elongation, the external work done on the tear must equal the energy lost by strand A (ignoring any work done by A on B). Therefore, since the energy loss incurred as the tear propagates a distance b is $\epsilon_0(bhd)$ and since T is defined as $(1/h)(\Delta W/\Delta C)$,

$$T = (1/h)(\epsilon_0 bhd)/b$$

or

$$T = \epsilon_0 d \tag{14.5}$$

Equation (14.5) has been obtained by Thomas through use of another approach (176). He has tested this equation by using various natural rubber gum stocks. Using Eq. (14.4), he computed T from a knowledge of F. This was done with tip diameters from 0.090 to 0.294 cm. His experimental results for T/d varied from 6.4 to 3.7 $\times$ 10^{-8} erg/cc in a more or less random way. These values are to be compared with the value of 4×10^{-8} erg/cc obtained by using a simple tensile breaking test and making use of Eq. (14.5). The value of T given by Eq. (14.5) is a little too low, but the result is probably as accurate as could be expected from such a simple model.

It is instructive to combine Eq. (14.5) with Eq. (14.4) to obtain the following equation for F:

$$F = h\, d\epsilon_0/2 \tag{14.6}$$

This equation shows that the predominant molecular quantity controlling tear strength is the energy which must be furnished to unit volume of rubber strand in order for it to break. Notice that the only dimension which enters, aside from the sample thickness h, is the diameter of the tip d. Since the width of the strand is of no importance, one therefore infers that the exact details of the model used for the computation of Eq. (14.5) are not critical.

Surprisingly enough, the tensile strength of the rubber, as such, does not determine the tear strength; instead, it is the energy furnished to the rubber in extending it to its maximum elongation that is important. This will involve not only the strength of the material but also its modulus and its viscous opposition to elongation. The latter quantity will become very important at low temperatures and high shear rates, where viscous loss effects may well overshadow the elastic effects.

In order to see the meaning of Eqs. (14.5) and (14.6) more clearly, consider the stress-strain curve shown in Figure 118.

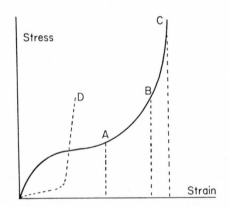

Figure 118.   Schematic stress-strain curves used to illustrate widely different tear behavior.

The quantity ϵ_0 is equal to the area under the curve up to the point of break. Suppose that one has three rubbers having equal moduli at low elongations but having low, moderate, and high strengths, respectively. These samples will break at points A, B, and C shown in the figure. It is clear that material A has about half the area under the curve up to the break point as compared with B; hence, the tear strength for B should be about double that for A. This is also in line with their tensile strengths. Material C, however, has an ϵ_0 value only about ⅔ as large as that for B, while its tensile strength is double that for B. Here, then, is a case where the tensile strength is a poor indication of tear strength.

One can, of course, envisage many modifications of the stress-strain curve shown in Figure 118 that would illustrate superficially anomalous behavior when comparing tensile and tear strength. They are obviously related, but it is quite possible for one material to show a higher tensile strength than another material while possessing a much inferior tear strength. The material illustrated by the broken curve in Figure 118, which breaks at D, would be a case in point when compared with polymer B.

3. Complicating Features in Tear

The conclusions drawn in the last section were based upon a very simplified picture of the actual situation. In practice, one is not sure exactly what the tear-tip diameter d will be. It may quite well be influenced by structural flaws within the rubber. However, there is no reason to think that the value of d should be independent of such things as the modulus of the rubber. For example, in the limit of a glass, the value of d will certainly be much smaller than in a rubber. Of course, the above derivations cannot be expected to hold for a glass, but one is unable to say at this time exactly where and how serious the possible modulus dependence of d will be. Measurements on practical rubbers (178) over a wide range of tear rates show d to be of the order of 0.8 mm for gum SBR and about 0.4 mm for SBR containing 50 parts carbon black. The latter material showed a tear strength nearly one hundred times higher than the former; thus, in this case at least, the tip-diameter variation is of no consequence.

A second complication relates to the fact that two general types of tearing occur. In the experimentally desirable case of smooth tearing, the above reasoning should be comparatively valid. However, under certain conditions one encounters "stick-slip" tearing or "knotty" tearing. In this case, the tearing force must be raised to a high value in order to start the tear. The tear then propagates under low force for a short distance and stops. To start the tear once again, it is necessary to increase the tearing force. This behavior appears to be associated with nonhomogeneity of the sample near the tip of the tear. Local crystallinity as a result of the high elongation, filler aggregates, and even Mullins softening are strongly suspected of being among the various causes of this behavior.

As mentioned before, the energy density at break ϵ_0 will be dependent upon the temperature and rate of test. This value includes not only the elastic energy needed to break a rubber under tensile stress, but it also includes work done against viscous forces during the stretching process. If the ideas outlined in the previous section are correct, ϵ_0 should vary in the same way in tensile-strength tests as it does in tear tests when the variables of rate and temperature are changed. This has been checked rather carefully by Greensmith, who shows that this is indeed the case (178).

The whole problem of tear strength is rather complicated, as can be seen from the above discussion. It is not that the process itself is intrinsically complicated, but more that the process contains several important variables. Although each of these variables alone is reasonably well understood, there are so many different types of tear behavior possible upon combining them that one is rather at a loss to describe all facets of the problem. In general, given a particular situation to analyze, one should be able to apply the principles outlined in these sections to the problem at hand. The interested reader is referred to two recent reviews of the subject for more detail (179,180).

4. Network Breakdown

The chemical mechanisms responsible for network breakdown are beyond the scope of this book; however, the behavior of the network itself as the chains in it are destroyed and reformed is an interesting mechanical phenomenon that will be discussed in some detail. For this purpose it is convenient to consider the stress relaxation of a rubber network when all the relaxation is the result of network chain scission. As indicated in previous chapters, appreciable stress relaxation will occur in a network if the network is not linked tightly enough. This effect will be ignored for the present purposes.

Suppose a network consists of ν_0 network chains at $t = 0$. If the network is elongated to an extension ratio α_0, the required force is σ_0, given by

$$\sigma_0 = \nu_0 k T (\alpha_0 - 1/\alpha_0{}^2) \tag{14.7}$$

If the network chains break without reforming, then the value of ν_0 will decrease to ν, and the stress needed to preserve an extension ratio α_0 will be given by

$$\sigma = \nu k T (\alpha_0 - 1/\alpha_0{}^2) \tag{14.8}$$

Dividing Eq. (14.8) by (14.7) gives

$$\nu = \nu_0 (\sigma/\sigma_0) \tag{14.9}$$

Hence the number of network chains at any time $t > 0$ is directly proportional to the stress at that time.

It is noticed that reforming of the broken network chains was not allowed in obtaining Eq. (14.9). There is a distinct possibility in any actual case, however, that some of the stretched chains may not be completely "dead" after they break. The new ends formed during the chain cleavage may well be reactive, in which case they could unite with other broken chains or become attached to an already existing network chain. Since the stretched chain will ordinarily retract very rapidly after scission, it is generally true that chain reformation will only occur in the relaxed state. As a result, these newly formed chains will not contribute to the stress in the yet unbroken portion of the network. This statement is only approximate, however, because the completely relaxed network itself will change as more chains in the stretched network break. This latter effect is found to be negligible for most purposes. As a result, Eq. (14.9) holds to a good approximation even if chains do reform as the network breaks.

The exact way in which ν changes with time is a function of the reaction mechanism involved. For example, if the chain scission reaction is assumed to occur at random with the probability that any given chain unit will break in time dt being $B\,dt$,

$$dv/dt = -(\nu/\nu_0)qB \qquad (14.10)$$

In this relation, q is the average number of units in the original ν_0 network chains, and the factor ν/ν_0 is required since only this fraction of the breaks will cause an unbroken chain to break.

Integration of Eq. (14.10) gives the following result:

$$\nu = \nu_0 \exp\left(-qBt/\nu_0\right) \qquad (14.11)$$

Or, upon placing this result in Eq. (14.9),

$$\sigma/\sigma_0 = \exp\left(-qBt/\nu_0\right) \qquad (14.12)$$

It is therefore indicated that the stress will relax exponentially with time. However, since this solution assumes a constant random scission rate, it would not be expected to apply in other more complicated cases.

It is also apparent from Eq. (14.12) that the stress should decay less rapidly in a highly crosslinked rubber than in a loosely crosslinked rubber. This follows from Eq. (14.12), since for a given rubber qB is constant and t/ν_0 is a reduced time variable. When $t/\nu_0 = 1/qB$, the stress will have decayed to e^{-1} of its original value. A more detailed examination of the use of facts such as these in determining the exact way in which a network breaks has been given in the literature and will not be pursued further here (91).

5. Intermittent and Continuous Stress Relaxation

Since it is often important to determine whether or not broken network chains reform after relaxation, two types of measurements are carried out on the same sample. The first measurement consists of measuring the relaxation of stress as the sample is maintained at constant elongation α_0. This was the type of test considered in the last section, and Eqs. (14.7), (14.8), and (14.9) apply.

A second type of test, the so-called "intermittent stress relaxation" test, consists of measuring the stress needed to elongate the sample to elongation α_0 at various times after chain scission has begun. The sample is retained in its relaxed state at all times except for the short interval needed to extend the rubber to α_0 and measure the tension. In this case, the chains that are reformed during the time the scission progresses will still contribute to the stress when the sample is elongated:

$$\sigma' = [\nu + \beta(\nu_0 - \nu)]kT(\alpha_0 - 1/\alpha_0^2) \qquad (14.13)$$

where β is the fraction of chains that break which are reformed. Notice that if β equals unity, the stress does not decrease in this type of experiment.

Taking ratios between Eq. (14.13) and Eq. (14.8) gives

$$\sigma'/\sigma = (1 - \beta) + \beta(\nu_0/\nu) \qquad (14.14)$$

This indicates that a plot of σ'/σ vs. ν_0/ν will yield a straight line of slope β and intercept $(1 - \beta)$. The quantity ν_0/ν can be found from Eq. (14.9). One therefore has a means for determining the fraction of recombination β. A similar treatment can also be used, of course, to describe the situation where additional crosslinking takes place during the time of the experiment.

6. Permanent Set

The term "permanent set" as used in this section is meant to designate the nonrecoverable elongation exhibited by a network after being released from a strained position. This nonrecoverable deformation is not to include the effects of true viscous flow and slow elastic retraction. These latter effects will only be negligible if one is dealing with a highly crosslinked system. It will be assumed for the following discussion that only the effects of network breakdown and reformation are present.

Suppose a network has been held at an extension ratio α_1 while network degradation and simultaneous network formation was occurring. Take the number of chains remaining in the stretched network after some time to be ν_1. At the same time, because of reforming of broken chains in the relaxed state and also possible simultaneous crosslinking, there will be built up a second relaxed network containing ν_2 chains. Now if the stress is removed from the sample, the ν_1 chains in the first network will cause the sample to retract, but the ν_2 relaxed chains will be compressed in the process. The sample will then reach an equilibrium elongation α_s, at which the force of the ν_1 network will exactly balance the compression of the ν_2 network:

$$-\alpha_1 \nu_1 k T(\alpha_s - 1/\alpha_s{}^2) = \nu_2 k T[(\alpha_s/\alpha_1) - (\alpha_1/\alpha_s)^2] \qquad (14.15)$$

The factor α_1 on the left side of Eq. (14.15) is needed to reduce the network to the same base area. Since network 1 was originally defined in the case $\alpha = 1$, its cross-section area was not unity at an extension ratio α_1 but was instead $1/\alpha_1$. The true force for a network of unit area at this elongation would be α_1 times as large; hence one must multiply by this factor. Equation (14.15) can be solved for $\alpha_s{}^3$ to give

$$\alpha_s{}^3 = \alpha_1{}^2(\nu_1 + \nu_2\alpha_1)/(\nu_1\alpha_1{}^2 + \nu_2) \qquad (14.16)$$

which is an explicit expression for the equilibrium elongation in terms of the original extension ratio and the number of chains in the network. It is sometimes convenient to define the permanent set as the percentage of the original elongation that is retained by the sample. Designating this quantity as P.S., one has

$$\text{P.S.} = 100[(\alpha_s - 1)/(\alpha_1 - 1)] \qquad (14.17)$$

where α_s is given by Eq. (14.16). Since ν_1 and ν_2 can be measured by continuous and intermittent stress-relaxation measurements, the results of such measurements can be used to predict permanent set. A typical comparison between the predicted and experimental values (181) is shown in Figure 119.

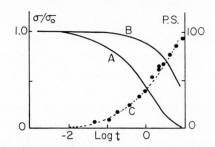

Figure 119. The broken curve C is the permanent set predicted from intermittent (curve A) and continuous (curve B) stress-relaxation measurements. Actual permanent-set data are shown by the points. The material is natural rubber gum stock at 130°C and 50 per cent elongation (181).

7. Mechanical Breakdown of Rubber

It is common practice to subject rubber and other molten polymers to very high shear stresses in various phases of polymer processing. Under these conditions it is found that the polymer molecules often break down to give a much lower final molecular weight (182). This section will be devoted to determining what molecular factors affect this degradation of the molecules. No attempt will be made to discuss subsequent reactions of the new chain ends caused by the degradation. This is equivalent to assuming the presence of a chemical inhibiting agent that renders the newly formed chain ends "dead" and nonreactive.

First, it must be recognized that chain breaking in shear does not ordinarily occur unless the polymer molecules possess a large number of entanglements with each other. Although this is not absolutely necessary, chain degradation in shear does not occur at any practical shear rates unless entanglements are present. The reason for this will be seen below.

Consider a polymer liquid consisting of highly entangled molecules and subjected to a shear rate $\dot{\gamma}$. Since the liquid shows true viscous flow, it must be assumed that the entanglements are slipping loose from the various molecules as the liquid is sheared; otherwise, the liquid would show only elastic deformation. As an entanglement point slips along the chain, it will rub against the chain in such a way as to stretch it. On the average, the entanglements on one side of the center of a chain will act to stretch the chain in that direction, while those on the other side of the chain center will be pulling in the opposite direction. Obviously, the center of the chain will be under the highest tension, and the ends will be under no tension. This means that the chain will break predominantly at its center.

The above ideas may be put on a quantitative basis (183), and this is done in Appendix 12. For a sample of average molecular weight M_t, the chance that a particular chain in the sample having molecular weight M will break at its center in time dt is

$$P \, dt = K \exp\left[-(E - F_0\delta)/kT\right] dt \qquad (14.18)$$

where E is the energy needed to break a chain bond. In this expression K is a constant of magnitude approximately equal to the bond vibration frequency, 2δ is about the length of a chain bond, and F_0 is given as

$$F_0 = (\text{constant})(\dot{\gamma}\eta/\rho)(M/M_t)^2 \qquad (14.19)$$

The constant in this expression will not vary markedly as long as one is dealing with a coiling polymer with many entanglements. It is of the order of magnitude of 10^{-13} cgs units.

As soon as $F_0\delta$ becomes comparable to E, mechanical chain breakdown should become appreciable. For a fractionated sample (where $M = M_t$), from the above equation then $\dot{\gamma}\eta/\rho$ must be of order 10^8 cgs units if one is to observe mechanical breakdown. Since this falls in the range found by experiment, some validity can be attached to the above ideas.

Equations (14.18) and (14.19) permit several predictions regarding mechanical breakdown. First, and most important, is the effect of viscosity on the shear rate needed to start degradation. For a fractionated sample, Eq. (14.19) states that the critical shear rate for breakdown will vary inversely with the sample viscosity. Thus, at low temperatures where η is very large, molecular breakdown will start at relatively low shear rates. Similarly, at high temperatures the viscosity will be much lower, and one will have to go to much higher shear rates to achieve breakdown. Also, since $\eta \sim M^{3.5}$, the shear rate at which breakdown becomes noticeable will vary rapidly with molecular weight. For example, if the sample molecular weight is doubled, the shear rate at which breakdown becomes appreciable will decrease by a factor of about 11.

It is also of interest to see what Eqs. (14.18) and (14.19) predict for the rate of degradation of two different molecular weights in a polydisperse polymer. If $F_0\delta/kT$ is about 20 for a certain molecular weight, its breakdown rate is proportional to exp (20). Since $F_0\delta$ varies as M^2, the breakdown rate for a molecular weight 20 per cent lower is proportional to exp (16). Hence these two molecules whose molecular weights differ by only 20 per cent will differ by a factor of about 55 in their breakdown rate. For this reason, it is apparent that a sample which has been mechanically degraded will show a rather sharp cutoff in the molecular-weight distribution at its upper molecular-weight limit.

From the above result it becomes evident that a polymer which contains a wide molecular-weight distribution will be altered as follows under the action of shear degradation. Essentially none of the shorter chains in the sample will be broken. All the chains with molecular weight higher than a certain critical size M_{max} will be broken down into low-molecular-weight material. The new low-molecular-weight material formed by breakdown will in general be within the molecular-weight region $M_{max} > M > M_{max}/3$. This fact is a consequence of the conclusion reached in Appendix 11 that the chains break preferentially near the center. As a result of this, the molecular-weight distribution of the original polymer will be narrowed by shear degradation. The highest molecular weights will always be lost.

Although the above discussion assumes that the broken chains cannot react chemically, very often in practice this will not be the case. In many cases, the free radical formed by the chain scission will attack a stable chain and form a branch on it. This will upset the conclusions reached above, since such a process will favor the formation of very large molecules or perhaps even gel. The gel formed under such conditions will be relatively tight, however, since loose, extended gel particles will readily break under the shearing action. This follows from the fact that, since the force on the center of a chain system is caused by the cumulative effect of a large number of entanglements slipping from the chain, short chains in compact branched systems will not break as easily as a linear molecule of the same molecular weight. The tightly branched system should be much more stable under shear than a linear molecule would be.

If one ignores the chemical reactions that might be possible for the broken chains in certain systems, the effect of shear on molecular breakdown is quite straightforward. In summary, the chains will break preferentially at their center; under a given shear rate and constant viscosity, all the chains above a certain critical molecular weight M_{max} will be lost by mechanical breakdown. These chains will augment the original molecular-weight distribution in the region $M_{max} > M > M_{max}/3$. Essentially no chains in the original distribution having $M < M_{max}/1.2$ will be broken. The value of M_{max} is strongly dependent upon shear rate and the viscosity of the system. In particular, an increase in η by means of temperature or diluent will decrease M_{max}, the relation being approximately $\eta \sim 1/M_{max}^2$. Since the viscosity enters only as a product with the shear rate, an increase in one is equivalent to a proportionate increase in the other.

APPENDIX 12
Shear Degradation (183)

Consider the polymer molecule shown schematically in Figure 120. It is supposed that there is a tensile shear with gradient $\dot{\gamma}$

in the x direction. The molecule under consideration will be taken to have Z links, each of molecular weight M_0, and the entanglements will be so spaced that the molecular weight between them is M_e. On the average, two entanglement points such as A and B will separate with a velocity $\dot{\gamma} b_0/2$ under the action of the shearing forces.

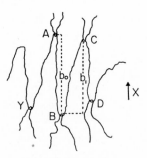

Figure 120.   A schematic diagram of a polymer chain restricted in its motion by entangled chains.

If the center of the chain is within the region AB of the chain, then on the average there will be as much force pulling one way on it as another. Therefore, if the chain pictured in Figure 120 is taken to be an average chain, the segment of the chain between A and B will not move. However, each link in the two adjacent segments, AY and BC, must move with a velocity $\dot{\gamma} b_0/2$. In general, each link in the i'th segment must move with a velocity

$$(\dot{\gamma}/2) \sum_{n=0}^{i-1} b_n \qquad (A11.1)$$

The velocities indicated are made possible by appropriate tensions along the chain. A link moving with velocity v resists movement by a viscous force fv, where f is a friction factor. The tension on the center link is the sum of all the forces needed to pull either side of the chain through its entanglements. This tension is

$$F_0 = \sum_{i=1}^{M/2M_e} \left[(M_e/M_0)(\dot{\gamma} f/2) \sum_{n=0}^{i-1} b_n \right] \qquad (A11.2)$$

which may be reduced to

$$F_0 = (\dot{\gamma}f/16)(M_e/M_0)^{3/2}(M/M_e)^2 a \qquad \text{(A11.3)}$$

where b, the mean x-directed end-to-end distance of a chain of molecular weight M_e, is taken to be $a(M_e/M_0)^{1/2}$, with a being the length of a chain link.

The tension in the q'th link from the center can be found in the same way and is

$$F_q = F_0[1 - (4q^2/Z^2)] \qquad \text{(A11.4)}$$

It is now necessary to consider the probability that a chain link subjected to a tension F will break. This problem was treated in Chapter 11, where it was found that the probability was proportional to $\exp[-(E - F\delta)/kT]$. If F is replaced by the value appropriate for any link as given by Eq. (A11.4), the result may be summed over all links to give the total probability that the chain will break:

$$P = K \exp[-(E - F_0\delta)/kT] \qquad \text{(A11.5)}$$

where K is a constant of the order of the bond vibration frequency.

Notice that, since the chance that the q'th segment from the center will break is proportional to $\exp(F_q\delta/kT)$, one is able to compare the rate with which chains break at various sites along the chain. For example, if $F_0\delta/kT = 20$, ten chains will break at the center for each chain that breaks $\frac{1}{3}$ of the way out from the center, i.e., where $2q/Z = \frac{1}{3}$.

Finally, the value of f in Eq. (A11.3) may be replaced by its value in terms of the viscosity as found in Chapter 3. The equations given in the text are then obtained.

PROBLEMS

1. In a particular chemical stress-relaxation experiment at 150 per cent elongation, the stress is allowed to decay until it is 60 per cent as large as its original value. The load is then removed and the sample is allowed to recover. Its final length is 10 per cent longer than its original length. What percentage of the network chains that broke is reformed?

2. Starting from the relation $T/d = \epsilon_0$, show that the energy expended per unit area of new tear surface as the tear propagates—namely, $\Delta W/2h\Delta C$—is given by $\epsilon_0 d/2$. Using the average experimental values of Thomas (176), namely, $d = 0.10$ cm and $\epsilon_0 = 5 \times 10^8$ ergs/cc, compute the energy lost in the tear for unit increase in tear surface area. Compare this value with the value of 100 ergs/cm² estimated by Berry (137) for the energy actually needed to break bonds in forming such a surface. Discuss the meaning of your answer.

3. A given polymer sample is mechanically degraded under shearing action at a temperature of 300°K. The energy of activation for viscous flow in this region is 20 Kcal/mole. If the temperature is now raised to 310°K, the same rate of degradation can be obtained only if the shear rate is increased (a) By what factor must the shear rate be increased? (b) If the shear rate were not increased, a higher-molecular-weight polymer of the same material would break down at the higher temperature at the same rate as the original material did at the original temperature. What is the ratio of molecular weights for these two polymers?

REFERENCES

1. P. J. Flory, *Principles of Polymer Chemistry*, Cornell University Press, Ithaca, N.Y., 1953.
2. W. Kuhn, *J. Polymer Sci.*, **1**, 380 (1946).
3. J. J. Hermans and J. T. G. Overbeek, *Rec. trav. chim.*, **67**, 761 (1948).
4. H. Tompa, *Polymer Solutions*, Academic Press, Inc., New York, 1956.
5. P. J. Flory, C. A. J. Hoeve, and A. Ciferri, *J. Polymer Sci.*, **34**, 337 (1959).
6. B. H. Zimm and W. H. Stockmayer, *J. Chem. Phys.*, **17**, 1301 (1949).
7. B. H. Zimm and R. W. Kilb, *J. Polymer Sci.*, **37**, 19 (1959).
8. F. Bueche, *J. Polymer Sci.*, **41**, 549 (1959).
9. S. Newman and P. J. Flory, *J. Polymer Sci.*, **10**, 121 (1953).
10. H. Eyring, *Phys. Rev.*, **39**, 746 (1932).
11. F. T. Wall, *J. Chem. Phys.*, **11**, 67 (1943).
12. P. Debye, *J. Chem. Phys.*, **14**, 636 (1946).
13. E. Guth and H. Mark, *Monatsh.*, **65**, 93 (1934).
14. Lord Rayleigh, *Phil. Mag.*, **37**, 321 (1919).
15. S. Chandrasekhar, *Revs. Mod. Phys.*, **15**, 3 (1943).
16. P. Debye and F. Bueche, *J. Chem. Phys.*, **20**, 1337 (1952).
17. A. Isihara, *J. Phys. Soc. Japan*, **5**, 201 (1950).
18. H. M. James and E. Guth, *J. Chem. Phys.*, **11**, 470 (1943).
19. W. Kuhn, *Kolloid-Z.*, **76**, 258 (1936).
20. L. R. G. Treloar, *Trans. Faraday Soc.*, **39**, 241 (1943).
21. P. J. Flory and J. Rehner, *J. Chem. Phys.*, **11**, 512 (1943).
22. L. R. G. Treloar, *Physics of Rubber Elasticity*, Oxford University Press, New York, 1958.
23. L. Mullins and A. G. Thomas, *J. Polymer Sci.*, **43**, 13 (1960).
24. J. Scanlan, *J. Polymer Sci.*, **43**, 501 (1960).
25. E. Guth, *J. Appl. Phy.*, **16**, 20 (1945).
26. L. H. Cohan, *Rubber World*, **117**, 343 (1947).
27. F. Bueche, *J. Appl. Polymer Sci.*, **4**, 107 (1960); **5**, 271 (1961).
28. A. M. Bueche, *J. Polymer Sci.*, **25**, 139 (1957).
29. L. Mullins, *J. Appl. Polymer Sci.*, **2**, 1 (1959).
30. P. J. Flory, *Ind. Eng. Chem.*, **38**, 417 (1946).
31. A. Ciferri and P. J. Flory, *J. Appl. Phy.*, **30**, 1498 (1959).
32. L. Mullins, *J. Appl. Polymer Sci.*, **2**, 257 (1959).
33. F. Bueche, *J. Chem. Phys.*, **20**, 1959 (1952); **25**, 599 (1956).
34. A. Einstein, *Ann. Physik*, **17**, 549 (1905).
35. P. Debye, *J. Chem. Phys.*, **14**, 636 (1946).

36. T. G. Fox and S. Loshaek, *J. Appl. Phy.*, **26**, 1080 (1955).
37. T. G. Fox and P. J. Flory, *J. Polymer Sci.*, **14**, 314 (1954).
38. F. Bueche, *J. Appl. Phy.*, **26**, 738 (1955); **24**, 423 (1953).
39. T. G. Fox and H. Nakayasu, *Rheol. Bull.*, **29**, 3 (1960).
40. D. W. McCall and D. C. Douglass, *J. Chem. Phys.*, **31**, 860 (1959).
41. F. Bueche, *J. Polymer Sci.*, **25**, 243 (1957).
42. T. G. Fox, S. Gratch, and S. Loshaek, in F. Eirich (ed.), *Rheology*, Vol. 1, Chap. 12, Academic Press, Inc., New York, 1956.
43. F. Bueche and F. N. Kelley, *J. Polymer Sci.*, **45**, 267 (1960).
44. J. F. Rudd, *J. Polymer Sci.*, **44**, 459 (1960).
45. F. Bueche, *J. Polymer Sci.*, **43**, 527 (1960).
46. See, for example, T. L. Hill, *Statistical Mechanics*, McGraw-Hill Book Company, Inc., New York, 1956.
47. T. G. Fox and P. J. Flory, *J. Am. Chem. Soc.*, **70**, 2384 (1948).
48. J. McLoughlin and A. V. Tobolsky, *J. Polymer Sci.*, **8**, 543 (1952).
49. M. L. Williams, R. F. Landel, and J. D. Ferry, *J. Am. Chem. Soc.*, **77**, 3701 (1955).
50. F. Bueche, *J. Chem. Phys.*, **21**, 1850 (1953); **24**, 418 (1956); **30**, 748 (1959).
51. M. H. Cohen and D. Turnbull, *J. Chem. Phys.*, **31**, 1164 (1959).
52. The observed variation of thermodynamic quantities near T_g has been reviewed by W. Kauzman, *Chem. Revs.*, **43**, 219 (1948).
53. T. G. Fox and P. J. Flory, *J. Appl. Phy.*, **21**, 581 (1950).
54. R. H. Wiley, G. M. Brauer, and A. R. Bennett, *J. Polymer Sci.*, **5**, 609 (1950).
55. J. McLoughlin and A. V. Tobolsky, *J. Polymer Sci.*, **7**, 658 (1951).
56. A. K. Doolittle, *J. Appl. Phy.*, **23**, 418 (1952).
57. M. L. Williams, *J. Appl. Phy.*, **29**, 1395 (1958).
58. R. F. Boyer, *J. Appl. Phy.*, **25**, 825 (1954).
59. R. G. Beaman, *J. Polymer Sci.*, **9**, 470 (1952).
60. L. A. Wood, *J. Polymer Sci.*, **28**, 319 (1958).
61. H. Singh and A. W. Nolle, *J. Appl. Phy.*, **30**, 337 (1959).
62. T. G. Fox and S. Loshaek, *J. Polymer Sci.*, **15**, 371, 391 (1955).
63. F. N. Kelley and F. Bueche, *J. Polymer Sci.*, **50**, 549 (1961).
64. T. G. Fox and P. J. Flory, *J. Polymer Sci.*, **14**, 315 (1954).
65. J. D. Ferry and R. A. Stratton, *Kolloid-Z.*, **171**, 107 (1960).
66. R. Buchdahl and L. Nielsen, *J. Polymer Sci.*, **15**, 1 (1955).
67. R. B. Beevers, E. White, and L. Brown, *Trans. Faraday Soc.*, **56**, 1529, 1535 (1960).
68. F. M. Merrett, *J. Polymer Sci.*, **24**, 467 (1957); D. J. Angier and D. T. Turner, *J. Polymer Sci.*, **28**, 265 (1958).
69. M. Gordon and J. S. Taylor, *J. Appl. Chem. (London)*, **2**, 493 (1952).
70. T. G. Fox, *Bull. Am. Phys. Soc.*, **1**, 123 (1956).

71. L. Mandelkern, G. M. Martin, and F. A. Quinn, *J. Research Natl. Bur. Standards*, **58,** 137 (1957).
72. F. Bueche, unpublished measurements.
73. F. Bueche, *J. Chem. Phys.*, **22,** 603 (1954).
74. See, for example, J. Slater and N. Frank, *Mechanics*, McGraw-Hill Book Company, Inc., New York, 1947, p. 157.
75. F. Bueche, *J. Appl. Polymer Sci.*, **1,** 240 (1959).
76. H. Leaderman, *Elastic and Creep Properties of Filamentous Materials*, Textile Foundation, Washington, D.C., 1943.
77. J. D. Ferry, *J. Am. Chem. Soc.*, **72,** 3746 (1950).
78. A. V. Tobolsky and R. D. Andrews, *J. Chem. Phys.*, **13,** 3 (1945).
79. P. Rouse, *J. Chem. Phys.*, **21,** 1272 (1953).
80. O. Nakada, *J. Phys. Soc. Japan*, **10,** 804 (1955).
81. B. Zimm, *J. Chem. Phys.*, **24,** 269 (1956).
82. J. D. Ferry, R. F. Landel, and M. L. Williams, *J. Appl. Phy.*, **26,** 359 (1955).
83. A. Miyake, *J. Polymer Sci.*, **26,** 239 (1957).
84. B. Gross and R. M. Fuoss, *J. Polymer Sci.*, **19,** 39 (1956).
85. H. Leaderman, in F. Eirich (ed.), *Rheology*, Vol. 2, Chap. 1, Academic Press, Inc., New York, 1958.
86. J. D. Ferry, *Viscoelastic Properties of Polymers*, John Wiley & Sons, Inc., New York, 1961.
87. A. J. Staverman and F. Schwarzl, in H. A. Stuart (ed.), *Die Physik der Hochpolymeren*, Vol. 4, Springer-Verlag, Berlin, 1956.
88. B. Gross and H. Pelzer, *J. Appl. Phy.*, **22,** 1035 (1951).
89. I. L. Hopkins and R. Hamming, *J. Appl. Phy.*, **28,** 906 (1957); **29,** 742 (1958).
90. V. Kolpe, unpublished results.
91. A. V. Tobolsky, *J. Appl. Phy.*, **27,** 673 (1956).
92. F. Bueche, *J. Polymer Sci.*, **25,** 305 (1957).
93. R. S. Marvin, in *Viscoelasticity: Phenomenological Aspects*, Academic Press, Inc., New York, 1960.
94. B. Gross, *J. Polymer Sci.*, **20,** 123, 371 (1956).
95. R. S. Marvin, *Proc. Second Intern. Congr. Rheol., London, 1953,* 156 (1954).
96. P. E. Rouse and K. Sittel, *J. Appl. Phy.*, **24,** 690 (1953).
97. F. J. Padden and T. W. DeWitt, *J. Appl. Phy.*, **25,** 1086 (1954).
98. T. W. DeWitt, H. Markovitz, F. Padden, and L. Zapas, *J. Colloid Sci.*, **10,** 174 (1955).
99. R. S. Porter and J. F. Johnson, *J. Appl. Polymer Sci.*, **3,** 107, 194, 200 (1960).
100. F. Bueche, *J. Chem. Phys.*, **22,** 1570 (1954).
101. A. Peterlin, *J. Polymer Sci.*, **8,** 621 (1952).

102. T. Takemura, *J. Polymer Sci.*, **27,** 549 (1958).
103. F. Bueche and S. Harding, *J. Polymer Sci.*, **32,** 177 (1958).
104. F. Bueche, *J. Appl. Phy.*, **30,** 1114 (1959).
105. Y. H. Pao, *J. Appl. Phy.*, **28,** 591 (1957); *J. Chem. Phys.*, **25,** 1294 (1956).
106. R. H. Boyd, *J. Appl. Phy.*, **29,** 953 (1958).
107. B. H. Zimm, *J. Chem. Phys.*, **24,** 269 (1956).
108. J. S. Ham, *J. Chem. Phys.*, **26,** 625 (1957).
109. B. H. Zimm and R. W. Kilb, *J. Polymer Sci.*, **37,** 19 (1959).
110. F. Bueche, *J. Polymer Sci.*, **41,** 551 (1959).
111. J. D. Ferry, L. Jordan, W. Evans, and M. Johnson, *J. Polymer Sci.*, **14,** 261 (1954).
112. J. M. Watkins, R. Spangler, and E. McKannan, *J. Appl. Phy.*, **27,** 685 (1956).
113. A. V. Tobolsky and K. Murakami, *J. Polymer Sci.*, **40,** 443 (1959).
114. P. U. A. Grossman, *J. Polymer Sci.*, **46,** 257 (1960).
115. T. Higuchi, H. Leeper, and D. Davis, *Anal. Chem.*, **20,** 1029 (1948).
116. A. M. Bueche and J. P. Berry, in B. L. Averbach (ed.), *Fracture*, Chap. 14, John Wiley & Sons, Inc., New York, 1959.
117. P. J. Flory, N. Rabjohn, and M. Shaffer, *J. Polymer Sci.*, **4,** 443 (1949).
118. P. J. Flory, *Ind. Eng. Chem.*, **38,** 417 (1946).
119. G. R. Taylor and S. Darin, *J. Polymer Sci.*, **17,** 511 (1955).
120. F. Bueche, *J. Polymer Sci.*, **33,** 259 (1958).
121. T. L. Smith, *J. Polymer Sci.*, **32,** 99 (1958); T. L. Smith and P. Stedry, *J. Appl. Phy.*, **31,** 1892 (1960).
122. F. Bueche, unpublished data.
123. F. Bueche, *J. Polymer Sci.*, **24,** 189 (1957).
124. A. M. Bueche, *J. Polymer Sci.*, **19,** 275 (1956).
125. F. Bueche, *Rubber Chem. and Technol.*, **32,** 1269 (1959).
126. F. Bueche, *J. Appl. Phy.*, **29,** 1231 (1958).
127. A. M. Borders and R. D. Juve, *Ind. Eng. Chem.*, **38,** 1066 (1946).
128. J. A. Sauer, J. Marin, and C. Hsiao, *J. Appl. Phy.*, **20,** 507 (1949).
129. W. N. Findley, *J. Appl. Phy.*, **21,** 258 (1950).
130. K. Deutsch, E. A. Hoff, and W. Reddish, *J. Polymer Sci.*, **13,** 565 (1954).
131. K. M. Sinnott, *J. Polymer Sci.*, **35,** 273 (1959).
132. E. A. Hoff, D. W. Robinson, and A. H. Willbourn, *J. Polymer Sci.*, **18,** 161 (1955).
133. F. Bueche, *J. Appl. Phy.*, **26,** 1133 (1955); **28,** 784 (1957); **29,** 1231 (1958).
134. C. C. Hsiao, *J. Appl. Phy.*, **30,** 1492 (1959); *J. Polymer Sci.*, **44,** 71 (1960).
135. A. Robinson, J. E. Osborn, and C. C. Hsiao, *J. Appl. Phy.*, **31,** 1602 (1960).
136. C. C. Hsiao and J. A. Sauer, *J. Appl. Phy.*, **21,** 1071 (1950).
137. J. P. Berry, *J. Polymer Sci.*, **50,** 107, 318 (1961).

138. P. Debye and F. Bueche, *J. Chem. Phys.*, **19**, 589 (1951).
139. R. M. Fuoss, *J. Am. Chem. Soc.*, **63**, 2410 (1941).
140. R. N. Work and Y. M. Trehu, *J. Appl. Phy.*, **27**, 1003 (1956).
141. H. Frohlich, *Theory of Dielectrics*, Oxford University Press, New York, 1949.
142. L. K. H. van Beek and J. J. Hermans, *J. Polymer Sci.*, **23**, 211 (1957).
143. F. Bueche, *J. Polymer Sci.*, **54**, 597 (1961).
144. A. J. Curtis, in J. Birks and J. Schulman (eds.), *Progress in Dielectrics*, Vol. 2, John Wiley & Sons, Inc., New York, 1960.
145. T. H. Sutherland and B. L. Funt, *J. Polymer Sci.*, **11**, 177 (1953).
146. P. C. Scherer, M. C. Hawkins, and D. W. Levi, *J. Polymer Sci.*, **31**, 105 (1958).
147. J. A. Sauer and A. E. Woodward, *Revs. Mod. Phys.*, **32**, 88 (1960).
148. J. G. Powles, *Proc. Phys. Soc. (London)*, **69**, 281 (1956).
149. K. Schmieder and K. Wolf, *Kolloid-Z.*, **134**, 149 (1953).
150. Odajima, Sohma, and Koike, *J. Phys. Soc. Japan*, **12**, 272 (1957).
151. J. G. Powles, *Polymer*, **1**, 219 (1960).
152. E. L. Warrick, *J. Polymer Sci.*, **27**, 1 (1958).
153. M. Davison and F. Bueche, unpublished work.
154. L. Mandelkern, *Chem. Revs.*, **56**, 903 (1956).
155. C. W. Bunn, *J. Polymer Sci.*, **16**, 323 (1955).
156. M. Dole and B. Wunderlich, *J. Polymer Sci.*, **24**, 139 (1957).
157. L. Mandelkern, M. Hellman, D. Brown, D. Roberts, and F. Quinn, *J. Am. Chem. Soc.*, **75**, 4093 (1953).
158. P. J. Flory, *J. Chem. Phys.*, **17**, 223 (1949).
159. P. J. Flory, *Trans. Faraday Soc.*, **51**, 848 (1955).
160. L. Mandelkern, F. Quinn, and D. Roberts, as quoted in ref. 154.
161. O. B. Edgar and R. Hill, *J. Polymer Sci.*, **8**, 1 (1952).
162. L. A. Wood, in *Advances in Colloid Science*, Vol. 2, Interscience Publishers, Inc., New York, 1946.
163. G. S. Whitby, personal communication.
164. P. J. Flory, *J. Chem. Phys.*, **15**, 397 (1947).
165. A. N. Gent, *J. Polymer Sci.*, **18**, 321 (1955).
166. B. G. Ranby, F. Moorehead, and N. M. Walter, *J. Polymer Sci.*, **44**, 349 (1960).
167. F. P. Price, *J. Polymer Sci.*, **42**, 49 (1960).
168. J. I. Lauritzen and J. D. Hoffman, *J. Research Natl. Bur. Standards*, **64A**, 1 (1960).
169. D. H. Reneker and P. H. Geil, *J. Appl. Phy.*, **31**, 1916 (1960).
170. A. Peterlin, *J. Appl. Phy.*, **31**, 1934 (1960).
171. W. P. Slichter, *J. Appl. Phy.*, **31**, 1865 (1960).
172. A. Keller, *J. Polymer Sci.*, **39**, 151 (1959).

173. G. Natta and P. Corradini, *J. Polymer Sci.*, **39,** 29 (1959).

174. R. L. Miller and L. E. Nielsen, *J. Polymer Sci.*, **44,** 391 (1960).

175. F. Billmeyer, *Textbook of Polymer Chemistry*, Interscience Publishers, Inc., New York, 1957.

176. A. G. Thomas, *J. Polymer Sci.*, **18,** 177 (1955).

177. A. G. Thomas, *J. Appl. Polymer Sci.*, **3,** 168 (1960).

178. H. W. Greensmith, *J. Appl. Polymer Sci.*, **3,** 183 (1960).

179. P. Kainradl and F. Handler, *Rubber Chem. and Technol.*, **33,** 1438 (1960); H. W. Greensmith, *Rheology of Elastomers* (P. Mason and N. Wookey, eds.) Pergamon Press, London, 1958.

180. L. Mullins, *Proc. Intern. Rubber Conf.*, American Chemical Society, Division of Rubber Chemistry, 1959.

181. R. D. Andrews, A. V. Tobolsky, and E. E. Hanson, *J. Appl. Phy.*, **17,** 352 (1946).

182. J. Scanlan and W. F. Watson, *Rubber Chem. and Technol.*, **33,** 1201 (1960).

183. F. Bueche, *J. Appl. Polymer Sci.*, **4,** 101 (1960).

INDEX

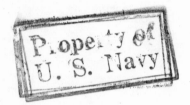